D1515967

ISOTOPIC CARBON

ISOTOPIC CARBON

Techniques in Its Measurement
and Chemical Manipulation

by

MELVIN CALVIN
PROFESSOR OF CHEMISTRY

CHARLES HEIDELBERGER

JAMES C. REID

BERT M. TOLBERT

PETER E. YANKWICH
INSTRUCTOR IN CHEMISTRY

ALL MEMBERS OF THE SCIENTIFIC STAFF
OF THE RADIATION LABORATORY

UNIVERSITY OF CALIFORNIA, BERKELEY

1949

JOHN WILEY & SONS, INC., NEW YORK

CHAPMAN & HALL, LIMITED, LONDON

ACKNOWLEDGMENTS

We would like to take this opportunity to acknowledge gratefully the cooperation of a large number of workers outside our own laboratory. These people not only gave permission to reproduce published work, but many of them generously supplied to us results and procedures as yet unpublished.

Permission to include material not published elsewhere was given by Arthur W. Adamson, S. Aronoff, H. A. Barker, James A. Bassham, Andrew A. Benson, Weldon G. Brown, Farrington Daniels, William G. Dauben, E. W. Fager, Bernard A. Fries, W. Z. Hassid, Gerhart R. Hennig, Louis R. Henrich, John L. Huston, Clinton D. Janney, William P. Jesse, Truman P. Kohman, Wright H. Langham, Richard M. Lemmon, W. B. Leslie, Willard F. Libby, Robert Loevinger, Robert B. Loftfield, Burton J. Moyer, Rosemarie Ostwald, Nello Pace, Charles N. Rice, Warwick Sakami, D. J. Salley, Hannah E. Silberstein, A. K. Solomon, L. B. Spector, Enrique Strajman, Richard B. Turner, John W. Weigl, and S. Weinhouse.

The following have allowed us to make use of previously published work: H. S. Anker, W. D. Armstrong, R. B. Bernstein, S. Gurin, F. C. Henriques, Jr., J. T. Kummer, R. B. Loftfield, J. R. Rachele, A. K. Solomon, and Vincent du Vigneaud.

Various parts of the manuscript were read by Freda Decker Christenson, Bernard A. Fries, Louis R. Henrich, and Truman P. Kohman, all of whom made valuable suggestions.

We are deeply indebted to Betty Davis Cohen and Marie Haumeder, who carried out the arduous task of typing the manuscript in all drafts, to Betty Reece Martinelli, who prepared the figures in the text, and to Marilyn Mack, who not only arranged and typed the index and bibliography but also took care of the multitude of clerical tasks associated with the final preparation of the book.

CONTENTS

vii

INTRODUCTION

The significance of having available considerable quantities of tracer isotopes of carbon, in both chemistry and biology, needs hardly be repeated. The usual definition of organic chemistry as the chemistry of carbon compounds, and its very name, "organic," can scarcely fail to impress even the uninitiated with the importance of this element in both life and industry. One of the chief impediments to the immediate large-scale application of carbon tracer work is the lack of any collection of the scattered information describing in detail the specific methods of measurement of the carbon isotopes and the procedures that have been used to incorporate the carbon isotopes into useful compounds for chemical and biological research.[1] It is the purpose of the present volume to fill this need.

Because of the present state of rapid growth of the field and its general unsettled nature, no attempt at a critical survey has been made. Rather have we tried to include sufficiently detailed descriptions of every synthesis with isotopic carbon that has been reported up to April of 1948, such that they might be used directly in the laboratory. In other words, this book is designed as a sort of laboratory manual for use in any group engaged in work involving isotopic carbon. Furthermore, the techniques of manipulation and measurement are discussed in terms of general principles. Thus do we have not only a record of past experience but also a guide to the solution of future problems.

Health Hazards

There does not seem to be any known health hazard connected with the use of C^{13}. However, certain facts should be known concerning C^{14} so that adequate precautions may be taken for the protection of laboratory personnel engaged in its use. Because the only radiation emitted by this isotope is a very weak β particle which cannot penetrate any but the very thinnest of barriers (less than a few milligrams per square centimeter), no danger is connected with the mere handling of material containing C^{14} in ordinary closed containers. What danger there is lies in the possibility of the actual ingestion of the isotope in

[1] *Radioactive Tracers in Biology*, M. D. Kamen, Academic Press, New York, 1947, contains an excellent discussion of the general methods of using all radioactive tracers in biology.

some form or another. At first sight this might also appear to be a relatively harmless situation in view of the fairly rapid turnover of carbon compounds in the living organism in spite of the very long life of C^{14}. Although this supposition seems to be true for the soft tissues of the body, there is some indication that carbon once laid down in the bone may not turn over very rapidly.[2] It has been calculated that if as much as 30 μc of carbon is evenly distributed in the hard tissues of an individual of average size he will be receiving the maximum daily dose (0.1 r/day) of radiation. It should be pointed out that this does not mean that the mere ingestion of 30 μc is the maximum allowable, since all present indications are that only a very small fraction of the radioactive carbon taken into the organism is laid down in the slowly transforming hard tissues. However, because of the many as yet unknown factors involved, it is wise to take all the convenient, and even sometimes inconvenient, precautions against the possible accidental ingestion of radioactive carbon. Generally, this involves arrangements so that any carbon radioactive gases, vapors, and dusts,[3] accidentally escaping, will have no opportunity of finding their way into the bodies of the workers. This is accomplished by working in closed systems, preferably vacuum systems, when handling gases or vapors. All other operations involving the manipulation of radioactive carbon should be performed in a well-ventilated hood. In some laboratories it has even been deemed advisable to build the vacuum system within an inclosed hood space so that accidental breakage will not contaminate the entire laboratory.

Nomenclature

Some suggestions have been made involving an introduction of a special naming system to describe in words the position of the isotopic carbon atom in an organic molecule, especially for problems of indexing. It does not seem wise to us to introduce more ramifications into the already complicated system of organic nomenclature. We have, therefore, sought to describe unequivocally a carbon-labeled compound as simply as possible in terms of the existing nomenclature.[4] The only additional convention that must be introduced is the recognition of the use of numbers and letters normally used to describe the carbon atom upon which a substituent is placed as indicating the position of the isotopic carbon atom. Very often it will be simpler to use the name of

[2] W. Bloom, H. J. Curtis, and F. C. McLean, *Science*, **105**, 485 (1947).

[3] Insoluble dusts such as $BaCO_3$ are particularly hazardous because of their tendency to collect in the lungs.

[4] See also J. W. Otvos and C. D. Wagner, *Science*, **106**, 409 (1947).

the functional group to describe a compound labeled in that group. Thus, any of the following names would be equivalent: carboxyl-labeled acetic acid, acetic acid-1-C^{14}, or carboxyl-C^{14}-acetic acid. Another acetic acid might be described by any of the following: methyl-labeled acetic acid, acetic acid-2-C^{14}, α-C^{14}-acetic acid. In some cases a name is available only in terms of a functional group, thus carboxyl-labeled benzoic acid or carboxyl-C^{14}-benzoic acid.

There is a special case in which this system of nomenclature is not explicit, namely, that of a symmetrical compound in which the symmetrically placed carbon atom(s) is labeled.[5] For example, it is possible to make two kinds of carbon-labeled ethylene. Thus, starting with 100% $C^{13}O_2$,[6] it is possible to make two different kinds of labeled ethylene. By passing through the sequence carbon dioxide → barium carbide → acetylene → ethylene, one would obtain an ethylene labeled in both carbon atoms and determinable as such on the mass spectrograph. But passing through the sequence unlabeled methyl Grignard plus labeled carbon dioxide → carboxyl-labeled acetic acid → methylene-labeled ethanol → ethylene, one would obtain an ethylene labeled only in one of the carbon atoms, as determined on the mass spectrograph. However, aside from any isotope effects on bond energies or reaction rates, these two ethylenes would behave identically in any subsequent reaction which would destroy the symmetrical relation of the two carbon atoms. For example, the hydration of either of these ethylenes will produce ethanol, which for tracer purposes is labeled equally in both carbon atoms. To the mass spectrograph, however, that ethanol resulting from the Grignard-produced ethylene will be an equimolar mixture of methylene-labeled ethanol and methyl-labeled ethanol, whereas that ethanol resulting from the carbide-produced ethylene will be a single species containing two labels in each molecule. For purposes of naming and indexing, the ethylene produced by the carbide route would be called ethylene-1,2-C^{13}, while that produced by the Grignard route would be called ethylene-1-C^{13}. However, the ethanol resulting from the hydration of either of these two ethylenes would be called ethanol-1,2-C^{13}. It should be noted that this difficulty will seldom arise in tracer work with C^{14}. It has its origin in the at-

[5] Much of the following material arose from a very helpful discussion with Drs. Otvos and Wagner, whose point of view is based upon mass-spectrograph analysis of isotopic compounds, and with Dr. Warren W. Miller.

[6] The choice of 100% C^{13} is made only for purposes of exposition. The same arguments would hold for any percentage composition of isotope, subject to the laws of statistics and any small direct isotope effect on the chemical bond energy that might be involved.

tempt to have the name of the compound correspond to the method of synthesis as well as to describe its subsequent chemical behavior.

Any attempt to be strictly rigorous in the physical sense in assigning names to isotopically labeled compounds in terms of individual molecular species therein contained seems to us entirely too cumbersome since it would involve, especially for compounds labeled with very small concentrations of C^{14}, a complete designation of the percentages of unlabeled species, species in which one atom contains the isotope, and species in which more than one of the symmetrical atoms contains the isotope. Therefore, for indexing purposes, the name of a compound labeled in a symmetrical carbon atom will be that derived from the method of synthesis. When a compound has been formed by passing through a symmetrical intermediate, it will be designated as a multiply labeled compound corresponding to the chemical behavior of the label. Such compounds will, of course, be a mixture of chemically inseparable singly labeled species. However, certain physical methods of analysis, such as the mass spectrograph or infra-red absorption, may be able to distinguish the individual species present and require a corresponding specific designation.

Mass Effects in Tracer Studies

It is well known that deuterium differs from hydrogen very appreciably in both its thermodynamic and kinetic properties, and that, when deuterium is used as a tracer for hydrogen as such, corrections frequently must be applied for this effect of the 100% difference in mass on the chemical behavior of deuterium. These effects, of course, are even larger when tritium is used as a tracer for hydrogen. However, it has been tacitly assumed that for any of the heavier elements, carbon, nitrogen, oxygen, and beyond, the chemical effects of different masses of the various isotopes would be completely negligible in any tracer study. This, however, will not be so, especially in cases involving one-carbon fragments reacting with or coming from larger molecules, for example, carboxylation and decarboxylation reactions, which are very common in chemical studies. Such effects may become appreciable, i.e., as much as 5% or more, especially in rate studies.

It is our conviction that isotopic carbon as a tracer will very soon find its place as a routine tool in many kinds of scientific laboratories. Its use on a routine basis for the investigation of physical, chemical, and biochemical transformations is comparable with that of the microscope, spectroscope, or x-ray analyses in their respective spheres. Because of their great diversity, the applications of this tool are beyond the scope of this book, and they have been included only as a bibliography, Appendix X, which contains all published tracer applications of isotopic carbon up to July, 1948.

MELVIN CALVIN
CHARLES HEIDELBERGER *
JAMES C. REID †
BERT M. TOLBERT
PETER E. YANKWICH ‡

Present Addresses (*January, 1949*):

* McArdle Memorial Laboratory, University of Wisconsin, Madison, Wisconsin.
† National Cancer Institute, Bethesda, Maryland.
‡ Department of Chemistry, University of Illinois, Urbana, Illinois.

Chapter 1

PRODUCTION AND PROPERTIES

OF ISOTOPIC CARBON

Five carbon isotopes are known, their mass numbers ranging from 10 to 14. Ordinary stable carbon is a mixture of carbon 12 and 13, the relative abundance of the heavier isotope being slightly more than one-hundredth that of the lighter. Two of the remaining isotopes, C^{10} and C^{11}, decay by the emission of energetic positrons, while the heaviest known carbon, C^{14}, is unstable with respect to negative β-ray emission. Isotopes of still greater mass number are not yet known, but the mass of the C^{15} atom has been estimated by Bethe. The half-life of C^{10} is very short, a few seconds, and this rapid decay has so far prevented its use in any tracer application; for this reason the production and properties of C^{10} will not be discussed in the paragraphs below. Carbon 11, enhanced mixtures of the stable isotopes, and carbon 14 have all found extensive applications in tracer-type experimentation.

Carbon 11 Production

Several target elements are known to yield C^{11} under suitable bombardment conditions. The first production of this isotope was noted during the proton irradiation of boron.[1] The reaction involved is B^{10} (p, γ) C^{11}.[2] Several laboratories investigated the deuteron bombardment of boric oxide [3] and found that the cross section for the (d, n) reaction was sufficiently great at the bombarding energies used (1–5 Mev) that large activities due to C^{11} were produced. In one research, the radioactivity volatilized by heating the target to 600° was subjected to a scheme of analysis which ruled out all elements but carbon.[4] A modification of this analysis was later used in the assignment of the

[1] H. C. Crane and T. Lauritsen, *Phys. Rev.*, **45**, 497 (1934); W. H. Barkas, *Phys. Rev.*, **56**, 287 (1939). See also R. Phillips and W. K. H. Panofsky, *Bull. Am. Phys. Soc.*, **23**, No. 5, 9 (1948).

[2] $_5B^{10} + _1H^1 = _6C^{11} + h\nu$.

[3] W. A. Fowler, L. A. Delsasso, and C. C. Lauritsen, *Phys. Rev.*, **49**, 561 (1936); J. D. Cockcroft, C. W. Gilbert, and E. T. S. Walton, *Proc. Roy. Soc. London*, **A148**, 225 (1935).

[4] D. M. Yost, L. Ridenour, and K. Shinohara, *J. Chem. Phys.*, **3**, 133 (1935).

C^{14} activity.[5] The B^{11} (p, n) and N^{14} (p, α) reactions [6] have been observed to yield C^{11}, as well as the transmutation C^{12} $(n, 2n)$ C^{11}.[7] Because of its short half-life, the isotope must be produced in the laboratory where it is to be used. Since most production of this type involves cyclotron bombardment, the reaction used should be economical of the available beam intensity. The $(n, 2n)$ reaction on carbon is not used since the target and product elements are the same, resulting in great dilution of the activity, and because the process is endothermic. Nitrogen bombardment has not been seriously contemplated for many reasons, chief of which is the ease with which the deuteron bombardment of boric oxide targets can be carried out. The techniques involved in the preparation of C^{11} by the irradiation of boron have been reviewed by Kamen.[8]

When boric oxide is irradiated, the principal products of the nuclear reaction are $C^{11}O$ and $C^{11}O_2$. These diffuse out of the oxide target rather rapidly. That both oxides are produced is fortunate, for, although the combustion of the monoxide to the dioxide can be easily and quite rapidly carried out, the reduction of the dioxide to the monoxide involves much more time-consuming procedures. When use is to be made of $C^{11}O$, carrier amounts of both gases are added to the hollow target chamber and the active carbon dioxide is trapped in a spiral frozen in liquid air. The monoxide is either swept out with an inert gas such as helium or is pumped into a suitable vessel by means of a Töppler pump. Approximately 30% of the gaseous activity is in the form of carbon monoxide.

Properties of C^{11}

The half-life of C^{11} is 20.5 minutes,[9,10] and its use is necessarily conditioned by this fact. However, as will be demonstrated in the sections on synthesis, certain reactions are available which give high yields

[5] S. Ruben and M. D. Kamen, Phys. Rev., **59**, 349 (1941).

[6] W. H. Barkas, Phys. Rev., **56**, 287 (1939). For results of studies on the reaction $C^{12}(p, pn)C^{11}$ see W. W. Chupp and E. M. McMillan, Phys. Rev., **72**, 873 (1947); E. M. McMillan and R. D. Miller, Phys. Rev., **73**, 80 (1948); W. Heckrotte and P. Wolff, Phys. Rev., **73**, 264 (1948); W. W. Chupp, E. Gardner, and T. B. Taylor, Phys. Rev., **73**, 742 (1948).

[7] M. L. Pool, J. M. Cork, and R. L. Thornton, Phys. Rev., **52**, 239 (1937). This reaction at high neutron energies has been studied by E. M. McMillan and H. F. York, Phys. Rev., **73**, 262 (1948); and W. Heckrotte and P. Wolff, Phys. Rev., **73**, 265 (1948). See also R. L. Thornton and R. W. Senseman, Phys. Rev., **72**, 872 (1947).

[8] M. D. Kamen, Radioactive Tracers in Biology, Academic Press, New York, 1947, pp. 149–151.

[9] A. K. Solomon, Phys. Rev., **60**, 279 (1941).

[10] A. A. Townsend, Proc. Roy. Soc. London, **A177**, 357 (1941).

in relatively short times and which incorporate the carbon activity into a number of useful compounds. If the experiments to be performed with the final product are designed and laid out with sufficient care, one can easily follow biological experiments through 12 half-lives; whenever there is an advantage in using the isotope for ordinary chemical work this time can be extended to 15 or 16 half-lives. Ultimately, the length of time available for the carrying out of experimental and counting procedures is dependent upon the bombardment intensity available. Little is to be gained by prolonging the irradiation of the target material beyond a half hour or so because of the rapid decay of the isotope.

C^{11} emits an energetic positron; the maximum energy has been determined by several methods. Observations of cloud-chamber tracks lead to a value of 0.95 ± 0.03 Mev for the maximum energy,[11] foil absorption measurements yield 1.03 ± 0.03 Mev,[12] while β-ray spectrometer studies give 0.980 ± 0.005 Mev.[10] A positron of this energy will penetrate about 400 mg/cm^2 of aluminum, which fact alone would make detection by ordinary means a simple matter. However, the production of annihilation radiation during the absorption of the positrons makes the detection very simple indeed. Almost any thick-walled Geiger-Müller counter tube can be used, and recourse need never be had to ionization chambers filled with active carbon dioxide. Because of its radioactive properties, carbon 11 is a useful tool for studying the processes of living systems. A good example of its use in this type of investigation is in the study of photosynthesis.[13] Radioactive carbon monoxide has been used to study the turnover in the "blood pools" of the human circulatory system.[14] In an experiment of this type one must devise a detector which is highly directional in its response; the manner in which this is accomplished is discussed in the sections on instruments.

Carbon 13

Of the three isotopes of carbon useful in tracer work, C^{13} [15] and C^{14} exist in nature.[16] "Normal" carbon is approximately 1.1% C^{13} and

[11] L. A. Delsasso, M. G. White, W. Barkas, and E. C. Creutz, Phys. Rev., **58**, 586 (1940).

[12] B. L. Moore, Phys. Rev., **57**, 355 (1940).

[13] S. Ruben et al., J. Am. Chem. Soc., **61**, 661 (1939), **62**, 3443, 3450, 3451 (1940).

[14] C. A. Tobias, J. H. Lawrence, F. J. W. Roughton, W. S. Root, and M. I. Gregersen, Am. J. Physiol., **145**, 253 (1945).

[15] Carbon from several sources has been analyzed by: A. O. Nier and E. Gulbransen, J. Am. Chem. Soc., **61**, 697 (1939); B. F. Murphy and A. O. Nier, Phys. Rev., **59**, 771 (1941).

[16] E. C. Anderson, W. F. Libby, S. Weinhouse, A. F. Reid, A. D. Kirshenbaum and A. V. Grosse, Science, **105**, 576 (1947); Phys. Rev., **72**, 931 (1947); A. V. Grosse and W. F. Libby, Science, **106**, 88 (1947).

98.9% C^{12}. For use in experiment, the concentration of the heavy isotope has been increased by chemical exchange and by thermal diffusion.[17] Thermal diffusion has been carried out with methane,[18] on a laboratory scale, furnishing the basis for a commercial method of concentration.[19]

Cosmic radiations produce a very small amount of C^{14}; computations carried out with data quoted in the paper by Anderson et al. lead to an abundance (in biologically derived methane) of about $10^{-10}\%$ C^{14} relative to ordinary carbon as 100%. It is doubtful that any tracer use can be made of naturally occurring C^{14}.

The chemical-exchange methods for isotope concentration depend upon the fact that there is a slight difference in the equilibrium constant for a reaction involving one isotope from the constant for the same reaction involving another isotope of the same element; the effect of this difference can be magnified many times, by methods commonly used in fractional distillation, to produce a concentration of one isotope at the expense of others.

The reaction now largely used in commercial production by the exchange method is

$$HC^{12}N \ (g) + C^{13}N^- = HC^{13}N \ (g) + C^{12}N^- \tag{1}$$

The equilibrium constant, calculated from spectroscopic data, is 1.012 at 25°.[20] The concentration is carried out by allowing a cyanide solution to flow down a packed column while hydrogen cyanide at low pressure is pumped up in countercurrent. At the top, hydrogen cyanide is continuously absorbed in sodium hydroxide and sent back down the column. When equilibrium has been reached, hydrogen cyanide enriched in C^{13} is drawn off at the top continuously while new normal alkali cyanide is added to the system.[21]

The exchange between bicarbonate ion and carbon dioxide is ordinarily

$$C^{13}O_2 \ (g) + HC^{12}O_3^- = HC^{13}O_3^- + C^{12}O_2 \ (g) \tag{2}$$

too slow for practical use, but successful heterogeneous catalysts have been discovered and used. The principal advantage of the use of the

[17] T. L. Ibbs, *Physica*, **4**, 1133 (1937); K. Clusius and G. Dickel, *Naturwissenschaften*, **26**, 546 (1938); H. S. Taylor, *Nature*, **144**, 8 (1939); A. O. Nier, *Phys. Rev.*, **56**, 1009 (1939), **57**, 358 (1940).

[18] A. O. Nier and J. Bardeen, *J. Chem. Phys.*, **9**, 690 (1941); see also T. I. Taylor and R. B. Bernstein, *J. Am. Chem. Soc.*, **69**, 2076 (1947).

[19] Houdry Process Co., Marcus Hook, Pennsylvania.

[20] H. C. Urey and L. J. Greiff, *J. Am. Chem. Soc.*, **57**, 321 (1935).

[21] I. Roberts, H. G. Thode, and H. C. Urey, *J. Chem. Phys.*, **7**, 137 (1939); C. A. Hutchinson, D. W. Stewart, and H. C. Urey, *J. Chem. Phys.*, **8**, 532 (1940).

carbon dioxide exchange is that there are no problems of toxicity or of polymer formation as there are with the cyanide reaction.[22]

Carbon 14 Production

The reaction N^{14} (n, p) C^{14} was suggested to account for the appearance of protons when nitrogen was bombarded with fast neutrons.[23] Later, what was evidently the same reaction was observed when slow neutrons were used.[24] In a deliberate search for the isotope, Ruben and Kamen were able to isolate and identify it from a graphite probe, enriched in C^{13}, which had been cyclotron-bombarded with deuterons of low energy (3–4 Mev), and later from solutions of ammonium nitrate which received, for several months, stray neutron radiation from the 60-inch Crocker Laboratory cyclotron.[25] The reaction O^{17} (n, α) C^{14} has also been observed.[26]

The investigation of Ruben and Kamen demonstrated that the relative efficiency of deuteron bombardment in no way compensated for the dilution of activity inherent in the use of a carbon target. It was also proved that the cross section for the (n, p) reaction was sufficiently large for quite profitable use to be made of the process if even moderate neutron fluxes were available. The development of nuclear reactors has therefore made possible large-scale production of C^{14} of very high specific activity by the neutron bombardment of nitrogenous substances.

Current production of the isotope for distribution is by irradiation of saturated ammonium nitrate solutions in the Clinton pile.[27] The bombardment of beryllium nitride has been investigated,[28] and work is in progress on calcium nitrate.[29] Though the activity from these sources will usually be received by the investigator in the form of solid barium carbonate, the target chemistry of the N^{14} (n, p) reaction is of consider-

²² A. F. Reid, in *Preparation and Measurement of Isotopic Tracers*, J. W. Edwards, Ann Arbor, Michigan, 1947, pp. 3–10; A. F. Reid and H. C. Urey, *J. Chem. Phys.*, **7**, 137 (1943).

²³ F. N. D. Kurie, *Phys. Rev.*, **45**, 904 (1934), **46**, 330 (1934); P. Huber and A. Stebler, *Phys. Rev.*, **73**, 89 (1948).

²⁴ T. W. Bonner and W. M. Brubaker, *Phys. Rev.*, **48**, 469 (1935); W. E. Burcham and M. Goldhaber, *Proc. Cambridge Phil. Soc.*, **32**, 632 (1936); P. Huber and A. Stebler, *Phys. Rev.*, **73**, 85 (1948); W. E. Shoupp and B. Jennings, *Bull. Am. Phys. Soc.*, **23**, No. 3, 39 (1948).

²⁵ M. D. Kamen and S. Ruben, *Phys. Rev.*, **58**, 149 (1940); S. Ruben and M. D. Kamen, *Phys. Rev.*, **59**, 349 (1941).

²⁶ E. P. Hincks, *Phys. Rev.*, **70**, 770 (1946).

²⁷ L. D. Norris and A. H. Snell, *Science*, **105**, 265 (1947).

²⁸ P. E. Yankwich, *J. Chem. Phys.*, **15**, 374 (1947).

²⁹ C. A. Thomas, *Chem. Eng. News*, **25**, 1572 (1947).

able interest. In the ammonium nitrate solutions, Ruben and Kamen found activities ascribable to carbon monoxide and dioxide, but none in any other one-carbon compound (formic acid, however, was not isolated). Later workers found the radioactive oxides but in addition discovered considerable activity in formic acid and a small amount in methanol. No radiocyanide or radioformaldehyde could be detected.[30] The existence, in the discarded solutions from the Clinton carbon factory, of approximately equal amounts of radiomethanol and radioformaldehyde [27,31] has been reported. The products of very low-intensity neutron irradiation of urea, hydrazine, glycine, pyridine, and aniline are reported in one of the earlier papers.[30]

Beryllium nitride presents an interesting picture. Of all the possible one-carbon compounds only formaldehyde is definitely inactive. Large percentages of the activity are found in methane and formic acid; smaller and approximately equal amounts are found in the other compounds. Cyanide is produced in a quantity much smaller than that expected, and it can be shown that the oxides have no lattice-trapped precursors; i.e., they are produced from air trapped in the powdered nitride. The production of a large amount of methane is important because its synthesis from the dioxide is rather time-consuming (see page 171).

In Table I are collected some of the data regarding the carbon compounds produced when nitrogen-containing substances are irradiated

TABLE I

RADIOACTIVE CARBON COMPOUNDS PRODUCED BY THE REACTION: N^{14} (n, p) C^{14}

Active Body	Target Substance—Percentage of Total Activity					
	Be_3N_2 solid	NH_4NO_3 solid	NH_4NO_3 saturated solution	H_2NCH_2COOH solid	H_2NCONH_2 solid	$N_2H_4 \cdot 2HCl$ moist crystals
CO	0.9	20	30	0	5	10
CH_4	63	0	<0.1	0	0	5
CO_2	3.3	80	60	10	40	20
CN^-	3.5	0	<0.1	15	55	70
HCHO	<0.01 } Total	0	1	0	0	0
CH_3OH	>1 } 27%	0	1	50	0	0
HCOOH	>16	0	10	30	0	0

30 P. E. Yankwich, G. K. Rollefson, and T. H. Norris, *J. Chem. Phys.*, **14**, 131 (1946).

31 W. B. Leslie, *Experimental Use of C^{14}*, Atomic Energy Commission, MDDC 674, Nov. 15, 1946. See also L. D. Norris and A. H. Snell, *Phys. Rev.*, **73**, 254 (1948).

with neutrons. Only the experiments with beryllium nitride were carried out on pile-bombarded material; the other analyses were made on cyclotron-irradiated samples and are not accurate because of the low activities produced. For comparison, the sample of Be_3N_2 analyzed had an activity of 3.3×10^7 c/min/g of contained nitrogen, while that of the most active sample obtained from cyclotron bombardment (ammonium nitrate solution) was only 80 c/min/g of contained nitrogen.

Properties of C¹⁴

The half-life of C^{14} has been the subject of several investigations because the β disintegration of this isotope probably proceeds through a forbidden transition, the observed half-life being much longer than that which one would expect, knowing the maximum β-particle energy to be about 0.15 Mev. The early estimates of Kamen ranged from 1,000 to 25,000 years, but such variety is understandable when one considers that the only data available on bombardment yield were very rough. Samples of known C^{14} content (determined by mass spectrograph) have been counted in a variety of ways by several investigators. The published values, all involving the use of solid samples, are $5,300 \pm 800$,[32] $5,100 \pm 200$,[32] and $4,700 \pm 500$ years.[33]

C^{14} emits β particles with a maximum energy of about 0.15 Mev. Ruben and Kamen quoted a figure of 0.145 ± 0.015 Mev, obtained from rough foil absorption data. Cloud-chamber experiments have led to the value 0.168 ± 0.010 Mev.[34] Accurate measurement of the maximum range in aluminum of C^{14} β particles has been made,[35] using the technique suggested by Feather,[36] which consists in comparing, at various points, the activity vs. absorber thickness curve for the radiations whose maximum range is desired with that obtained for RaE under identical geometrical conditions. The data of Marshall and Ward [37] were used to convert the maximum range to an energy value. The observed range of 27.9 ± 0.3 mg/cm² corresponds to a maximum energy

[32] L. D. Norris and M. G. Inghram, *Phys. Rev.*, **70**, 772 (1946); **73**, 350 (1948).

[33] A. F. Reid, J. R. Dunning, S. Weinhouse, and A. V. Grosse, *Phys. Rev.*, **70**, 431 (1946).

[34] R. C. Raymond, doctoral dissertation, University of California, 1941.

[35] A. K. Solomon, R. G. Gould, and C. B. Anfinsen, *Phys. Rev.*, **72**, 1097 (1947). The maximum energy has been obtained from β-ray spectrometer measurements. The following values have been reported: 0.154 Mev, P. W. Levy, *Phys. Rev.*, **72**, 248 (1947); 0.155 ± 0.002 Mev, J. L. Berggren and R. K. Osborne, *Bull. Am. Phys. Soc.*, **23**, No. 3, 46 (1948); 0.1563 ± 0.0010 Mev, L. M. Langer, C. S. Cook, and H. C. Price, Jr., *Bull. Am. Phys. Soc.*, **23**, No. 4, 15 (1948).

[36] N. Feather, *Proc. Cambridge Phil. Soc.*, **35**, 599 (1938).

[37] J. S. Marshall and A. G. Ward, *Can. J. Research*, **15**, 29 (1939).

of 0.154 ± 0.004 Mev. In Table II are collected some of the important characteristics of the several isotopes of carbon.[38]

TABLE II

PROPERTIES OF THE CARBON NUCLIDES

	Abundance, %	Exact Mass $O^{16} = 16.000000$	Nuclear Spin	Radiation	Maximum Energy Mev	Half-Life	Usual Production
C^{10}	......	10.0210 ± 0.0003		β^+	3.4 ± 0.1	8.8 sec	B (p, n)
C^{11}	......	11.01495 ± 0.00009		β^+	0.98 ± 0.01	20.5 min	B (d, n)
C^{12}	98.9	12.00382 ± 0.00004	0				
C^{13}	1.1	13.00751 ± 0.00010	½				
C^{14}	$<10^{-10}$	14.00767 ± 0.00005	0	β^-	0.154 ± 0.004	5,100 yr	N (n, p)
(C^{15})	......	(15.0165)		(β^-)	(11)	(Short)	

[38] The mass values are taken from the table of nuclear species contained in H. A. Bethe, *Elementary Nuclear Theory*, John Wiley & Sons, New York, 1947.

Chapter 2

MEASUREMENT OF CARBON 13

The radioactive isotopes are detected and measured, directly or indirectly, by means of their nuclear radiations. The radioactive isotope is not usually present in an amount so large that the isotopic constitution of the element is appreciably altered. However, enrichment of the normal mixture of stable isotopes in one particular isotope produces a change in constitution which can be detected and measured with suitable instruments. The use of C^{13} as a tracer depends upon the fact that one can detect an amount of this isotope only slightly in excess of that normally found.

If two ions of different mass but identical charge and velocity pass through a uniform magnetic field which is perpendicular to the plane of their motion, they will describe circular paths of different radii, the ion of greater mass being less deflected. Ions of the same specific charge, e/m, will traverse paths with identical curvature, regardless of the absolute magnitudes of either the charges or masses. Instruments which combine ions of the same specific charge into discrete beams, so that the intensities or curvatures of several such beams can be compared, are known as mass spectrometers or mass spectrographs.

These instruments can usually be divided into two classes: the first consists of those of the "double-focusing" type, ions of originally differing direction and velocity but the same e/m being combined into a single beam; the second class consists of instruments which have moderate direction focusing power and in the use of which ion sources yielding essentially monoenergetic beams must be employed. The double-focusing instruments were developed by Bainbridge, Dempster, and Mattauch and Herzog; [1] they are normally used with photographic recording and are best suited for analyses in which the greatest importance must be attached to high resolving power, large dispersion, and high accuracy in the measurement of the relative masses of several nuclei. The second type, often called "magnetic spectrometers," use electrical

---

[1] K. T. Bainbridge, *J. Franklin Inst.*, **215**, 509 (1933); K. T. Bainbridge and E. B. Jordan, *Phys. Rev.*, **50**, 282 (1936); A. J. Dempster, *Proc. Am. Phil. Soc.*, **75**, 755 (1935); J. Mattauch and R. Herzog, *Z. Physik*, **89**, 786 (1934).

recording and are favored where relative abundances are to be measured. The simplicity of this type of instrument has resulted in a rapid increase in the number of laboratories equipped to measure isotopic abundances on a routine basis. Many of the recent refinements and simplifications have been due to Nier, and the major portion of commercially available instruments are constructed according to his designs.

Principles of Mass Separation in Electric and Magnetic Fields

In the Dempster magnetic spectrometer, as modified by Nier, positive ions are produced by electron bombardment of a gas containing the sample submitted for analysis, usually carbon dioxide in work with C^{13}. A monoenergetic beam of particles is formed by accelerating a collimated pencil of ions through a potential difference of several hundred volts. If m is the mass of a particular positive ion, e the charge which it carries, and V the accelerating potential, then

$$Ve = \tfrac{1}{2}mv^2 \tag{1}$$

After acceleration the ion enters a magnetic field of strength H in which it follows a circular path of radius R according to the relation

$$He = \frac{mv}{R} \tag{2}$$

If these equations are combined, it is found that

$$\frac{e}{m} = \frac{2V}{H^2R^2} \tag{3}$$

The ions emerging from the field pass through a narrow slit and impinge upon a collecting electrode. It is clear that, for constant values of V, H, and R, only ions having a particular value of e/m will pass into the detector. As it is usually convenient to keep the magnetic field strength constant, the mass scale is scanned by varying the accelerating potential.

Ion Production and Acceleration

The function of the ion source is to produce positive ions containing the desired element, usually by electron impact; further, the particles thus ionized must be formed into a monoenergetic beam. The type of source used in most instruments today is based upon that devised by Bleakney and modified by Nier.[2] It is important that the electrons

---

[2] W. Bleakney, *Phys. Rev.*, **34**, 157 (1929), **40**, 496 (1932); A. O. Nier, *Rev. Sci. Instruments*, **11**, 212 (1940). See also A. O. Nier, *Phys. Rev.*, **52**, 933 (1937), **53**, 282 (1938), and *Rev. Sci. Instruments*, **18**, 398 (1947).

used to bombard the sample be themselves of one energy; achievement of this is dependent upon the stability of the filament supply, which is now usually regulated electronically. The accelerating potentials used vary from 500 to 1,500 volts, depending upon the instrument. Regulation of the accelerating voltage is also accomplished by means of electronic stabilizing circuits.

Magnetic Analysis and Beam Measurement

In the original Dempster instrument [3] magnetic focusing was achieved by turning the ion beam through 180°; geometrical focusing properties are obtained which were first achieved by Classen [4] in the measurement of e/m for electrons. The use of 180° focusing necessitates large magnets; smaller instruments employing magnetic deviations of 45° to 90° have been constructed, [5] with a great reduction in the bulk of the instrument. After leaving the magnetic analyzer the ions are focused at a slit defining the detector. Generally, they are allowed to fall upon a collecting plate, and this ion current is measured with an electrometer.

Nier has reviewed the application of the mass spectrometer to the measurement of C^{13} concentrations, and the reader is referred to these articles for greater detail concerning instrumentation. [6]

Vacuum Requirements

An important part of these instruments is the vacuum system necessary for their operation. The vacuum apparatus is in two parts, one pumping on the spectrometer tube, source, and detector, and the other used for handling the gas samples. In order that the various ions follow their predicted paths, collisions with other ions, or with molecules of residual gases in the system, must be kept to the minimum. So that this condition may be satisfied, it is necessary that the path length in the spectrometer be small relative to the mean free path of the positive ion; therefore the apparatus is operated at pressures of the order of 10^{-5} to 10^{-7} mm of Hg. Vacuum systems for mass spectrographs are discussed in some detail on pages 146–147.

Background Effects

A systematic background is associated with mass spectrometers, somewhat analogous to that encountered in radioactivity detectors.

[3] A. J. Dempster, *Phil. Mag.*, **31**, 438 (1916).

[4] E. J. Classen, *Physik. Z.*, **9**, 762 (1908).

[5] J. A. Hipple, *J. Applied Phys.*, **13**, 551 (1942), for example.

[6] A. O. Nier, in *Preparation and Measurement of Isotopic Tracers*, J. W. Edwards, Ann Arbor, Michigan, 1947; in *Report of a Symposium on the Use of Isotopes in Biological Research*, Chicago, March 3–4, 1947.

It is caused by polymerization and hold-up of sample materials in the ion source, by leaks in the system, and by adsorption of various substances on the interior surfaces of the spectrometer. If many different materials are presented for analysis the background can become quite large, and it may be necessary to pump the instrument for long periods before use and to heat the analyzer tube. System contamination results in large background peaks at mass 18, $(H_2O^{16})^+$, and mass 28, $(C^{12}O^{16})^+$. The peak due to water is very difficult to remove; so difficult, in fact, that samples to be analyzed for deuterium must be submitted as hydrogen gas. Air leaks contribute mostly to peak heights at mass 28, N_2^+, and 32, O_2^+.[7]

The sample is introduced into the ion source through a controlled leak. The amount of gas necessary for the usual routine analysis is very small. The relative abundances of the krypton and xenon isotopes was measured with a sample which would have occupied only a cubic millimeter at standard temperature and pressure.[8] About four or five times this amount of carbon dioxide is sufficient for very accurate measurements with carbon.[9]

Carbon dioxide has been found to be a satisfactory gas for analysis since its ions do not appear close to those of any large background contaminant, it can be transferred from one part of the system to another with either mercury pumps or liquid air, and it can be stored in solid form as a carbonate. The mass numbers scanned in the analysis of carbon dioxide range from 44, $(C^{12}O^{16}O^{16})^+$, to 50, $(C^{14}O^{18}O^{18})^+$. The peaks from 28 to 32, due to the various CO^+ ions, are not as useful because of backgrounds caused by nitrogen and by carbon monoxide contamination of the system. Not all the possible isotopic species make a measurable contribution to the various peaks scanned. For instance, even in a sample containing a high percentage of C^{13}, the peak at 49 due to $C^{13}O^{18}O^{18}$ is not usually observable because of the low abundance of O^{18}. If very accurate measurements are to be made, the observed peak heights must be corrected for the small contribution of dioxide ions containing a lighter carbon but a heavier oxygen, and vice versa. For example, let us suppose that a determination is made involving a sample known to contain about ten times as much C^{12} as C^{13}; the most accurate analysis possible is desired. Oxygen is a mixture of isotopes

---

[7] The high sensitivity of the mass spectrometer in the absence of an appreciable background has been applied to leak detection. A small spectrometer is attached to the pumping system of a large piece of apparatus, and leaks are located by passing over the outer surfaces and joints a probe which releases a fine jet of tank helium. There is no appreciable background at mass 4.

[8] H. G. Thode and R. L. Graham, *Can. J. Research*, **A25**, 1 (1947).

[9] A. O. Nier, *Rev. Sci. Instruments*, **11**, 212 (1940).

of masses 16, 17, and 18; the relative abundances of the three are 490, 1.00, and 0.20, respectively.[8,10] If the result of the carbon analysis is based on the ratio (mass 44)/(mass 45), the denominator must be corrected for the contribution of $C^{12}O^{16}O^{17}$. If the relative amount of C^{13} were closely that in the naturally occurring mixture an important correction might have to be made for the contribution due to the $C^{12}O^{16}O^{17}$ combination. In analyses for C^{14} the situation is of greater importance, for at mass 46 contributions due to $C^{13}O^{16}O^{17}$ and $C^{12}O^{16}O^{18}$ may be appreciable.

Accuracy

When the corrected peak heights are known, the relative isotopic abundances are easily computed. The accuracy obtainable in tracer work is determined by the precision with which the concentrations in an experimentally derived sample are compared with those of a standard. With the instruments commercially available measurement of changes in the isotope ratios of carbon can be made to 0.5–1% with relative ease. There are many instances in which this accuracy can be improved by care in taking the measurements. As an example of how this may affect the planning of an experiment involving considerable dilution, it has been calculated that a sample enriched tenfold in C^{13} can be diluted a thousandfold and still be detected if the ratio C^{13}/C^{12} can be determined to $\pm 1\%$.

The refinements in relative abundance measurements can be based upon the fact that the absolute intensities of several beams may vary continuously but their relative strengths remain the same. Accuracy is improved, therefore, when the intensities of all collector currents are read simultaneously. This type of measurement is practical where the relative abundance of two isotopes is to be determined. A double collector is used, and the ion currents from each are balanced against those from the other by a null circuit. The operation of such a method has been described,[11] and it was found that isotopic abundance ratios in two samples which were very nearly alike, and in which the abundance ratio of the two isotopes was approximately 100 to 1, could be measured with an accuracy considerably better than 0.1%.

In stable isotope work the data are expressed in several ways. Sometimes the figure quoted is the atom percentage of a certain isotope in the sample, based on all isotopes of the element. For instance, if the ratio R, C^{13}/C^{12}, is determined, then the atom percentage of C^{13} in a

[10] B. F. Murphy and A. O. Nier, *Phys. Rev.*, **59**, 771 (1941).

[11] A. O. Nier, E. P. Ney, and M. G. Inghram, *Phys. Rev.*, **70**, 116 (1946); *Rev. Sci. Instruments*, **18**, 294 (1947).

given sample is equal to $100R/(R + 1)$. The abundance of C^{13} in naturally occurring tissues and minerals varies somewhat from source to source. The atom percentage excess is often used to express the tracer concentration. It is equal to $100 \left[\dfrac{R}{R + 1} - \dfrac{R_{standard}}{R_{standard} + 1} \right]$; depending upon the sample and standard, it may have positive or negative values.

The techniques of isotope dilution, and the interrelations of the various methods of expressing isotope abundance and dilution data, are discussed in detail in Appendix I.

Chapter 3

CHARACTERISTICS

OF CARBON TRACER RADIATIONS

The process known as radioactive decay is brought about because of the existence or production of certain unstable combinations and configurations of the elemental particles of which nuclei are made.[1] Decay may proceed by the emission from the nucleus of an α particle (α, $_2\text{He}^{4\,++}$), a β particle (β^-, $_{-1}\beta^0$), a positron (β^+, $_1\beta^0$), or a γ ray (γ, $h\nu$); only β-particle and positron emission are of interest in tracer work with the isotopes of carbon, but the properties of γ rays must be discussed because of the appearance of electromagnetic radiation with positrons.

The two stable isotopes of carbon are made up of six protons and either six or seven neutrons. C^{12} is almost a hundred times as abundant as the heavier isotope,[2] and, as might be inferred, it has the higher total binding energy of the two.

There are three known unstable isotopes of carbon. The lightest of these is C^{10}; it is a positron emitter [3] of very short half-life, 8.8 sec-

---

[1] General references on relation of structure to decay:

H. A. Bethe and R. F. Bacher, Nuclear Physics, A, Stationary States of Nuclei, *Revs. Modern Phys.*, **8**, 82–299 (1936).

H. A. Bethe, Nuclear Dynamics, B, Theoretical, *Revs. Modern Phys.*, **9**, 69–244 (1937).

M. S. Livingston and H. A. Bethe, Nuclear Dynamics, C, Experimental, *Revs. Modern Phys.*, **9**, 245–390 (1937).

G. Gamow, *Structure of Atomic Nuclei and Nuclear Transformations*, Oxford University Press, 1937.

F. Rasetti, *Elements of Nuclear Physics*, Prentice-Hall, New York, 1936.

C. F. von Weizsaker, *Die Atomkerne*, Akademische Verlagsgesellschaft, Leipzig, 1937.

H. Kallman, *Einführung in die Kernphysik*, Deuticke, Vienna, 1937.

H. A. Bethe, *Elementary Nuclear Theory*, John Wiley & Sons, New York, 1947.

E. M. McMillan and E. Segré, in *Lecture Series in Nuclear Physics*, Atomic Energy Commission, MDDC 1175.

[2] A. O. Nier and E. Gulbransen, *J. Am. Chem. Soc.*, **61**, 697 (1939).

[3] L. A. Delsasso, M. G. White, W. H. Barkas, and E. C. Creutz, *Phys. Rev.*, **58**, 586 (1941).

onds.[4]   Another positron-emitting carbon is the isotope of mass 11; its half-life, 20.5 minutes [5] though short, is long enough to permit certain types of experimentation.   Decay by positron emission makes it particularly valuable for *in vivo* tracer work because of the production during absorption of the positrons of penetrating γ rays.   The third radioactive carbon isotope is C^{14}.[6]   It decays by the emission of a β particle of moderate energy [7] but with a very long half-life,[8] several thousand years.

In general, a proton-neutron ratio lower than those of the neighboring stable isotopes results in a nucleus which can gain stability by emitting a negative particle, β particle, while positron emission results from a proton-neutron ratio larger than those of nearby stable nuclei of the same element.   Positron emission is always accompanied by γ rays, known as annihilation radiation, which are produced by the union of positron-electron pairs.[9]

In the discussion to follow, the term β particles will be used for negative electrons of nuclear origin in discussions requiring specificity; the term β rays will be understood to mean electrons of nuclear origin having either positive or negative signs.

Radioactivity is a chance phenomenon,[10] and its rate cannot be affected by any known physical or chemical process or condition. Experimental determinations of the rates of decay of radioactive substances have shown that these processes take place according to an exponential law, the rate of decay at any instant being proportional

[4] W. H. Barkas, E. C. Creutz, L. A. Delsasso, J. G. Fox, and M. G. White, *Phys. Rev.*, **57**, 562 (1940).

[5] A. K. Solomon, *Phys. Rev.*, **60**, 279 (1941); A. A. Townsend, *Proc. Roy. Soc. London*, **A177**, 357 (1941).

[6] S. Ruben and M. D. Kamen, *Phys. Rev.*, **59**, 349 (1941).

[7] P. W. Levy, *Phys. Rev.*, **72**, 248 (1947).   See reference 35, Chapter 1.

[8] L. D. Norris and M. G. Inghram, *Phys. Rev.*, **70**, 772 (1946), **73**, 350 (1948); A. F. Reid, J. R. Dunning, S. Weinhouse, and A. von Grosse, *Phys. Rev.*, **70**, 431 (1946).   Compare with early estimate by M. D. Kamen and S. Ruben, *Phys. Rev.*, **58**, 194 (1940).

[9] C. Y. Chao, *Phys. Rev.*, **36**, 1519 (1930), *Proc. Natl. Acad. Sci. U. S.*, **16**, 431 (1931); L. Meitner and H. H. Hapfeld, *Z. Physik*, **67**, 147 (1930).

[10] F. Kohlrausch, *Ergeb. exakt. Naturw.*, **5**, 197 (1926); L. F. Curtiss, *J. Research Natl. Bur. Standards*, **4**, 595 (1930); A. F. Kovarik, *Phys. Rev.*, **13**, 272 (1919); E. Rutherford, J. Chadwick, and C. D. Ellis, *Radiations from Radioactive Substances*, Cambridge University Press, 1930, pp. 167–174; E. Rutherford, H. Geiger, and H. Bateman, *Phil. Mag.*, **20**, 698 (1910); K. W. F. Kohlrausch in *Handbuch der exptl. Physik*, **XV**, 786, W. Wein and F. Harms, Editors, Leipzig, 1928.   There is evidence that the rate of K-electron capture in isotopes of the lightest elements may be affected by chemical condition.

to the number of unstable nuclei present.[11]   The fundamental relation is expressed as follows:

$$\frac{-dN}{dt} = \lambda N \tag{1}$$

Integration of this equation gives

$$N_t = N_0 e^{-\lambda t} \tag{2}$$

where N_0 is the original number of unstable nuclei ($t = 0$), N_t is the number present after a time t, and λ is the disintegration constant.   The time $1/\lambda$ is that necessary for an active deposit to decay to $1/e$ [12] its original strength and is known as the average life.   It is now more common to speak of a "half-life" for an active body; this time is that required for the radioactivity from a deposit to fall to one-half its original intensity; the half-life is equal to $(\ln 2)/\lambda$.   As with any random process, certain momentary departures from the exponential decay relation can be observed, especially when small numbers of events are considered. These deviations have been found to follow the Poisson distribution relation; use will be made of this fact in the appendix treating the statistical errors associated with the measurement of radioactive samples.

Half-Lives

The half-lives of known radioactive nuclei range from 10^{-6} second to 10^{13} years.   Since many experiments are performed over periods which are commensurate with the half-life of the particular isotope being used, accurate knowledge of this time is often essential.

The simplest method of half-life determination is the direct observation of the decay rate at suitable time intervals.   This procedure can be applied only where the time available for experimentation differs from the half-life by no more than a factor of 100 or so.   For very short half-lives, flow methods,[13] which are in many respects identical with that type of analysis applied to chemical reaction kinetics, are sometimes used for single decay processes; for multiple or chain processes, such as are observed in the naturally occurring radioactivities, use can be made of the known family relationships between the various decaying nuclei. In many cases, the half-lives are so long that no detectable decrease in the rate of decay of a particular sample could be observed over many

[11] E. Rutherford, J. Chadwick, and C. D. Ellis, *op. cit.*, pp. 1–37; G. Hevesy and F. A. Paneth, *A Manual of Radioactivity*, 2nd Ed., Oxford University Press, 1938, pp. 126–140

[12] The e used here is the base of natural logarithms. $e = 2.71828+$.

[13] See also A. C. Graves and R. L. Walker, *Phys. Rev.*, **71**, 1 (1947).

years; in these instances, one must determine by some means the actual number of unstable nuclei that are present. From a knowledge of this quantity and a measurement of the decay rate, the disintegration constant, and thus the half-life, can be evaluated by substituting the experimental observations into equation 1.

The half-life of C^{11} is always determined by actually following the decay of the activity since $T_{1/2} = 20.5$ minutes; a plot of the decay curve for this isotope is shown in Fig. 1. The half-life of C^{14}, approximately

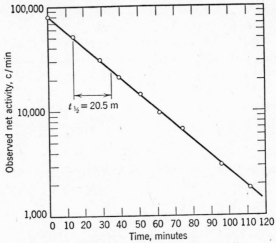

Fig. 1. Decay of a sample containing C^{11}.

5,100 years, is so long that the second method noted above must be used. Usually one measures with a mass spectrometer the C^{14} content of a very active sample of carbonate and then determines the radioactive strength of a diluted aliquot.[8] There is, however, the possibility of determining the half-life from bombardment yield data. For example, if a sample containing nitrogen is irradiated with neutrons and one knows the neutron flux, time of bombardment, capture cross section of N^{14} for these particular neutrons, and the number of N^{14} atoms in the sample, then the amount of C^{14} produced during the bombardment is given by the relation

$$ft\sigma N_N = N_0 \tag{3}$$

where the various factors are those named above, in order. The carbon is separated from the exposed material by some chemical process and its radioactivity measured; the disintegration constant can then be determined from equation 1. Work on cross sections [14] is of sufficient

14 See, for example, D. H. Frisch, *Phys. Rev.*, **70**, 589 (1946); and J. Rainwater and W. W. Havens, Jr., *Phys. Rev.*, **70**, 136 (1946).

accuracy for such determinations, but the methods available for monitoring neutron fluxes over extended periods leave much to be desired.

β Radiations

β Radiations consist of singly charged positive or negative electrons of nuclear origin.[15] They are produced as the result of instabilities conferred by certain nuclear combinations and configurations of neutrons and protons. β Particles (negative electrons) and positrons (positive electrons) are identical in their physical properties and interactions with matter with the single exception of the sign of the charge of the particle. Positrons unite with electrons to form the "annihilation radiation," the particle masses being converted to electromagnetic energy in the form of γ rays. Since positrons are foreign to extranuclear space this effect is observed in conjunction with positron emission but not with β-particle emission.

The β particle bears a charge of one electron unit, 4.803×10^{-10} absolute electrostatic unit, and at zero kinetic energy has a "rest mass" of 9.107×10^{-28} gram. The mass is so small that β particles of even the most moderate energies have very high velocities. Often these velocities are appreciable fractions of that of electromagnetic radiation, 2.998×10^{10} cm/sec, and under these circumstances the mass is given by the relativistic formula

$$m_v = \frac{m_0}{\sqrt{1 - (v/c)^2}} \tag{4}$$

where m_0 is the rest mass, c is the velocity of light, and m_v the mass at a velocity v. It is common practice to refer to the energies of β particles in terms of the potentials necessary to accelerate them to a given energy. Thus the kinetic energy E in Mev (millions of electron volts) is related to the velocity as follows:

$$E_{\text{Mev}} = 0.511 \left[\frac{1}{\sqrt{1 - (v/c)^2}} - 1 \right] \tag{5}$$

For example, a particle with 0.60 the velocity of light has a kinetic energy of 0.128 Mev.[16]

[15] For reviews of the theory of the β disintegration process, see E. J. Konopinski, *Revs. Modern Phys.*, **15**, 209 (1943); H. A. Bethe, *Elementary Nuclear Theory*, John Wiley & Sons, New York, 1947, pp. 10–12, 20–22, 97–108.

[16] The energy is often recorded in units of $H\rho$ since this quantity is measured directly in the β-ray spectrometer. The relation between $H\rho$ and energy is given by

$$E_{\text{Mev}} = -0.51085 + \sqrt{0.2611 + 8.9854 \times 10^{-8}(H\rho)^2}$$

where H is the magnetic field strength in gauss, ρ is the particle path radius in centimeters, and E is the energy in Mev.

Interactions of β Radiations with Matter

The absorption of β rays, except for scattering and the production of annihilation radiation, is due to energy losses by excitation and ionization of the atoms of the absorber and to radiation of energy by the β ray during acceleration in close collisions with nuclei.[17]

The first two processes account for practically all the energy loss for β rays below 1 Mev in energy. The decrease in energy due to the radiative process results in the formation of "Bremsstrahlung" which are identical with continuous x rays. There is no definite range for a β ray of given energy because of the great variation in the amount of energy which may be transferred at each instance of one of the above-

TABLE III

MAXIMUM RANGES OF HOMOGENEOUS β-PARTICLE BEAMS IN ALUMINUM

E, Mev	Range, mg/cm^2
0.02	0.8
0.05	4.2
0.10	13.9
0.20	42
0.50	170
1.00	430
2.00	980

named processes; this energy can vary from practically zero up to the whole energy of the ray. A maximum range, however, can be observed with comparative ease, and many data have been obtained for the maximum ranges in various absorbers of homogeneous β-particle beams of different energies.[18]

Because of their relatively high specific charge, β rays are quite easily deflected from their paths; to indicate the magnitude of this effect, it is sufficient to point out that from ⅕ to ½ of the β particles directed perpendicularly at a thick plate will be irregularly reflected (see pages 308–312). Because scattering is so important in the weakening of β-ray beams, the experimentally observed absorption curves include scattering as well as true absorption events.

[17] Energy loss by excitation of the nuclei of the absorber is observed only at very great energies.

[18] R. Varder, *Phil. Mag.*, **29**, 725 (1915); B. F. J. Schonland, *Proc. Roy. Soc. London*, **A108**, 187 (1925); E. Madgwick, *Proc. Cambridge Phil. Soc.*, **23**, 970 (1927); C. E. Eddy, *Proc. Cambridge Phil. Soc.*, **25**, 50 (1929); J. S. Marshall and A. G. Ward, *Can. J. Research*, **15**, 29 (1937). For a brief review, see L. E. Glendenin, *Nucleonics*, **2**, No. 1, 12 (1948).

Absorption Curves and Energy Spectra

The weakening of an initially homogeneous beam of β rays follows an approximate linear relation as the thickness of the absorbing material is increased. The slope of the curve decreases at large absorber thicknesses and the actual maximum observable penetration is indistinct and extremely sensitive to the arrangement of source and detector; the defined maximum range is obtained by extrapolating the straight portion to zero net activity. A schematic absorption curve for homogeneous β rays is shown in Fig. 2. As is the case with all such measurements, the results obtained are strongly dependent upon the spatial arrangement of the source, absorber, and detector.

The absorption curve observed for a source emitting β rays inhomogeneous in energy falls relatively more rapidly than that for a source emitting a homogeneous beam of the same maximum energy, because of the initial presence of lower-energy rays. The shape of the curve and the extrapolated maximum range obtainable from it are of great importance in tracer applications, since all β-active bodies emit particles which vary continuously in energy from practically zero up to a well-defined maximum. Because of a fortunate combination of absorption (by radiative and ionization energy loss), scat-

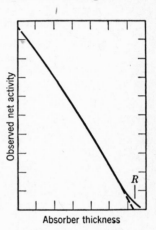

Fig. 2. Absorption curve of homogeneous β rays. The letter R indicates the extrapolated range.

tering, and the distribution of initial energies, the absorption curves of many β-emitting isotopes are approximately exponential. Thus if N_0 particles are measured with no absorbing layer present between source and detector, $N^t = N_0 e^{-\mu t}$ particles will be observed through an absorber of thickness t. The absorption coefficient μ is determined by the emitter and absorber, but its dependence upon the nature of the absorber can be greatly reduced by expressing absorber thicknesses in terms of surface density, i.e., mg/cm^2. In order that the value of μ be independent of the experimental arrangement, corrections must ordinarily be applied to it to allow for the fact that the path lengths through the absorber vary upwards from the perpendicular absorber thickness. These corrections for path obliquity are discussed on pages 312–315.

C^{11} and C^{14} emit continuous spectra of positrons and β particles, respectively. The maximum energy of the C^{11} positrons has been determined to be 0.95 Mev,[3] while that of C^{14} β rays is around 0.15 Mev [7,19] (see Table II).

The energy spectrum of the C^{14} radiations is of particular interest because the half-life is much longer than that which one would predict from the observed maximum energy. This situation usually indicates that the decay proceeds by what is termed a "forbidden transition"; i.e., the actual rate of the disintegration is much different from that

TABLE IV

ABSORPTION OF C^{14} β PARTICLES IN ALUMINUM

Total Absorber, mg/cm²	Activity Observed, c/min
0	76,000 (extrapolated)
3.36	34,000
5.28	21,400
6.15	17,300
7.37	12,700
8.68	9,150
11.0	5,020
15.2	1,610
18.1	670
19.9	410
27.9	24
34.1	5
37.6	3

calculated on the basis of contemporary theory. Information concerning the β-ray spectrum of an isotope can often be accurately obtained from β-ray spectrometer studies. In an early instance of this type of investigation of the spectrum of C^{14},[7] considerable difficulty was encountered in the preparation of a strong sample free from self-absorption, and reliability was claimed only for the maximum energy value, 0.154 Mev. A similar method involves the measurement of cloud-chamber tracks when the paths of the disintegration electrons are observed with an applied homogeneous magnetic field. This type of investigation has been used to determine the energy of C^{11} positrons; but only limited work of this nature has been carried out with the long-lived activity.[20]

For the β particles from a thin sample of calcium carbonate having an activity of approximately 6,000 disintegrations per minute, values of 0.168 ± 0.007 Mev and 0.041 ± 0.002 Mev for the maximum and mean energies respectively were obtained. The actual mean energy is prob-

[19] M. D. Kamen and S. Ruben, *Phys. Rev.*, **59**, 349 (1941).

[20] R. C. Raymond, doctoral dissertation, University of California, 1941.

ably greater since the conditions of the experiment were such that the measurement of low-energy particle tracks was somewhat favored.

A procedure which, though not so delicate as those above, yields data especially useful for laboratory work consists in the determination of the desired quantities from absorption measurements.[21] Typical data

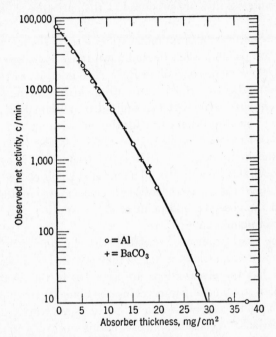

FIG. 3. Absorption curves of C^{14} β rays. (Thin sample mounted on aluminum; data not corrected for backscattering.)

for the absorption of the β particles from a very thin sample of C^{14} are shown in Table IV.

The figures were obtained using a sample of barium carbonate less than 0.05 mg/cm² in thickness. In the plot in Fig. 3, the dashed line represents exponential absorption behavior; the deviation from this line is less than 5% out to 15 mg/cm². The samples were counted with an end-window counter; the aluminum equivalent of the window was 2.6 mg/cm² while that of the air path was 0.8 mg/cm². The maximum energy obtained from these data [18] is 0.155 ± 0.010 Mev, and the mean energy is 0.051 ± 0.003 Mev. It will be noted that the activities at

---

[21] The mean energy can also be obtained calorimetrically. See C. D. Ellis and W. A. Wooster, *Proc. Roy. Soc. London*, **A117**, 109 (1927).

the very end of the table form a small tail; in the case of C^{14} this more penetrating radiation accounts for no more than a fraction of a per cent of the total activity observable. Analysis of this phenomenon in other β emitters has shown that this effect is due to the production of Bremsstrahlung in the absorbers in a manner entirely analogous to that in which continuous x rays are produced at the anticathode of a Coolidge tube.

Much more accurate absorption measurements of the maximum range and energy are possible when the unknown range is compared with the known range and energy of radium E.[22] The intensity of the radiation from the source being studied transmitted through aluminum foil absorbers is compared with that transmitted by radium E at several foil thicknesses. The absorption curve for the radiation under investigation is superimposed on that for RaE (two abscissa scales being used) and the known maximum range of the RaE β particles used in extrapolating the other curve to zero activity. The method has been applied to C^{14}, and the value of 0.154 ± 0.004 Mev has been computed for the maximum energy from the observed end point of the absorption curve at 27.9 ± 0.3 mg/cm^2 of aluminum.[23]

One of the great problems associated with the correct interpretation of absorption curves, at least as far as they are used to measure particle energies, is that the observations are sensitive to the arrangement of the source, detector, and any intervening absorbing layers.[24] The effects noted are due to the ease with which β particles are scattered from their original directions. A considerable part of this sensitivity to the arrangement of the detector and source is due to reflection into the sensitive volume, by the materials of which the sample and its mount are made, of β particles originally directed away from the detector. This effect, known as backscattering, increases with increasing particle energy, with atomic number of the scatterer, and with the thickness of the sample and mounting materials. For a given array of sample and detector, the backscattering is maximized when the thickness of the mount is equal to one-half the maximum absorption thickness; particles which penetrate deeper are completely absorbed before emerging from the surface. Where absolute disintegration rates must be computed from those observed, suitable corrections must be applied to account for the increase

[22] N. Feather, *Proc. Cambridge Phil. Soc.*, **35**, 599 (1938).

[23] A. K. Solomon, R. G. Gould, and C. B. Anfinsen, *Phys. Rev.*, **72**, 1097 (1947).

[24] See, for example, M. Deutsch, J. R. Downing, L. G. Elliot, J. W. Irvine, Jr., and A. Roberts, *Phys. Rev.*, **62**, 3 (1942); M. Deutsch, *Phys. Rev.*, **61**, 672 (1942).

in apparent activity which is due to backscattering. The problem is discussed in considerable detail on pages 308–312.[25]

The Annihilation Radiation

The difference in charge between positrons and β particles greatly simplifies the detection of the positrons under certain conditions. Positrons are foreign to extranuclear space and are relatively short lived.[26] They are annihilated by combination with electrons according to the scheme $\beta^+ + e^- + M = 2h\nu + M$; M represents a massive third body the presence of which usually is required so that both momentum and energy can be conserved, and $h\nu$ represents a quantum of electromagnetic radiation of energy m_0c^2 (0.51 Mev). Occasionally conditions are such that only a single γ ray of double this energy is produced. The formation of this "annihilation radiation" during the absorption of positrons is important to tracer experimentation because it enables carbon 11 to be measured through thicknesses of absorber which are sufficient to mask completely the actual positron emission.[27] The positron emitted by C^{11} has a maximum range in aluminum of 400 mg/cm^2.

Interaction of Annihilation Radiation with Matter

γ Rays of 0.51 Mev energy can interact with matter in three important ways:[28] (1) elastic (coherent) scattering; (2) inelastic (Compton) scattering; (3) photoelectron production.

γ Rays of much higher energy can excite nuclei and thus induce photodisintegration; those of 1.02 Mev energy or greater can produce positron-electron pairs by a process which is the reverse of that which accounts for the annihilation radiation.

The probability that a γ quantum can interact with the electric field of an atom so that it suffers only a change in direction, coherent scatter-

[25] See also Rutherford, Chadwick, and Ellis, *op. cit.*, p. 420; J. A. Chalmers, *Proc. Cambridge Phil. Soc.*, **25**, 331 (1929), **26**, 252 (1930); B. F. J. Schonland, *Proc. Roy. Soc. London*, **A104**, 235 (1923), **A108**, 187 (1925); with UX, H. W. Schmidt, *Ann. Physik*, **23**, 671 (1907); with RaE and AcC, A. F. Kovarik, *Phil. Mag.*, **20**, 849 (1910); A. F. Kovarik and W. Wilson, *Phil. Mag.*, **20**, 866 (1910); P. B. Wagner, *Phys. Rev.*, **35**, 98 (1930).

[26] C. D. Anderson, *Science*, **76**, 238 (1932), **77**, 432 (1933); *Phys. Rev.*, **43**, 491 (1933); P. M. S. Blackett and G. P. S. Occialini, *Proc. Roy. Soc. London*, **A139**, 699 (1933); I. Curie and F. Joliot, *Compt. rend.*, **196**, 1105 (1933).

[27] See, for example, C. A. Tobais, J. H. Lawrence, F. J. W. Roughton, W. S. Root, and M. I. Gregersen, *Am. J. Physiol.*, **145**, 253 (1945). $C^{11}O$ was measured while combined with hemoglobin in a living subject; such experiments cannot be performed with C^{13} or C^{14} since they are not detectable under these conditions.

[28] See Rutherford, Chadwick, and Ellis, *op. cit.*, pp. 451–494, for greater detail.

ing, diminishes rapidly with increasing photon energy. Coherent scattering, which is responsible for diffraction phenomena, is not an important effect with the annihilation radiation from positron absorption, but it may be of great significance to the interactions with the absorber of those photons whose energy (frequency) is diminished by inelastic scattering (Compton effect).

If an electron is bound to an atom with an energy small in comparison with that of an incident γ ray, inelastic scattering may occur, resulting in the production of an energetic unbound electron and a γ quantum of diminished energy.[29] This process is important in the absorption of quanta whose energies are of the order of that of the annihilation radiation, and the probability for its occurrence increases with increasing atomic number of the absorber, although in the lighter elements it is favored because photoelectron production is not very likely.

If a photon of energy $h\nu$ interacts with an electron bound by energy W, it may give up its entire energy to the electron, which will then be ejected with a kinetic energy E given by the relation $E = h\nu - W$. For a given value of the photon energy, the probability that the process can occur is dependent upon the value of W. A photon cannot eject an electron whose binding energy is greater than $h\nu$, and the ejection is not favored if the photon energy is very large compared with W. The photoelectric effect is most often observed when the energy of binding, W, is slightly less than $h\nu$. Where the incident photon is a quantum of 0.51 Mev, W is always less than $h\nu$ even for the very tightly bound s electrons of uranium. Since these inner shells are the ones that contain electrons for which W is commensurate with $h\nu$, and since W increases with increasing Z, the photoelectric effect increases rapidly in importance as heavier elements are used as absorbers. Essentially free electrons, such as are found in the outer valence shells, cannot give rise to the effect with high-energy quanta because of the diminished possibility that momentum can be conserved.

Photoelectron emission, whether brought about by the original γ rays or by quanta of diminished energy, is critical in the measurement of carbon 11 through thick absorbers, because it is this emission, and the production of Compton recoil electrons, both in the materials of which the detector is made, which permit detection of the photons.

[29] A. H. Compton, *Bull. Natl. Research Council U.S.*, **4**, 1 (1922); *Phys. Rev.*, **21**, 207, 483 (1923); A. H. Compton and S. K. Allison, *X-Rays in Theory and Experiment*, 2nd Ed., D. Van Nostrand Co., New York, 1935; N. S. Gingrich, *Phys. Rev.*, **36**, 1050 (1930); A. H. Compton and A. W. Simon, *Phys. Rev.*, **26**, 289 (1925).

Absorption Curves of γ Rays

γ Rays are absorbed to a certain extent by all absorbing layers through which they pass. What fraction of an homogeneous beam is absorbed depends upon the nature and extent of the absorber and the energy of the γ quanta, since the relative contributions of the various processes named above are dependent upon these factors. X rays and γ rays are absorbed exponentially, a constant fraction of the flux being removed per unit thickness of absorber. If μ_t is the total absorption coefficient for all processes, then $I_x = I_0 e^{-\mu_t x}$, where I_0 is the original intensity of the beam and I_x is that after passing through an absorber of thickness x. μ_t is the gross absorption coefficient for all flux weakening

TABLE V

ABSORPTION COEFFICIENTS FOR 0.51 MEV γ RAYS

Absorber	μ_t linear, cm^{-1}	μ_t mass, cm^2/g
H_2O	0.095	0.095
$C_{(graphite)}$	0.20	0.088
Al	0.22	0.082
Cu	0.70	0.079
Pb	1.7	0.15

courses of action; it is called the total absorption coefficient and is equal to $(\mu_{Compton} + \mu_{photoelectric} + \mu_{scattering})$. The coefficient may be expressed in various units; the use mentioned above implies units of reciprocal length. The value of μ_{linear} is therefore dependent upon the physical and chemical state of the absorber. If divided by the density of the absorbing material the quotient (called the mass absorption coefficient) has the dimensions of reciprocal surface density, $L^2 M^{-1}$ and is independent of the state of the absorber. The atomic absorption coefficient, having properties similar to those of μ_t mass, is obtained by dividing μ_t linear by the number of absorbing atoms per cubic centimeter. In Table V are collected the mass and linear absorption coefficients of annihilation radiation in several absorbers.[30]

Self-Absorption

Observed Phenomena

If one measures the activity of a series of samples of varying weight but constant area, there will be noted a deviation from linear dependence

30 W. Heitler, *The Quantum Theory of Radiation*, Oxford, The Clarendon Press, 1936, pp. 215–216; W. Gentner, *J. phys. radium*, **6**, 274 (1935), *Physik. Z.*, **38**, 836 (1937); G. T. Seaborg, S. G. English, V. C. Wilson, and C. D. Coryell, *An Introduction to Nuclear Chemistry*, Lecture Series (1942), Atomic Energy Commission, MDDC 763.

upon the mass of sample material; this effect is caused by self-absorption. The linear relation between the observed activity and the sample mass is possible only where the radiations are so penetrating that the upper layers of the sample cannot appreciably absorb the radiation which originates in the lower laminae. In an earlier section it was noted that the backscattering effect is saturated when the thickness of the sample mount is one-half the maximum penetration thickness. A similar effect occurs in self-absorption. The observed activity reaches the maximum

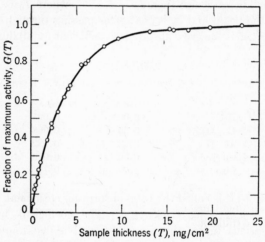

Fig. 4. Activity saturation curve of barium carbonate samples containing $BaC^{14}O_3$. (Thin-window counter data, geometry $\sim 30\%$; samples mounted on aluminum.)

when the sample is so thick that the radiations originating in the layer farthest removed from the detector are completely absorbed by the intervening sample layers. Any further increase in the amount of sample material will not affect the observed strength of the sample. Figure 4 shows such a saturation curve for barium carbonate samples containing $BaC^{14}O_3$.[31] When tracer experiments are carried out with an isotope whose radiations are of such low energy that the ordinary solid or liquid sample thicknesses represent an appreciable fraction of the mean particle range, self-absorption losses introduce large errors in activity measurements for which correction must be made.

There are four procedures by which this correction can be made or the need for it eliminated.

First, it is often possible to mount the samples in such thin layers that the small self-absorption loss can be neglected when compared with

[31] See also W. D. Armstrong and J. Schubert, *Anal. Chem.*, **20**, 270 (1948); M. Haïssinsky and B. Pullman, *J. phys. radium*, **8**, 33 (1947).

other errors in the experiment. With carbon 14 this method cannot usually be followed, except with very thin samples, ca. 0.1–0.2 mg/cm^2, since about 13% of the activity is lost when a layer only 1 mg/cm^2 thick is mounted. This procedure is very often used in determining the radioactivity of substances emitting α particles, but its application to the measurement of isotopes such as C^{14} and S^{35} is limited by the frequency with which one is called upon to measure samples of low specific activity.

Second, an attempt can be made to reproduce accurately a standard sample thickness. The method is based upon the ability of the experimenter to make samples of an identical thickness and area from a constant amount of the sample material. Actually such a technique is ordinarily very difficult to apply; the only recent work in which any success is evident, for the application of this type of sample preparation to routine analysis, is that concerned with metallic arsenic.[32]

Third, the sample material can be mounted in a layer so thick that the saturation activity is observed. Often such samples are called "infinitely thick" layers; the activity observed is proportional to the specific activity of the sample. This procedure is of quite general applicability when low-energy particles are to be detected, but it is often wasteful of sample material. Frequently the amount of sample available is small and its activity so great that the capacity of the detecting instrument may be exceeded. In this situation recourse must be had either to dilution of the sample or to the fourth method of sample preparation.

Fourth, the relation between the observable specific activity and the thickness of the sample can be obtained, and by its use the activity observed at any thickness can be related to that which would have been observed at some standard thickness. Clearly, this is the most general approach to the problem. No limits are placed on the amount of activity or of material which can or must be used in preparing the substance for radioactive analysis.

Calculation of Self-Absorption Corrections

If it is assumed that the absorption is essentially exponential, the equation of the absorption curve is of the form $F(T) = e^{-\mu T}$. Where μ can be evaluated for the sample material, the activity of a deposit of thickness T is given by the integral

$$G(T) \sim \int_0^T e^{-\mu T}\, dT \sim 1 - e^{-\mu T}$$

[32] F. C. Henriques, Jr., and C. Margnetti, *Ind. Eng. Chem.*, *Anal. Ed.*, **18**, 415 (1946).

Since the self-absorption loss results in an apparent diminution of specific activity, we can define a correction "denominator" as being the ratio of the observed and maximum observable specific activities.

$$\frac{G(T)}{G(0)} = J(T) \sim \frac{1 - e^{-\mu T}}{\mu T}$$

Thus, correction factors can be calculated if μ for the sample material is known and if it is very nearly the same for the other absorbing layers (air path and window) usually present.

Libby [33] has given an empirical relation between the maximum energy, maximum range, and mass absorption coefficient for β emitters with E_{max} less than 0.2 Mev. The formula is

$$T_{max} = \frac{5}{\mu} = \frac{[E_{kv}]^{5/3}}{150}$$

In certain cases this formula yields excellent results. For C^{14} β-particle absorption in barium carbonate, μ is 0.285 ± 0.008 cm^2/mg.[23, 35]

Sometimes the absorption in the sample material is not even approximately exponential; when this situation exists or the character of the absorption curve is unknown, recourse must be had to experimental methods for the evaluation of the function J. The simplest procedure is to make a plot, normalized to unity at zero sample thickness, of the apparent specific activity per unit sample thickness for various source surface densities. In effect, one calculates for each value of T the ratio $G(T)/[T \times G(0)]$. The J function thus obtained corrects the observed activities to zero sample thickness; such a graph of J for samples of barium carbonate is shown in Fig. 5. Correction of the observed activity to zero thickness is not necessary, though usually desirable. Division by G at some other T than zero produces a J function which will correct all activities to that thickness.[34]

A general graphical method for obtaining self-absorption corrections is often useful; one needs only to have an absorption or saturation curve involving the sample material used. The procedure is applicable when the absorption coefficients for the sample and window materials are very nearly the same. A graphical method of this type has been outlined

[33] W. F. Libby, *Ind. Eng. Chem., Anal. Ed.*, **19**, 2 (1947). In the investigation cited in reference 23, the authors state that, for C^{14}, $T_{max} = 8.6/\mu$ mg/cm^2.

[34] See, for example, F. C. Henriques, Jr., G. B. Kistiakowsky, C. Margnetti, and W. F. Schneider, *Ind. Eng. Chem., Anal. Ed.*, **18**, 349 (1946). The plot of $1/J$ vs. T is often used.

elsewhere and will not be repeated here.[35]   It must be remembered that the shape of the absorption curve depends upon the detector; a curve obtained with a counter will ordinarily be different from that obtained with an ionization chamber.   Some data for benzidine sulfate containing S^{35} may be consulted as an example.[34]

Self-absorption is related to scattering as is simple absorption.   For this reason the effect exhibits a sensitivity to the geometry of the detection arrangement other than that associated with simple obliquity of

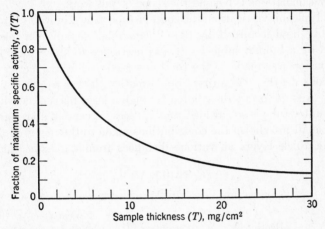

FIG. 5.   Self-absorption correction curve.   (Data from Fig. 4.)

particle paths.   Sometimes this dependence upon geometry is considerable, and the self-absorption correction function, J, must be separately evaluated for each arrangement of source and detector.   This is obviously a lot of work, and since laboratories operating on a routine basis commonly have several counters in use, it is advisable to inquire into the magnitude of this dependence for C^{14}.   When samples of varying thickness were measured with geometric efficiencies ranging from 7.6 to 20.5%, the relative activities in each instance were the same within the mounting and counting error of $\pm 2\%$. The obliquity corrections for these geometries go as high as 1.4 (see page 314).   Thus, for the efficiencies encountered with counter tubes of ordinary design, the J function is relatively insensitive to the geometry of the measuring array.   Reflection processes cause pronounced differences in J functions when different sample and mounting materials are used; the nature and extent of these effects are discussed in detail on pages 105 and 311.

[35] P. E. Yankwich, T. H. Norris, and J. L. Huston, *Ind. Eng. Chem., Anal. Ed.*, **19,** 439 (1947).

In vivo measurement of carbon 11 involves a self-absorption phenomenon slightly different from that encountered with solid samples of carbon 14; in such measurements, where the activity is dispersed vertically along the detection axis as well as horizontally, the geometric efficiency is very different for various sample layers. Because of the importance which must be attached to the accuracy of data obtained from living tissues, several workers have engaged in exploring the various detection problems associated with the *in vivo* use of C^{11}. An exposition of their calculations is beyond the scope of this work.

In a typical investigation, the counter tube shown in Fig. 19 (page 67) was to be used in measuring the C^{11} annihilation radiation from $C^{11}O$ inhaled by a human subject. It was necessary to know what relative contribution was made to the total observed activity by active tissues at various depths. As a first approximation, it was assumed that the activity was uniformly distributed through a large mass of density 1.05. The counter tube is so shielded that it "sees" a cone of apex angle 46°. In Table VI are shown the contributions made to the observed activity by 1-cm thick layers at various distances from the *tissue* surface.[36]

TABLE VI

SELF-ABSORPTION EFFECT IN MEASUREMENT OF C^{11} *in vivo*

Depth, cm (density 1.05)	Percentage of Observed Activity	Percentage of Observed Activity to This Depth
0– 1	10.7	10.7
1– 2	8.9	19.6
2– 3	7.5	27.1
3– 4	7.1	34.2
4– 5	7.0	41.2
9–10	4.0	68.0
10–11	3.3	71.3
14–15	2.1	81.5
15–16	2.0	83.5
19–20	1.4	89.8
20–21	1.3	91.1

Thus, the tissue layer lying from 4 to 5 cm from the *surface* (not from the sensitive volume of the detector) contributes 7.0% of the total activity, and all layers from 0 to 5 cm contribute 41.2% of the total. Experimental data agree with the calculation within an error of a few per cent.

[36] N. Pace, R. Loevinger, and E. Strajman, *Science*, **107**, 71 (1948). See also R. D. Evans and R. O. Evans, *Revs. Modern Phys.*, **20**, 305 (1948).

Chapter 4

INSTRUMENTS FOR

RADIOACTIVITY MEASUREMENT

β Rays are detected by the ionization which they produce directly; γ rays, by the charged secondaries which they release and which are directly measurable. Suppose that the ionizing events take place between two electrodes. When there is no potential difference across the system, the ions produced are subjected only to ordinary thermal agitation and recombine during various excursions thus instigated; only a very small fraction will be collected on either of the electrodes. As a potential difference is applied to the system and slowly increased, the ion cloud will be more and more completely collected before recombination is finished. At field strengths of about 10 volts/cm practically all the ions will be collected on the electrodes. As the potential is further increased, various avalanche processes become important which result in multiplication of the ionization produced. In the first voltage range where processes of this type take place, the multiplication factor is essentially constant and the ionization collected is a direct function of that produced. This is known as the "proportional region." At higher potentials the multiplication approaches a saturation condition where all pulses of ionization, regardless of initial strength, are multiplied to a constant final size. In this region, known as the Geiger region, the pulses collected are all of the same size, regardless of the number of primary ions produced during the initiating ionization event.

The instruments commonly used in the measurement of radioactivity in tracer work confined to β-active isotopes are the ionization chamber and the Geiger-Müller counter tube. The ion chamber operates at potentials which are in the low to moderate voltage range. The measurement is made by collecting all the ions produced in a well-defined region, and the number of ions collected is proportional to the number of disintegration events. The Geiger-Müller counter is operated in the high-voltage range mentioned above; the ionization produced by each particle passing through the sensitive volume of the tube is multiplied to a given size, and the resultant pulse actuates a suitable recording mechanism.

Detailed descriptions of the operation of counter tubes, as well as ion chambers, have been given by several authors.[1,2] Depending upon whether the time constants of the associated circuits are small or large, ion chambers are either "counting," responding separately to each event, or "integrating," collecting the ionization produced over a relatively long period; [3] in the usual application the integrating type of chamber is used in conjunction with a suitable electroscope or electrometer. The actual measuring instruments may be divided into three classes: electroscopes and electrometers dependent upon mechanical restorative forces for their operation, vacuum-tube electrometers, and dynamic condenser electrometers.

Electroscopes and Electrometers

Mechanical Instruments

The familiar gold-leaf and quartz-fiber electroscopes and the various "string" and quadrant electrometers are examples of the first type. The deflection of a fiber or vane, or the rate at which an auxiliary voltage must be applied to halt this drift (null method), is used to indicate the magnitude of the charge on the collecting system.[4]

Lauritsen Electroscope

The Lauritsen electroscope [5] is now a familiar piece of equipment in most laboratories equipped for tracer work. The sensitive element is sketched in Fig. 6. It consists of a small quartz fiber, 6 mm long and about 0.005 mm in diameter, cemented to a supporting wire with shellac or other suitable adhesive. The fiber is made conducting by a film of sputtered gold and has a short index fiber cemented to its end. The supporting wire is attached to a good insulator by a small plate, with which contact is made to the charging system and to ground. The response of the instrument

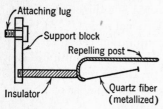

FIG. 6. Sensitive element of the Lauritsen electroscope (schematic).

[1] S. A. Korff, *Electron and Nuclear Counters*, D. Van Nostrand Co., New York, 1946.

[2] C. G. Montgomery and D. D. Montgomery, *J. Franklin Inst.*, **231**, 447, 509 (1941).

[3] W. B. Lewis, *Electrical Counting*, The Macmillan Co., New York, 1943.

[4] See H. V. Neher in J. Strong, *Procedures in Experimental Physics*, Prentice-Hall, New York, 1938, pp. 217–258.

[5] C. C. Lauritsen and T. Lauritsen, *Rev. Sci. Instruments*, **8**, 483 (1937).

is approximately linear over the greater part of the scale. Most often the sensitive element is placed inside an aluminum case which serves to protect the delicate fiber from air currents and dust; the case may be grounded in use or held at a small negative potential. A part of the ionization produced by an external sample in the space thus defined is collected on the charged system and the case, resulting in a decrease in the deflection of the fiber from its support.

The Lauritsen electroscope is frequently used to measure the radioactivity of solid samples. When the radiations emitted by the tracer isotope are of such low energy that they are appreciably absorbed in passing through the protecting outer case, the measurable ionization is reduced; when C^{14} is the tracer isotope, the thickness of the usual electroscope case is such that none of the radiations penetrate into the sensitive volume. Some use has been made of cases having "windows" of thin aluminum foil, through which the softer radiations can enter the confined volumes of the cases. A better solution to the problem is to place the sample inside the outer case of the electroscope and thus eliminate all absorption losses other than self-absorption. A modified case has been developed for use with such samples; [6] however, greater efficiency is obtained when the samples are introduced directly into an ionization chamber operated at 100–200 volts. When such a chamber is employed, essentially all the ionization produced is collected upon the fiber system, whereas the operation of a modified grounded case depends upon the drift of the ions in a much weaker field.

A particularly ingenious application of the Lauritsen instrument to the measurement of gaseous samples containing carbon 14 has been worked out. [7] The apparatus is shown in Fig. 7. Essentially, the chamber consists of a quartz flask silvered inside except for a small spot at one end. Through the center of this unsilvered area is sealed a collecting probe which is connected to the repelling post of the sensitive element. A power pack of more or less standard design, employing a 5R4 rectifier and three VR 150 regulator tubes, provides the necessary potentials. The chamber is ordinarily filled to a pressure of 2 atmospheres with carbon dioxide. The chamber volume is approximately 200 cc and at the pressure used requires a filling of 20 mmoles of gas. Under these conditions the β particles from C^{14} produce in the chamber about 97% of the total possible ionization (see page 316); the sensitivity is 5×10^{-11}

[6] F. C. Henriques, Jr., G. B. Kistiakowsky, C. Margnetti, and W. G. Schneider, *Ind. Eng. Chem., Anal. Ed.*, **18**, 349 (1946); F. C. Henriques, Jr., and C. Margnetti, *Ind. Eng. Chem., Anal. Ed.*, **18**, 415 (1946).

[7] F. C. Henriques, Jr., and C. Margnetti, *Ind. Eng. Chem., Anal. Ed.*, **18**, 417 (1946).

curie, corresponding to a dilution of 2×10^{-10} curie/gram of carbon. Activities at least equal to the background can be determined to 2% on a routine basis, and the time required for such an analysis is about 3 hours, all steps being considered; the actual measuring time for $\pm 2\%$ standard deviation is somewhat less than 2 hours under the usual conditions.

It is difficult to compare the sensitivities of various ionization chamber-electroscope (or electrometer) combinations from the kind of data ordi-

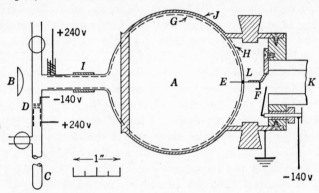

Fig. 7.   Quartz-bulb ionization chamber apparatus.   (F. C. Henriques, Jr., et al.)

A	200-cc bulb	G	Chemically deposited silver
B	Light source	H	Colloidal graphite
C	Condensing tube	I	Graded seal
D	Ion trap	J	Brass adapter and collar
E	Collection probe	K	Telescope tube
F	Repelling post	L	Ceresin wax

narily included in published work.   However, data believed to be indicative of the performance of a given instrument are tabulated when the instrument is described.

In Table VII are shown the results of dilution experiments performed with the modified Lauritsen electroscope just described.   The symbol R_x represents the observed net activity of a particular sample, and it is given by $R_x = R_s - R_b$, where R_b is the background activity and R_s is that observed when the sample material is used to fill the chamber. The measurements were made in duplicate, and no sample was measured for more than 1 hour.

A temperature-controlled pressure ion chamber has been used in conjunction with a Lutz-Edelman (single fiber) electrometer to measure external C^{11} samples.[8]   The radioactive material was in the form of

[8] J. H. C. Smith and D. B. Cowie, *Plant Physiol.*, **16**, 257 (1941); *J. Applied Phys.*, **12**, 78 (1941).

carbonate in normal potassium hydroxide; approximately 4 ml of the solution was pipetted into a hard rubber dish which was covered with a thin aluminum foil to prevent evaporation and placed in a standard position near a window in the ion chamber.

The ion chamber was 250 cc in volume and was filled to approximately 2.5 atmospheres pressure with dry nitrogen. A circular window of aluminum, 8 cm in diameter and 0.1 mm thick, was located in the end

TABLE VII

RADIOACTIVITY MEASUREMENTS AS A FUNCTION OF SAMPLE DILUTION

Lauritsen Electroscope-Quartz Ion Chamber Apparatus [7]

Relative Activity R_x/R_b		Per Cent Standard Deviation	
Computed	Observed Mean	from Computed R_x/R_b	of Observed Mean R_x/R_b
83.2	83.5	0.4	0.1
41.6	41.7	0.4	0.4
20.8	20.5	2.1	1.2
10.4	10.4	1.0	1.0
5.20	5.24	1.0	1.5
2.60	2.64	1.7	0.9
1.30	1.29	2.2	1.9
0.65	0.67	3.3	2.2

Operational data:

$T = 25°$ C $\quad$ CO_2 used $= 20$ mmoles
$P_{CO_2} = 170$ cm Hg $\quad$ Weight C $= 0.240$ gram
$V_{chamber} = 219$ cc $\quad$ $R_b \cong 8 \times 10^{-11}$ curie

of the chamber opposite the insulator. Dilution experiments showed that the response of the chamber-electrometer combination was linear over a 250-fold range of positron activities. A similar array has been used in neutron absorption and diffusion studies.[9]

Lindemann Electrometer

The Lindemann electrometer [10] was developed for use in astronomical observations with equatorial telescopes, the desired features being small size, low electrical capacity, high sensitivity, and lack of dependence of the zero and sensitivity on tilt; the instrument is now widely used for radioactivity determinations. The sensitive element is sketched in Fig. 8. Between the quadrants, the quartz needle is suspended at its center on a torsion fiber about 0.006 mm thick; when charge is collected on the

[9] E. Amaldi and E. Fermi, *Phys. Rev.*, **50**, 899 (1936).
[10] F. A. Lindemann, A. F. Lindemann, and T. C. Kerley, *Phil. Mag.*, **47**, 577 (1924).

needle it rotates about the torsion support and the deflection of the tip. is noted with a microscope and scale. Ordinarily potentials of plus and minus 20–25 volts are put across the quadrants; under these conditions the instrument can be used with a sensitivity as high as 3,000–5,000 divisions per volt for short measuring times. If the time of observation is long, shifts of the zero are usually noted, but even very weak biological samples can be quite easily measured in reasonable lengths of time at a sensitivity of 1,000 divisions per volt.

Several workers [11] have studied the measurement with this electrometer of carbon 14 samples of very low specific activity. The versatile

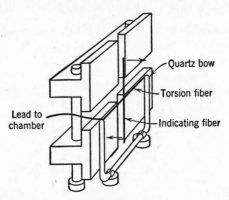

FIG. 8.   Sensitive element of the Lindemann electrometer (one set of quadrants is not shown).

circuit used is shown in Fig. 9, and a diagram of the chamber and its relation to the other parts of the instrument is shown in Fig. 10. The essential components of the circuit are the quadrant voltage supply, the collection voltage supply, a bridge circuit which prevents changes in the collection voltage from affecting the potential on the charge collecting system (needle), and a null method circuit for drawing the collected charge onto the standard condenser C, thus restoring the needle to its zero. When the null method is employed, the activity in the chamber is proportional to the voltage which must be applied in unit time to keep the fiber at zero.

If a very high resistance is put in place of the standard capacitance, the instrument becomes a null voltmeter of moderate period. When operating in this manner, the unit can be used in conjunction with a

[11] C. D. Janney and B. J. Moyer, Atomic Energy Commission, MDDC 1303, July 31, 1947; see also W. P. Jesse, L. A. Hannum, H. Forstat, and A. L. Hart, *Phys. Rev.*, **71**, 478 (1947).

recording device and the operator merely keeps the fiber at zero. This type of application is not desirable when the activities of a number of samples are to be compared because its sensitivity is considerably less than that obtained by means of the null method. However, in certain types of experiments the operation of the ion chamber in this manner,

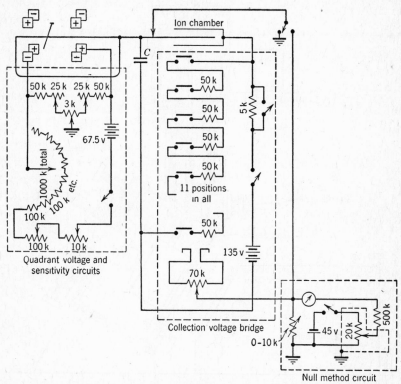

FIG. 9. Lindemann electrometer circuit. (C. D. Janney and B. J. Moyer.)

essentially as a counting rate meter, is practical. (One such investigation [12] employed a 10-cc ion chamber connected in series with an oxygen meter and a photosynthesis reaction chamber; the apparatus was used to follow continuously the respiration of barley plants in an atmosphere containing $C^{14}O_2$. Under these conditions, the instrument has a period of about 2 seconds and it will not respond to an activity of less than 3×10^{-8} curie.)

When a chamber of 100- to 150-cc volume is used, the instrument will measure samples as weak as 1.6×10^{-10} curie to 5% in less than

[12] J. Weigl and M. Calvin, unpublished experiments.

1 hour total counting time. This corresponds to a specific activity of about 3×10^{-9} curie/gram of carbon when the chamber is filled to a pressure of 1 atmosphere. If the α-particle contribution to the background can be subtracted (see page 56), the sensible lower activity limit

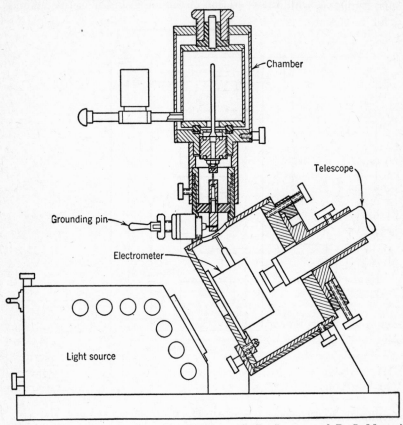

Fig. 10.   Lindemann electrometer assembly.   (C. D. Janney and B. J. Moyer.)

is 0.5×10^{-11} curie and the corresponding specific activity 6×10^{-11} curie/gram of carbon. These activity figures are based on a total counting time of 30 minutes divided equally between the sample and background, and an observed standard error of 10%. A counting period four times as long would give a result to 5%, or one could determine one-fourth the activity to 10% error (see Appendix II). The use of ion chamber-electrometer combinations is advantageous in that the equipment is not difficult to operate or adjust, the circuits are so simple that a relatively inexperienced person can construct and maintain them, and the sensitivity is high enough so that the very weak samples encountered in biological work can be measured in quite reasonable times; the disadvantages are that the method is wasteful of time when samples of greater than very moderate activity are to be measured (small samples must be diluted with inactive material to furnish enough carbon dioxide to fill the chamber to the standard pressure) and the time to prepare one

TABLE VIII

LINDEMANN ELECTROMETER DATA [11]

Relative Activity		Per Cent Standard Deviation of Observed Mean	Observation Time (Sample Only), min	Approximate Specific Activity, curies/gram carbon
Computed	Observed Mean			
1.0000	1.0000	0.2	20	3.7×10^{-7}
0.1493	0.1503	0.7	34	5.5×10^{-8}
0.0519	0.0533	1.7	45	1.9×10^{-8}
0.0248	0.0246	1.2	62	9.6×10^{-9}
0.0100	0.0096	4.0	62	4.1×10^{-9}
Background	0.0000	6.0	180	(2.2×10^{-9})

Operational data:

$T = 25°C$ CO_2 used = 4.17 mmoles
$P_{CO_2} = 76.0$ cm Hg   Weight C = 0.050 gram
$V_{chamber} = 102$ cc $R_b \cong 1.1 \times 10^{-10}$ curie

sample for measurement is often longer than that required to prepare solid samples for counter measurement.

Typical data obtained with active carbon dioxide are shown in Table VIII; a Ryerson-Lindemann electrometer was used at a sensitivity of 1,000 div/volt.[11]

Vacuum-Tube Electrometers

Vacuum-tube amplifiers commonly employing an "electrometer tube" such as the FP-54 or D-96475 have been widely used in photometric studies.[13] Because of the skill necessary for their maintenance they have not gained favor rapidly for the measurement of radioactivity.

The direct-current amplifier in this modification employs a vacuum tube across two elements of which a potential difference is built up by the collection of charge from an ionization chamber. The flow of current to a third electrode in the tube is controlled by this potential difference. Almost any amplifier tube has this function and certain of the desirable

[13] A. E. Whitford, in J. Strong, *Procedures in Experimental Physics*, Prentice-Hall, New York, 1938, pp. 412–430.

properties as well, but in order to attain high voltage sensitivity the design of special tubes has been necessary. Such tubes have been constructed so that effects due to positive-ion bombardment of the control grid, temperature changes in the filament, and low grid-filament resistance are reduced. The amplification factor of a properly designed and adjusted circuit can be made so great that a galvanometer of only moderate sensitivity will register even the lowest ion currents in the chamber; if the galvanometer shunt resistance is varied, very high currents can be measured. The response of the instrument is very nearly linear over its entire range.[14]

The principal advantages associated with the use of vacuum-tube electrometers are the great ease of routine operation when the instrument has been properly stabilized and adjusted, the ease with which the signal can be recorded, extremely great sensitivity, and linearity of response over a wide detection range. The instrument is rugged in some respects but extremely delicate in others; it is not easily stabilized, and the rate of zero drift is ordinarily quite high. The associated circuits are not extraordinarily complex, but more than a slight familiarity with electronics is necessary for their repair and readjustment. The principal disadvantages are associated with the great sensitivity of vacuum tubes to stray electromagnetic disturbances; the elimination of operational trouble from this source requires complete and elaborate shielding. The real advantage of the device is its ability to handle both very high and very low ionization currents, but at present it is not an instrument that can be used easily for routine work.

The Dynamic Condenser Electrometer

The great inherent instability of all multistage d-c amplifiers lies in the fact that practically the whole plate voltage of one stage must be put on the grid of the next. A slight change in the supply voltage to the first stage produces a proportionately large effect in those succeeding. One-tube balancing circuits such as those developed by DuBridge and Brown [14] eliminate this problem to such an extent that single-stage operation is possible. In alternating-current amplifiers these difficulties are of much less importance. Electrometers have been perfected which make use of a-c amplifying circuits of conventional design; [15] these are

14 L. A. DuBridge, *Phys. Rev.*, **37**, 392 (1931); C. E. Wynn-Williams, *Phil. Mag.*, **6**, 324 (1928); L. A. DuBridge and H. Brown, *Rev. Sci. Instruments*, **4**, 532 (1933); L. A. Turner, *Rev. Sci. Instruments*, **4**, 665 (1933); D. B. Penick, *Rev. Sci. Instruments*, **6**, 115 (1935).

15 H. Palevsky, R. K. Swank, and R. Grenchik, *Bull. Am. Phys. Soc.*, **21**, No. 3, 23 (1946); *Rev. Sci. Instruments*, **18**, 298 (1947).

known as dynamic condenser electrometers, and the two types which were developed are called the "vibrating-reed" and the "vibrating-diaphragm" electrometers. These instruments employ an oscillating collector which moves an impressed charge in the field of a cylindrical condenser; the motion of the charge results in the production of an a-c signal the magnitude of which is dependent upon that of the charge, which is in turn a function of the ionization current in the chamber. The electrometer is ordinarily operated as a null instrument in a man-

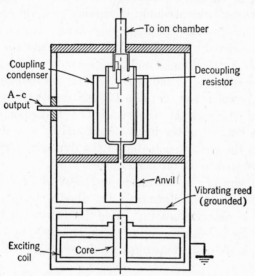

FIG. 11. Vibrating-reed unit (schematic).

ner similar to that described before. In Fig. 11 are sketched the working parts of the vibrating-reed unit.

In actual practice the electrometer output is fed to a converter unit and a conventional balancing and recording circuit, which produces a graphical trace of the output. Graphical recording of the a-c output signal is especially useful and desirable when samples of low total activity are encountered, because the subtraction of the α-particle contribution is made simple. Of course, one can note the registration of α events with a fiber electrometer if a sufficiently high sensitivity is employed; however, this procedure is always tiring and rarely accurate. A graphical record shows α-particle events as distinct "jumps" in the trace of signal strength against time. The great increase in detection sensitivity upon correction for α events has been mentioned in the section on the Lindemann electrometer.

The use of duplicate detectors in opposition on a single output circuit has been suggested as a method for reducing the background effect; the practical difficulties associated with the preparation of such identical ion chambers and counter tubes have prevented the development of these instruments for routine use.

The difficulties associated with the instrument are almost entirely constructional. The reed or diaphragm must be very carefully prepared and mounted to eliminate transient effects, such as variable contact potentials, but once the assembly is working properly and is sealed it need never be readjusted. The amplifying circuits are much more rugged than those associated with FP-54 electrometers, and considerably less skill is required for their repair and readjustment. The instrument as a whole is unusually stable and sensitive, and its routine operation is simpler, for example, than that of a Lindemann electrometer. The design suggested [15] is such that the sensitivity is limited only by the thermal agitation "noise" in the input circuit and by zero drift; the drift depends upon the contact potential of the dynamic condenser surface and can be reduced to 0.1 mv per 24 hours.

The advantages of the instrument are great sensitivity and ease of operation, repair, and readjustment. The disadvantages are due largely to difficulties in manufacture, but, since the instrument will ordinarily be purchased by the experimenter rather than built by him, these are reflected only in the cost; at the moment, the availability of the electrometer is limited.

Some data obtained with a vibrating-reed electrometer are summarized in Table IX.[16] There appears to be a systematic trend for the more dilute samples to give higher relative values than those calculated from the actual dilution data; the reasons for this trend are being investigated, and at present it is believed that the discrepancies are due to errors in sample preparation rather than to errors in the measurements.[17] It must be noted here that, for the first three samples measured, a single observation gave a relative current value sufficiently precise for use in tracer studies. For example: the average deviation from the observed mean was only 0.9% for the determinations made with the 170 disintegrations per minute sample, and the average deviation from the computed current was 5.1%; this sample was only a little more than four times as active as the background.

16 W. P. Jesse, L. A. Hannum, H. Forstat, and A. L. Hart, Atomic Energy Commission, MDDC 622.

17 W. P. Jesse, private communication.

TABLE IX

VIBRATING-REED ELECTROMETER DATA[16]

Relative Current, amperes		Number of Measurements	Total Time, min	Per Cent Standard Deviation		Approximate Specific Activity, curies/g C	Disintegrations per Minute in Chamber
Computed Current	Observed Mean			from Computed Current	of Observed Mean		
....	2.201×10^{-13}	5	112	...	0.1	4×10^{-7}	73,000
1.073×10^{-14}	1.089×10^{-14}	6	300	2.2	0.15	2×10^{-8}	3,600
5.24×10^{-16}	5.51×10^{-16}	5	401	2.7	0.8	1×10^{-9}	170
3.85×10^{-17}	3.7×10^{-17}	4	226	10	10	7×10^{-11}	13
Background	1.2×10^{-16}	.	..	....	....	....	.....

Operational data:

$T = 27°$ C CO_2 used = 6.86 mmoles

$P_{CO_2} = 81.9$ cm Hg   Weight C = 0.0824 gram

$V_{chamber} = 156$ cc $R_b = 1.7 \times 10^{-11}$ curie

Geiger-Müller Counters

Though some ion chamber-electrometer combinations can be used to register the detection of single particles (see page 34), the device usually employed in "counting" is the Geiger-Müller counter or "Zählrohr." [18] Instruments of this type which respond equally to various ionizing events are widely used in carbon tracer studies. Certain counter-circuit combinations are constructed so as to operate in a voltage range where the pulse delivered by the circuit is proportional to the primary ionization produced by the various kinds of events. These are known as proportional counters [19] and are sometimes used where several different isotopes may be present in a single sample; discrimination is made between the various isotopes by arbitrarily adjusting the circuit so that it accepts pulses of only a certain size.

In its usual form, the counter tube consists of a cylindrical cathode made of brass or copper and a coaxial wire anode of tungsten, iron, or other suitable metal. The space between the electrodes is filled with either a pure or mixed gas, and the whole array is enclosed in a suitable envelope; in some forms, the cathode forms a part of the outer shell and the wire is supported by insulating plugs in the ends of the cylinder.

Counter tubes may be divided into classes on the basis of their fillings. Tubes filled with monatomic or diatomic gases, single or in combination, are known as *non-selfquenching* counters; fillings having as one component a gas with at least four atoms per molecule produce *selfquenching counters*.[21] Triatomic gases constitute a special class; the use of certain of them produces non-selfquenching counters, while combinations may result in counters which are selfquenching in their action.

Action of the Counter

A schematic diagram of the fundamental Geiger-Müller circuit is shown in Fig. 12. The arrangement consists of a source of high potential V, a resistance R, and a coupling condenser C (which, numerically, will be considered to represent the distributed capacity of the associated circuit). Circuit action may be of one of three types: resistance quenching, vacuum-tube quenching, and selfquenching. If an ionizing particle enters the sensitive volume of the counter tube, an ion-multiplying

[18] H. Geiger, *Ber. deut. physik. Ges.*, **15**, 534 (1913), *Physik. Z.*, **14**, 1129 (1913); E. Rutherford and H. Geiger, *Proc. Roy. Soc. London*, **A81**, 141 (1908); H. Geiger and W. Müller, *Physik. Z.*, **29**, 839 (1928), **30**, 489 (1929).

[19] H. Geiger and O. Klemperer, *Z. Physik*, **49**, 753 (1928). A complete review of modern proportional counter practice is given by S. A. Korff, *Electron and Nuclear Counters*, D. Van Nostrand Co., New York, 1946.

avalanche is produced in the neighborhood of the wire. The mechanism by which this discharge is stopped and the counter returned to a sensitive condition is called quenching. When resistance quenching is used, the value of R is of the order of 10^9 ohms; the onset of the avalanche impresses a large potential drop across R which lowers the voltage across the tube, rendering it incapable of sustaining the discharge. Circuits operated in this manner have a large time constant, $R \times C$, and are necessarily slow in their action. With vacuum-tube quenching, an auxiliary circuit is employed which automatically lowers the voltage across the tube when a discharge starts. The action of such a combination is usually of intermediate speed; counters thus quenched are useful

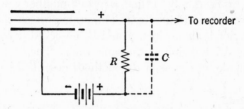

FIG. 12. Fundamental Geiger-Müller counter circuit (C represents effective distributed capacity).

to relatively high counting rates, being able to accept up to about 70,000 counts per minute without blocking or going into a continuous discharge and with only reasonable losses due to coincidences; either selfquenching or non-selfquenching fillings can be used with these types of circuit. The resistance-quenched circuit is now obsolete for tracer experimentation; the vacuum-tube-quenching circuits ordinarily employed are those due to Neher, Harper, and Pickering.[20]

The electrons produced in an ion-multiplication avalanche are collected in a time so short, compared with the time necessary for the collection of the positive ions, that the internal recovery mechanism may be considered as wholly a property of these positive ions. Photon emission takes place both during the ionization processes and when the positive-ion cloud is collected at the cathode; if these photons are not scavenged out of the sensitive volume before they cause further electron emission, the counter will go into a continuous discharge. The external mechanisms for accomplishing this by reducing the potential between the electrodes have already been mentioned. In selfquenching counters, the added polyatomic gas performs this function by being dissociated

[20] H. V. Neher and W. W. Harper, *Phys. Rev.*, **49**, 940 (1936); H. V. Neher and W. H. Pickering, *Phys. Rev.*, **53**, 316 (1938); C. E. Wynn-Williams, British patent 421341.

by both the emitted photons and the positive ions themselves; thus, the useful lifetime of the filling is determined by the amount of quenching gas available.[21]

Even though the positive ions are collected relatively slowly, recovery of selfquenched tubes can take place in times as short as a few times 10^{-5} second. The product $R \times C$ of the associated circuits can be made very small, R is often less than 1,000 ohms, and instruments of rather conventional design can discriminate between pulses as close together as 1 or 2×10^{-6} second.[22] The recovery time of the counter tube is thus the principal factor limiting the rate at which a given tube-circuit combination can accept and record ionizing events. Since the disintegration events are spaced randomly in time, a certain number will be undetected even at moderate counting rates. This is known as coincidence loss, since the behavior is that which would be observed if two particles arrived in the sensitive region at the same time. The corrections for this effect can be made by means of the methods described in Appendix III.

Auxiliary Circuits

Each complete counting unit consists of three elements—counter, high-voltage circuit, and mechanical recorder—which have different upper limits to the rates at which they can record or transmit ionizing events; the fastest of the three is the circuit, the slowest is the mechanical recorder. Since it is the detector that is most advantageously the limiting element, ordinarily some way must be found to raise the upper limit of the mechanical recorder; the usual device of this type will accept without loss about 3,000–4,000 evenly spaced pulses per minute, but less than 1,500 if the events are spaced in a random manner. One solution to the problem has been to develop a circuit or other device which feeds pulses to the register at a rate at which they can be accepted and recorded without loss; this feat is accomplished by "scaling circuits," which usually are combinations of the Wynn-Williams "scale-of-2" circuit.[23] Each "unit" in the scaler passes on to the next stage only

---

[21] S. S. Friedland, *Phys. Rev.*, **71**, 377 (1947); see also S. A. Korff and R. D. Present, *Phys. Rev.*, **65**, 274 (1944), and R. D. Present, *Phys. Rev.*, **72**, 243 (1947). The last paper describes the selfquenching action of halogen fillings.

[22] One manufacturer tests scaling circuits by feeding a bank of five with pulses from a generator at the rate of 200,000 per second for 10 hours. All five must show the same reading at the end of this time on the "interpolate" indicator.

[23] C. E. Wynn-Williams, *Proc. Roy. Soc. London*, **A136**, 312 (1932); W. H. Eccles and F. W. Jordan, *Radio Rev.*, **1**, 143 (1919); W. G. Shepard and R. O. Haxby, *Rev. Sci. Instruments*, **7**, 425 (1936); E. C. Stevenson and I. A. Getting, *Rev. Sci. Instruments*, **8**, 414 (1937); H. Lifschutz and J. L. Lawson, *Rev. Sci. Instruments*, **9**, 83 (1938), **10**, 21 (1939).

half of the pulses which it receives. The register receives $(\frac{1}{2})^n$ of the events actuating the detector if there are n stages in the scaler.

When samples of moderate activity are counted for short periods the register reading may not give an accurate activity value, since an appreciable fraction of the pulses delivered by the counter tube may be "tied-up" in the scalers. For example, if a sample whose activity is 150 c/min is counted with a scale-of-64 circuit for 1 minute, the register reading will be 2 and the activity computed from this figure alone will be 128 c/min. The 22 counts which are apparently missing are indicated upon a suitable dial or series of lights connected to the scaling pairs.[24]

Circuits with scales of 8 and 64 are the most common, though scalers for α-particle counting are often constructed with a scale of 4,096. Some instruments of this type are equipped with a variable contact pick-off which enables any number of the available scaling units to be used; the higher the counting rate, the greater the number of stages necessary. In automatic counting (see page 50) it is necessary, especially for relatively short counting periods, to have the scaling factor as small as possible because the "interpolate" is thrown away when detection is shifted from sample to background, and vice versa. However, the factor cannot usually be reduced below 4 because, even at counting rates as low as 50 c/min, there is an appreciable number of pulses arriving so close together that the usual mechanical registers lose counts when driven by a scale-of-2 circuit.

Counting Control

Counting, when carried out as a completely manual operation, is often tedious, and several auxiliary circuits and controlling devices have been designed to put the operation of scaling circuits on a more nearly automatic basis. Most of these controlling apparatuses require manual starting, but they turn off the counting circuit after a predetermined time interval or after a certain number of counts have been collected; both controllers have the advantage that the experimenter need not be in constant attendance. One advantage in counting a constant number of pulses is that all samples may be determined to the same statistical error without resetting the controller; this is especially useful if large numbers of samples of approximately the same activity are encountered.

[24] Scale-of-64 circuits require 6 "interpolate" lights; these are wired into the scaler across each scaling pair. The arrival of a pulse at the pair turns the light on; the next pulse fires the scaling pair, turns the light off, and sends a pulse to the next pair, which pulse turns its interpolate light on. If a lighted light is represented by X
1 2 4 8 16 32
and an extinguished light by O, an interpolate of 22 counts would be OXXOXO, 2 counts OXOOOO, 10 counts OXOXOO, 62 counts OXXXXX, etc.

Several devices have been designed for counting automatically a large number of samples; these usually involve a rotating wheel on the periphery of which are mounted various experimental, blank, and standard samples.[25]   All these samples are counted for the same length of time, or to a constant error, and the number of counts registered, or the time of counting, for each sample is printed on a moving tape.   Instruments

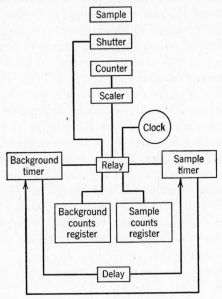

FIG. 13.   Block diagram of automatic counter circuit.   (J. E. Fredrickson et al.)

of this type enable sample counting to be carried on at night or over weekends.

A circuit of rather similar type has been developed for counting extremely weak samples.[26]   A switching unit is placed after the scaler; by means of suitable timing devices and relays, this unit operates a thick shutter, between the sample and counter tube, and two registers, thus permitting alternate counting of the background and the sample. The impulses collected at each instance are passed to the proper register, and a clock records the total length of time during which impulses are collected; a switch is provided which allows a complete cycle of the instrument to be finished before the circuit is shut off.   The advantage of this type of operation is that samples whose activities are small fractions of the background can be counted in the presence of a rapidly

25 W. C. Peacock and W. M. Good, *Rev. Sci. Instruments*, **17**, 255 (1946).
26 J. E. Fredrickson, A. A. Benson, and P. E. Yankwich, unpublished work.

fluctuating background; the greater and more rapid the fluctuations, the shorter is made the total length of the counting cycle. Since only impulses directed to the registers from the last scaling pair are recorded, the scaling factor must be made as small as possible, the interpolate being thrown away when the shutter is moved. A block diagram of the instrument is shown in Fig. 13.

Counting-Rate Meters

The usual scaling circuit actuates a mechanical register which records the number of impulses produced in the detector over a given period of time. Some circuits have been constructed to operate, directly or indirectly, a continuously reading dial meter, which records the rate at which the impulses are produced; these instruments are known as counting-rate meters.[27] They are usually quite rugged and are capable of handling both very low and very high counting rates; the linearity of the response is determined by the detector, as with more conventional Geiger-Müller tube circuits. The random pulses produced in the counter tube are impressed upon a capacity resistance tank circuit which exerts a powerful damping effect on the fluctuating yield of the detector; thus, the meter may be thought of as a radioactivity "speedometer." The determination of the statistical accuracy of the results is a rather special problem, but it has received thorough treatment.[28]

[27] See, for example, N. S. Gingrich, R. D. Evans, and H. E. Edgerton, *Rev. Sci. Instruments*, **7**, 450 (1936).

[28] L. I. Schiff and R. D. Evans, *Rev. Sci. Instruments*, **7**, 456 (1936).

Chapter 5

DETECTORS FOR
RADIOACTIVITY MEASUREMENTS

Ionization Chambers

Design Considerations

Ionization chambers have been used for the determination of both C^{11} and C^{14}, though present usage is restricted largely to measurement of the latter isotope. Regardless of which isotope is to be measured, certain general requirements should be satisfied in the chamber design for efficient and reproducible detection. The principal features of the electrode system are shown in Fig. 14.

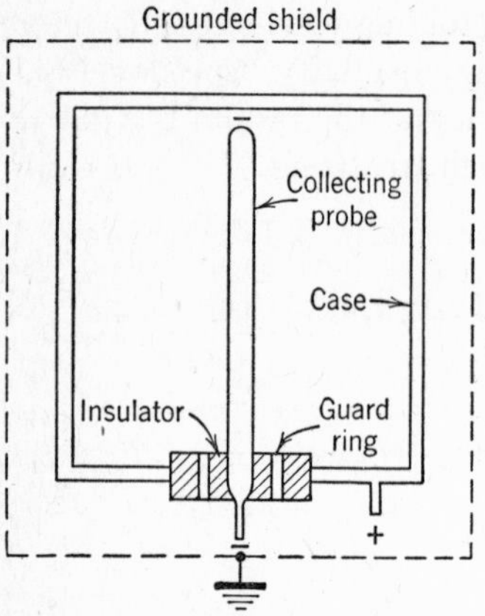

The collecting probe is usually no more than a few millimeters in diameter; if the chamber were operated with the probe at a high positive potential, the original ion current would be at least partially increased by ion-multiplication events occurring in the vicinity of the probe. This condition does not exist if the potential across the electrodes is reversed, and nearly all chambers are operated with a positive outer electrode and a negative or grounded probe. If the outer electrode is not grounded, the system is usually surrounded by a grounded electrostatic shield. The guard ring serves as a shield for the collecting probe; the greater part of the leakage current across the insulator is stopped by the ring, which may be grounded or operated at a potential near that of the probe. The ring serves the additional purpose of intercepting a large fraction of the low-frequency electromagnetic radiation which the probe would otherwise "see" (from light bulbs, cables, motors, etc.), since it is so arranged that any straight line to the collecting electrode must pass either through the outer electrode or the guard ring.

Fig. 14. Ionization chamber (schematic).

52

The insulator is made of sulfur, Bakelite, amber, or polystyrene. Extreme care must be taken in machining the insulator, for its final treatment determines to a large extent the leakage current that it will pass when assembled with the electrodes. This leak is primarily a surface effect and is minimized by making the last cuts with lathe tools that have been carefully freed from oil and grit. Since the outer surface may be exposed to humid laboratory atmospheres, some investigators paint the whole outside with melted natural ceresin wax, which has unusually fine moisture-resistance qualities as well as high surface and volume resistance. The insulator should not be handled with the fingers after the final shaping has been carried out; sterilized cotton or disposable cleansing tissues, which have been dried, are convenient to use for what little handling may be necessary.

In the determination of C^{11} one uses either a chamber with a moderately thin window filled with air or other gas at 1 atmosphere, or a chamber with somewhat thicker walls filled to a pressure of several atmospheres with a gas such as argon or carbon dioxide. The samples are usually exterior to the chamber, since the C^{11} positrons and annihilation γ rays are quite penetrating. The design to be employed and the overall size depend upon the samples to be measured. If solid samples, of calcium carbonate for example, are to be measured, it will ordinarily be desirable to use a thin-walled chamber so that the positrons will produce as many ions as possible in the chamber instead of being absorbed in its walls, or it may be practical to place the active sample inside the chamber. In experiments on living systems, it is often best to use an ion chamber of small size to measure the annihilation radiation through rather thick layers of tissue; the thick-walled high-pressure ion chamber is then to be preferred since there is greater probability that secondaries will be produced in the sensitive volume (carbon 11 has not been measured in this manner in any published research).

Ionization chambers for the measurement of the radiations from C^{14} present a somewhat different problem. Only rarely is it desired to employ external samples which would have to be measured through a thin window in the chamber wall. The usual technique consists in filling the chamber with the radioactive carbon dioxide obtained from the research samples by combustion, and several difficulties are immediately introduced when such a technique is followed.

The first of these is associated with the background current observed when the chamber is evacuated and then filled with inactive gas; it is usually noted that there is a very high residual "activity" which may take as long as several hours to die out. This effect is due to piezoelectric currents in the insulator which are the result of strains introduced into the insulator during evacuation of the chamber; the behavior of the two most convenient insulating materials, polystyrene and Bakelite, is particularly objectionable. It has been found that there are three ways to correct for this difficulty: the first, most obvious, and often most practical, is to wait until the currents die out; the second is to minimize the size of the insulator as far as is compatible with good design; the third is to keep to the minimum the time during which the chamber is

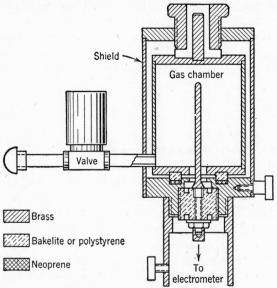

Shield

Gas chamber

Valve

▨ Brass

▨ Bakelite or polystyrene

▨ Neoprene

To electrometer

FIG. 15.   Ionization chamber for C*O₂ measurement.   (C. D. Janney and B. J. Moyer.)

allowed to remain evacuated. In chambers constructed according to the design in Fig. 15, these currents fall to a negligible value in 15 to 45 minutes if the collection voltage is left on, and in 3 to 4 hours if the electrodes are grounded. If several chambers are in use this time need not be wasted, for while one chamber is in place on the electrometer those that have been more recently evacuated and filled can be set on a dummy so arranged that the full collection voltage is applied.

Chamber size is especially important in work with carbon 14, since samples of biological origin with extremely low specific activities are quite often encountered, especially in preliminary and survey experiments. The mean energy of C^{14} β particles is roughly equivalent to 2.2 cm atm of carbon dioxide at 25° C,[1] while that of the particles of

---

[1] At this temperature a centimeter cube of carbon dioxide at 1 atmosphere pressure weighs 1.80 mg. Its apparent surface density is therefore 1.80 mg/cm² per atmosphere pressure. The C^{14} β rays of mean energy will penetrate about 4 mg/cm² of absorber, or 4/1.8 = 2.22 cm atm of carbon dioxide.

maximum energy is approximately equivalent to 17 cm atm of the gas. In order that the detection be at all efficient, the dimensions of the chamber must be of this order of magnitude, the filling pressure being considered. In one research [2] it was reported that 97% of the maximum ionization current is observed when a spherical chamber 7.46 cm in diameter is filled to a pressure of 2 atmospheres with active carbon dioxide; this is 14.9 cm atm along a diameter and about 10 cm atm along the mean chord. Other workers [3] have observed the ion current when a stubby cylindrical chamber of 125-cc volume is filled to different pres-

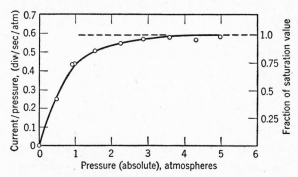

FIG. 16. Observed ion current as a function of the chamber filling pressure. (C. D. Janney.)

sures with active carbon dioxide from a large sample. The data are shown in Fig. 16. Two designs for ion chambers useful in the measurement of carbon 14 are shown in Figs. 7 and 15. (A vacuum system designed especially for use with ionization chambers is described on pages 143–146.)

The Background Effect

The background in ionization chambers is the sum of contributions from three sources: cosmic rays, which are very penetrating and produce few ions along their paths in the sensitive volume; α particles, emitted from substances that contaminate many of the materials of which chambers are made, which produce many ions per unit path length but are not very penetrating; artificial or natural γ or β contamination. If sufficient care is exercised in constructing and shielding the chamber, the contribution due to the third source can be largely eliminated. Let us assume then that the background is made up only of ions produced by cosmic rays and α particles. Let G and H be the average rates at which

[2] F. C. Henriques, Jr., and C. Margnetti, *Ind. Eng. Chem., Anal. Ed.*, **18**, 417 (1946).

[3] C. D. Janney and B. J. Moyer, private communication.

these events occur, and let g and h represent the average number of ion pairs produced per event in the sensitive volume, and F and f represent the same quantities for the C^{14} activity. The background activity will be $(gG + hH)$, and the activity of the sample plus background will be $(fF + gG + hH)$. The standard deviations to be expected in the use of ion-chamber counting technique can be calculated if one knows these six factors. For chambers of ordinary size (volume at least 75 cc), the value of f is approximately 1,000 ion pairs per β disintegration at a pressure of 1 atmosphere of carbon dioxide; F is obtained by computation from the net sample activity. The value of g is approximately 2.7 ion pairs per second per cubic centimeter of chamber volume,[4] while G corresponds to 0.025 cosmic rays per second per square centimeter of projected horizontal area of the chamber.[5] Each α particle emitted from ordinary brass produces, on the average, about 1.4×10^5 ion pairs, and this figure may be used to approximate h.[6] The α rate, H, must be evaluated from the observed background, and in practice one finds from 10^{-4} to 10^{-2} α event per minute per square centimeter of chamber surface.

Because of their intense ionization the α particles constitute a serious problem where attempts to minimize the background are concerned. A common approach to the problem involves the use of a positive screen for an outer electrode. This serves to repel the secondaries produced by α events, excluding them from the sensitive volume. This approach has several disadvantages when the chamber must be filled with an active gas, the greatest of which is that a large fraction of the activity makes no contribution to the observed ion current. A more effective method is to reduce the activity of the chamber surface by painting it with a very pure substance such as collodion or lampblack; the material chosen should be inert to the chamber filling. However, since chambers used in carbon counting must ordinarily be occasionally disassembled for cleaning, this manner of coating the internal surface is a time-consuming procedure which too often does not produce a diminution in background commensurate with the effort expended. Electroplating with gold or silver does not often result in a large reduction in the α effect, but some silver paints have been found to lower the background contribution from this source. Ion chambers are usually constructed from brass, and careful choice, unfortunately by trial and error, of the particular stock to be used is probably the best solution to this problem;

[4] J. Clay and P. H. Clay, *Physica*, **5**, 898 (1938).

[5] J. C. Street and R. H. Woodward, *Phys. Rev.*, **46**, 1029 (1934).

[6] H. Palevsky, R. K. Swank, and R. Grenchik, *Rev. Sci. Instruments*, **18**, 298 (1947).

various samples of commercial brass tubing vary as much as fivefold in their contamination, and the activity observed when the parts of the chamber are milled from solid bar stock is usually less than that found when drawn tubing is used.

Memory

When the sample is completely external to the detector, its removal results in the fall of the observed activity to that of the background. There is a tendency in instruments which use a sample-filled detection volume for this fall to fail; the result is a very high background activity known as "memory." Effects due to memory are most important where the increase in background due to this source of contamination is of the same order of magnitude as the activity to be measured. For example, suppose that a strong sample filling is first used and the chamber is next filled with a sample only one-hundredth as strong. If only 0.1% of the stronger sample is retained by the chamber, the activity observed for the weaker sample will be 10% high, unless the new background of the chamber is determined between every two samples.

Ionization chambers and certain gas-filled counter cathodes, see page 67, are commonly made of yellow brass, which is 67% copper and 33% zinc. If we assume that these surfaces are carefully cleaned before assembly, memory is due to the physical or chemical adsorption of the active filling, usually carbon dioxide, on the surface. It is usually impossible to remove the greater part of the retained activity by prolonged high-vacuum pumping, but the adsorbed or absorbed material can be removed by washing of the affected parts with dilute acids. These observations, and other considerations, have led various investigators to conclude that the effect is due to true chemisorption of active carbon dioxide on the clean surface. Zinc carbonate will form much more rapidly than copper carbonate under the conditions usually existing, and the treatment of the memory effect is based upon this fact.

A procedure that has been of considerable value to the authors is due to Libby [7] with certain modifications.[3] For cathodes to be used in Geiger-Müller counters filled with carbon dioxide, the following procedure is suggested: The cathode is carefully cleaned with dilute acid, say 0.05 M HNO_3, and the counter is quickly assembled. The counter tube is connected to a high-vacuum system and pumped, then filled with inert carbon dioxide to a pressure of 1 atmosphere and allowed to stand for at least 12 hours, a somewhat longer time being favored. The inert filling is then pumped out and the counter is ready for use. Counters thus stabilized show no tendency to remember very high activities

---

[7] W. F. Libby, private communication.

even after several months of continuous use, provided that these high activities are not permitted to remain in the counter for more than a few hours. This scheme was changed somewhat for use with ionization chambers, though the procedure as outlined may be effective. If an assembled chamber is to be cleaned and stabilized without take-down and reassembly, the following steps are carried out: The chamber is filled with 0.005 M HCl, which is allowed to act for 10 to 15 minutes; the chamber is then connected to a water aspirator and the greater part of the solution is pumped out. The valve is closed while the aspirator is on, to prevent filling with laboratory air, and the chamber is removed and connected to a high-vacuum system where it is pumped on for about 20 minutes, or until dry. It is then filled to a pressure of 1 atmosphere with inert carbon dioxide and allowed to stand, as above.

Counters

Up to a few years ago, when commercial manufacture was greatly increased in scale, virtually all counters were "home-made." The individual experimenter had to design and fabricate the instrument for himself, with the aid of colleagues' experience and a great body of uncoordinated publications. At present there are several good reviews of the subjects of counter design and construction,[8] and commercial production is reaching such proportions that many laboratories now engaged in tracer experimentation have no experience in building counters. Counter tubes made outside the laboratory are expensive in money (the least expensive counter suitable for work with C^{14} retails at around \$40) while those made in the laboratory may involve a much greater expenditure in time. Often the size, type, or design of counter desired is not available commercially; then, recourse must be had to the talent of the investigator. In the following sections no attempt will be made to describe *all* the many different tube designs that have been found satisfactory for the measurement of the radiations from isotopic carbon, nor will any effort be made to explore completely the construction problems involved.

General Design Considerations

Size and Geometry Factors. The design of any counter tube must take into account the nature of the radiations to be measured. The β

---

8 S. A. Korff, *Electron and Nuclear Counters*, D. Van Nostrand Co., New York, 1946; H. V. Neher, in J. Strong, *Procedures in Experimental Physics*, Prentice-Hall, New York, 1938; C. G. and D. D. Montgomery, *J. Franklin Inst.*, **231**, 447, 509 (1941); H. Fränz, in F. Kohlrausch, *Praktische Physik*, 18th Ed., B. G. Teubner, Leipzig and Berlin, 1943; S. C. Curran and J. M. Reid, *Rev. Sci. Instruments*, **19**, 67 (1948); D. R. Corson and R. R. Wilson, *Rev. Sci. Instruments*, **19**, 207 (1948).

particles from C^{14} cannot penetrate absorber thicknesses greater than about 25–30 mg/cm^2; therefore samples containing this isotope must either be placed inside the counter or be measured through very thin windows. The positrons of C^{11} can penetrate aluminum, for example, of such a thickness that aluminum tubes below a certain maximum diameter can withstand atmospheric pressure when evacuated and still pass the positron radiation without great loss; the annihilation radiation of this isotope is detectable through considerable absorber thicknesses, but the detection efficiency for γ rays of this energy is not large, at best 1–2% of that for β radiation.[9]

The source-detector geometry must usually be large, though inefficient detection may be desirable where very high activities are encountered; the achievement of good geometry requires the placement of the sample very close to the sensitive volume of the counter, if not inside it. A consideration in the geometric arrangement is the reproducibility of the sample position, but since such manipulations are usually carried out with devices that are properly part of the shield they will not be detailed here.

Reduction of Background. A very desirable, and often attainable, attribute of counters is a low background effect. A counter responds with equal result to any single ionizing event, whether it be an α, β, γ, or cosmic ray; β and γ events are usually of external origin (local contamination of the laboratory, etc.) and are usually either of small magnitude or easily made so; α-particle events have their origin in the materials of which the counter is made, while cosmic rays are of undetermined ancestry.

The background due to α particles, and what internal β and γ contamination there may be, is proportional to the area of surface presented to the sensitive volume. It can be minimized for a given volume by making the length and diameter of the cathode, and envelope, nearly the same. Since most β particles and positrons will have a high ionization probability for relatively short lengths of path in the counting gas, the background under the conditions above can sometimes be profitably reduced by making the length of the cylindrical cathode small with respect to the diameter, without greatly reducing the β-ray detection efficiency. However, the plateaus of counters so constructed are usually short and quite steep, and resort to this design should be had only in rather special circumstances.

The effects due to cosmic radiation and external contamination are proportional to the effective cross-sectional area of the sensitive volume

⁹ See H. Maier-Leibnitz, *Z. Naturforsch.*, **1**, 243 (1946); R. D. Evans and R. A. Mugele, *Rev. Sci. Instruments*, **7**, 441 (1936); M. Pohl and A. Faessler, *Z. Physik*, **102**, 562 (1936); see also H. M. Sullivan, *Rev. Sci. Instruments*, **11**, 356 (1940); N. Marty, *J. phys. radium*, **8**, 29 (1947).

perpendicular to the line of origin of the particular radiation; the background due to cosmic rays can be reduced to the minimum for a given sensitive volume by making the cathode in the form of a long cylinder oriented vertically. The effects due to local external contamination are most easily reduced by proper shielding of the counter tube, except where a local γ activity of high energy must be tolerated for some reason; then the area of the cathode material should be kept to the minimum.

The counter and its contents, if permanently sealed, should be chemically stable. The fulfillment of this requirement is dependent upon careful choice and manipulation of the materials of construction. A low rate of incidence of "spurious" counts, events not due to ionization events initiated in the sensitive volume by tracer or background radiations, can be achieved by proper arrangement and treatment of the electrodes and by the choice of a suitable filling.

The Cathode. Counter cathodes are usually made of brass or copper, though aluminum and silver are used often and many other metals have been employed for special purposes. Plastic or glass insulating supports are usually free from radioactive contamination; brass cathodes give higher backgrounds than copper ones of the same size, but the effect observed varies greatly with different samples of brass. Silver is usually in the form of a thin mirror chemically deposited on a glass envelope; such cathodes are not difficult to prepare, are relatively free from active contaminants, and have fairly high photoelectric work functions, thus being relatively insensitive to visible light. Brass is more photosensitive than copper, owing to its zinc content (the photoelectric efficiency of both is of the order of 0.01 to 0.05%). The cathode should have a uniform surface free from tears, cracks, and points; aluminum is especially difficult to handle in small diameters because of the great ease with which the inner surface can be torn by lathe tools. Points can be easily removed with fine abrasive paper or cloth.

The characteristics of the cathode are important in determining the "speed" of the counter and the plateau characteristics. Various techniques are available for decreasing or enhancing the photosensitivity of the surface, or for making "fast" or "slow" cathodes.[8, 9]

The Anode. The anode is usually a wire of small diameter. Chromel, iron, and tungsten are the preferred materials, the last being especially popular because of its uniformly high quality as received from the manufacturers and for various constructional reasons. For best performance the anode should be coaxial with the cathode, free from small sharp bends and points, and mechanically stable; Chromel and iron wires smaller than 0.004 inch in diameter cannot satisfy the last requirement,

and tungsten fails at about 0.0025 inch.   The wire should be as straight
as possible; iron and Chromel can be straightened easily by stretching,
but this work with tungsten must either be done with the fingers or by
heating and stretching *in vacuo*.   The threshold voltage is very much
dependent upon the diameters of the anode and cathode, decreasing as
they are made smaller; since low voltages are easier to stabilize, one can
often use a counter of large cathode diameter by making the anode wire
small.   A tiny glass bead is melted over the free end of an unsupported
wire to minimize the number of spurious counts caused by surface
irregularities at the end; the bead also helps to weight small wires and
thus increases their mechanical stability.   These beads are easy to form
only on wires of tungsten because of the much lower softening points
of the other materials.

Envelopes.   In the most common designs the two electrodes are suspended in and supported by a complete glass envelope.   These counters
are useful in carbon tracer work where they can be filled with a radioactive gas or where only the most penetrating radiations are to be detected.   Where these situations are not encountered, the envelope must
be modified in some manner so that the radiations can be detected.   The
end-window counter is such a modification: a very thin mica or foil
window is stretched across the end of a glass envelope which is in the
form of a cylinder at one end.   Much work with carbon 11 has been
done with small counter tubes so designed that a very thin tubular
cathode serves as the body of the envelope and insulating glass plugs
support the anode and retain the filling.   In the "screen-wall" counter
(see page 72) the sample is exterior to the sensitive volume but all are
contained within a sealed envelope.   Which of the many designs to
choose depends upon the special analytical problems involved.

Seals.   The construction of any counter tube requires at least one
insulator-conductor seal, most designs requiring several.   The usual
cosmic-ray-type tube, which consists of the electrodes completely surrounded by a glass envelope, requires two metal-glass seals for the
electrical leads; these are usually made with 0.030-inch tungsten wire.
The simplest end-window tube has, in addition to these, a seal of rather
large area necessary to support the transmitting foil over the open
end of the envelope.   In general all joints must be vacuum tight, and
it is usually desired that they be electrically non-conducting.   Glass-
metal seals are not difficult to make vacuum tight, are insensitive to
rather great temperature changes, and are very rugged; wax-glass seals
are difficult to make vacuum tight, are very sensitive to large changes in
temperature, and are rather delicate, especially in warm climates.   Both
types of seal have good insulating properties.

Lately, the double wax seal has found some favor in the construction of end-window counters.[10]   Two waxes of very different properties are used; in a typical application the mechanical strength of a deKhotinsky-type wax is used in conjunction with the great wetting and sealing power of "Apiezon W." [11]   In Fig. 17 are shown enlarged diagrams of the two most common joints involved in end-window counters made by this technique.   Note how the fillets of Apiezon W prevent the counter filling from coming into contact with the deKhotinsky wax.

A very unusual seal has been developed [12] for use with end-window counter tubes.   A permanent bond is made between the glass envelope

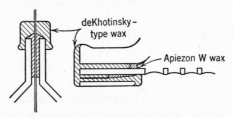

FIG. 17.   Double-wax seals.

and the mica of the window by means of lead glass having a low softening temperature.

Stopcocks are often used on counters for ease in refilling, and they constitute an important part of the sealing problem.   The lubricant in most cocks striates and leaks after a few weeks if not kept under pressure with rubber bands.   This difficulty can be reduced by using very tacky greases, such as Apiezon L, or by regrinding the stopcock with an aqueous or glycerin suspension of No. 600 Carborundum powder.   Counter tubes constructed with carefully ground and greased stopcocks show no leakage from this source.

Counter Fillings and Performance

After assembly the counter is ready for filling and use.   In order that the filling be uncontaminated by outgassing of various parts, the counter is connected to a high-vacuum system and pumped for an hour or so. (Obviously, large thin windows which are unsupported will not stand evacuation on one side; both sides of the window must be evacuated so that no breaking forces come into play.)   After this preliminary evacuation, which will remove the greater part of the occluded gases, the tube

[10] W. G. Dauben, J. C. Reid, and P. E. Yankwich, *Anal. Chem.*, **19**, 828 (1947).

[11] Manufactured for Apiezon Products, Ltd.

[12] C. S. Wu, C. L. Meaker, and H. A. Glassford, *Rev. Sci. Instruments*, **18**, 693 (1947).

is disconnected from the manifold and allowed to stand for several hours, after which it is reconnected to the high-vacuum system and opened into a manometer of small volume; any gross leakage is immediately apparent. If only small leaks are discovered, the wax parts are painted with a thick coat of plastic varnish. (If larger leaks are found, a search must be made for them; pinholes in windows and seals are common offenders. Ordinarily it is easier to reassemble a counter than to correct a leak that is not obvious from a very rapid inspection.) After the varnish has dried hard, the tube is pumped out for an hour or two, slowly flushed three or four times with the selected filling mixture, and then filled to the desired pressure. The counter is then tested on the counting circuit and its starting and threshold voltages are recorded.[13] The plateau is followed rapidly for about 200 volts and its slope roughly estimated. After an hour's operation at 100 volts above the original threshold, the starting and threshold voltages are again determined; they should not differ by more than 20–30 volts from those originally observed. The counter tube is then removed from the circuit and allowed to stand overnight. The next morning the starting voltage is redetermined; it should not be more than 20 volts higher than the second value determined the preceding day. On successive mornings the same procedure is repeated, and, if the starting voltage remains for at least a week within 20–30 volts of the second value obtained on the first day, the tube has no leaks which will change its characteristics greatly during 2–3 months of use. The sensitivity of this method for detecting leaks is quite good; even with counters whose gas volume is as great as 400 ml, small leaks show up very rapidly. For example, the data in Table X were observed for two different counters over a period of 2 weeks.

TABLE X

EFFECT OF LEAKAGE ON STARTING VOLTAGE

Days

t_s	0	1	2	3	4	5	10	12	14
A	870; 890	900	910	910	910	915	900	915	910
B	890; 900	915	920	915	920	920	930	935	935+

The gas volumes were 375 and 390 ml respectively, and the filling was 10 cm of 95% argon-5% ethanol mixture. Counter B was connected to the manifold and its gas pressure noted; the rise in the starting voltage had been caused by a pressure of approximately 1.5 mm of air.

[13] The starting voltage is that potential at which counts are first passed by the scaling circuit. The threshold voltage is that at which the Geiger plateau apparently starts; see page 33.

In any counter tube which makes use of a selfquenching mixture, each discharge reduces the amount of the quenching component available; [14] therefore, a given counter tube has a rather definite useful life. The observable effect of this decomposition is shortening and steepening of the plateau; the starting voltage is also raised and is a good index of counter "age." The data in Table XI serve to illustrate the phenomena observed in a typical tube. The tube receives, on the average, about 10^5 counts per day.

TABLE XI

EFFECT OF AGE ON COUNTER-TUBE PERFORMANCE

Counter tube GP4 Months after service started	0	3	6	12	18	21
Starting voltage	1,020	1,025	1,040	1,050	1,080	1,100
Approximate plateau length, volts	350	350	325	310	260	260
Approximate slope, %/100 volts	0	0	0.5	.....	0.8	1.0
Dead time, minutes	1.12×10^{-5}	1.1×10^{-5}	1.2×10^{-5}	1.3×10^{-5}	1.8×10^{-5}	2.0×10^{-5}
Sensitivity to standard, c/min	1,110	1,110	1,125	1,120	1,105	1,120

Many gases have been tried as counter fillings in the search for desirable characteristics, which are determined to a large extent by the nature of the gas or gases used. The problem has been discussed in considerable detail.[8]

Helium has a rather low specific ionization, see page 316, and therefore must be used at relatively high pressures if good efficiencies are to be obtained.[15] At 1 atmosphere the starting potential of a counter with a cathode $2\frac{1}{2}$ inches in diameter and a 0.008-inch anode is 1,600–1,800 volts, which is not too high; [16] for this reason helium is now coming into use as a filling for end-window tubes of high efficiency (see page 69). Neon has been employed in many counter designs, especially with ether as a quenching additive. A peculiar property of this mixture is that counters filled with it become very photosensitive after passing 10^7 or so counts. Argon is perhaps the most familiar counting gas; it is relatively inexpensively obtained in high purity and, in common with neon, produces counters with low starting voltages. Both these gases have high specific ionizations, and small counters can be made very efficient detectors through their use.

[14] W. D. B. Spatz, *Phys. Rev.*, **64**, 236 (1943); S. S. Friedland, *Phys. Rev.*, **71**,377 (1947). See G. E. Hagen and D. H. Loughridge, *Phys. Rev.*, **73**, 1131 (1948).

[15] S. C. Brown, L. A. Elliot, and R. D. Evans, *Rev. Sci. Instruments*, **13**, 147 (1942); I. A. Bearden and C. L. Haines, *Phys. Rev.*, **40**, 1048 (1932).

[16] P. E. Yankwich, G. K. Rollefson, and T. H. Norris, *J. Chem. Phys.*,**14**, 131(1946).

Nitrogen, hydrogen, oxygen, and air were formerly common as counter fillings, but they result in high threshold voltages and long recovery times; for these reasons they have fallen into comparative disuse.[17] Krypton and xenon are very expensive but have high specific ionizations and result in counters having low starting voltages; their only advantage is their high atomic number, which makes them efficient as fillings for γ-ray detectors.

Numerous organic vapors have been employed as quenching gases; those most successfully incorporated into counter fillings have been

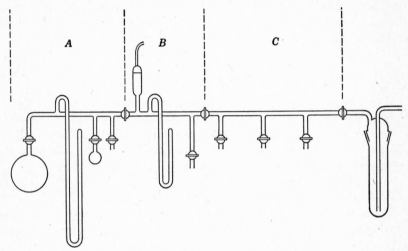

FIG. 18. A vacuum system for filling counter tubes.

ethanol, ethyl ether, xylene, and amyl acetate.[18] Counters filled with argon-alcohol, neon-ether, argon-amyl acetate, etc., all have short recovery times and high detection efficiencies.[19] Of these, the "fastest" mixture is 95% argon-5% ethanol at a total pressure of 10 cm of mercury. In counters operating near atmospheric pressure, a filling of 1 cm ethanol and 74 cm helium is often used. Some selfquenching counters are being filled commercially with tetramethyllead and dimethylmercury, which act as their own quenching gases.[20] Because of the large number of atoms in the molecule, amyl acetate fillings have long useful lives. Triatomic gases constitute a special class of fillings; the use of carbon dioxide and disulfide will be discussed below.

[17] C. L. Haines, *Rev. Sci. Instruments,* **7,** 411 (1936).

[18] E. der Mateosian and H. Friedman, *Bull. Am. Phys. Soc.,* **21,** No. 2, 20 (1946).

[19] S. A. Korff, *Electron and Nuclear Counters,* D. Van Nostrand Co., New York, 1946, p. 95.

[20] A. S. Keston, *Rev. Sci. Instruments,* **14,** 293 (1943).

A simple vacuum system for filling counter tubes is shown in Fig. 18. Section A, the storage line for the filling mixture, consists of a large storage bulb for prepared filling, a small removable bulb filled with absolute ethanol or other quenching additive, and a differential manometer capable of reading pressures as high as 80–90 cm of mercury. The filling gas is made up as follows: system A is evacuated while the alcohol is frozen in liquid air, then filled to a pressure of 4 cm with the ethanol. Argon, or some other base gas, is then added until the total pressure is 80 cm. Section B is a small manifold containing a differential manometer reading to 15 cm for filling the counter tubes, a thermocouple gauge for leak detection, and a connection to the counter tube. Section C is used for preliminary or final pumping of several counters simultaneously.

Specific Designs of Counter Tubes

For the purposes of description and comparison, all counter tubes can be classified in three groups: (1) tubes that are used with completely external samples; (2) those in which the sample is internal but no part of the tube itself; (3) those in which the sample forms an integral part of the instrument.

1. External-Sample Counters

All but a few counter designs fall into this classification; tubes of this variety have more constant detecting properties and are usually more easily operated than those of either of the other types. These tubes are filled with a selected counting mixture and used until the tube is destroyed by accident or until the quenching gas is used up; their sensitivity is easily checked with an external standard. Three counters of this type are in everyday use in carbon tracer work.

Thick-Walled Tubes. The first subtype is used to measure C^{11} by means of its annihilation radiation. The standard cosmic-ray type of tube can be used, and its properties and methods of construction are well described elsewhere.[21] A small tube has been designed for use with living subjects;[22] a diagram of this instrument and the small lead shield for defining the region from which it will accept counts is shown in Fig. 19. This counter does not have a high overall efficiency, but its directional specificity is good and its use in research is based upon this property (see page 32). The filling normally used is helium at 1 atmosphere saturated with xylene or alcohol; under these conditions the threshold is at about 1,500 volts.

[21] H. V. Neher, reference 8.
[22] N. Pace, R. Loevinger, and E. Strajman, *Science*, **107**, 71 (1948).

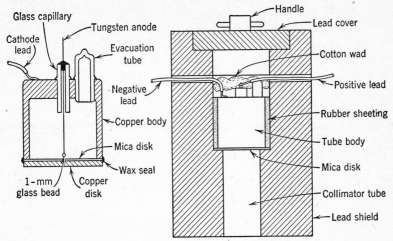

FIG. 19. A counter for clinical use. (N. Pace, R. Loevinger, and E. Strajman.)

Thin-Walled Tubes. A second tube in this general category is shown in Fig. 20.[23] Its aluminum cathode is machined to a thickness of a few thousandths of an inch; such a thickness of aluminum will absorb all the radiation from a carbon 14 sample but allows the positrons

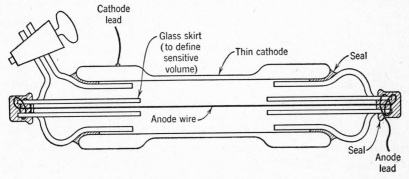

FIG. 20. Thin-walled counter tube.

from C^{11} to be counted with only a small absorption loss. The samples to be measured are placed close to the tube in a standard and easily reproduced position. Some investigators have used tubes of similar design to count solutions, with high geometric efficiency.[24] For this

---

[23] See M. D. Kamen, *Radioactive Tracers in Biology*, Academic Press, New York, 1947, page 71.

[24] A. R. Olson, W. F. Libby, F. A. Long, and R. S. Halford, *J. Am. Chem. Soc.*, **58,** 1313 (1936); H. Suess, *Naturwissenschaften*, **27,** 702 (1939).

purpose the outer surface of the cathode is painted with a thin layer of chemically resistant varnish and surrounded by a jacket of small volume. The liquid samples are pipetted into this annular space for measurement.

A third modification of this class has been described, particularly for use with liquid samples.[25] The counter tube consists of a very thin-walled glass tube, or "finger," to which is attached a rather large gas reservoir which also supports the anode; the inner surface of the finger is chemically silvered and serves as cathode. In practice the instrument is attached to a gear-operated raising device which enables the operator to move a cup containing the sample to be measured over the finger. The relative size of the cup can be so varied that as little as 1 ml of solution will cover an area of several square centimeters of cathode; this counter tube is diagrammed in Fig. 21. An end-window counter of similar design has been developed for insertion into the body orifices; the tube is used in research on cancer of the cervix.[26]

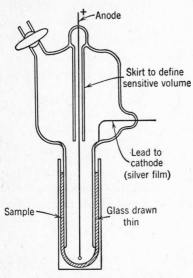

Fig. 21.   Counter for liquid samples. (After W. F. Bale, K. E. Zimens, et al.)

End-Window Counters. The very low energy of the β particles emitted by C^{14} necessitates the use of a counter tube with a very thin wall, less than 8–10 mg/cm² in thickness, if the samples are to be counted externally with high efficiency. Thin-wall tubes of this thickness, made from the ordinary materials of construction, will not support atmospheric pressure in the diameters necessary. This difficulty has resulted in the development of the "end-window" counter tube.

Counter tubes of this kind usually consist of a thick envelope of cylindrical form, over one end of which is stretched a very thin "window" of mica, beryllium, aluminum, or other suitable foil of high β-particle transmission. Depending upon the area of the open end of the envelope, and the pressure of filling to be used, the window may or may not be

[25] A. H. Barnes, *Rev. Sci. Instruments*, **7**, 106 (1936); W. F. Bale, F. L. Haven, and M. L. LeFevre, *Rev. Sci. Instruments*, **10**, 193 (1939). See also A. K. Solomon and H. D. Estes, *Rev. Sci. Instruments*, **19**, 47 (1948).
[26] E. Strajman, *Rev. Sci. Instruments*, **17**, 232 (1946).

supported by a grid of some kind. Several designs of this type [27] are available; one of them uses the cathode as the main body of the counter, a glass top containing the pumping connection and supporting the anode wire. A flange about ½ inch wide is soldered to the open end of the body, and the thin window is attached to this. Since no provision is made to support the window, counters of this design are limited to a cathode diameter of about 1¼ inches when low-pressure fillings are used. An all-glass seal has been developed for use with glass envelopes and

TABLE XII

TRANSMISSION OF C^{14} β PARTICLES BY MICA WINDOWS

Per Cent Transmission	Window Thickness, mg/cm^2
100	0.00
90	0.72
75	1.4
50	3.1
25	5.9
10	9.4
5	11.9
2	15.5
1	17.6

(Note: the window thicknesses are the actual oblique equivalents; since the data were obtained with a point source at about 30% geometry, perpendicular thicknesses are obtained by dividing those listed above by 1.5.)

mica windows.[12] Several authors have used lead or rubber gaskets to effect the mounting of the window. One advantage of this procedure is that disassembly and remounting are much less trouble than with the wax or glass seals.[28] It is quite easy to prepare and mount successfully windows of mica as thin as 1.5 mg/cm^2, which will support a pressure difference of 1 atmosphere, and if the helium-alcohol atmospheric pressure filling can be used, the size of the tube is limited only by that of the thin mica available.

The operational characteristics of all counters are somewhat dependent upon the nature of the cathode material, usually copper or brass,

[27] D. H. Copp and D. M. Greenberg, *Rev. Sci. Instruments*, **14**, 205 (1943); H. Weltin, *Rev. Sci. Instruments*, **14**, 278 (1943); see also F. C. Henriques, Jr., G. B. Kistiakowsky, C. Margnetti, and W. G. Schneider, *Ind. Eng. Chem., Anal. Ed.*, **18**, 349 (1946).

[28] W. C. Peacock and W. M. Good, *Rev. Sci. Instruments*, **17**, 261 (1946); W. M. Good, A. Kip, and S. Brown, *Rev. Sci. Instruments*, **17**, 262 (1946); M. D. Kamen, reference 23, p. 77.

and the treatment accorded it before assembly. Photosensitivity is increased by the formation of very thick oxide layers on the cathode surface but is reduced by thin ones. A surface of metal sulfide, formed by dipping the carefully cleaned cathode in dilute ammonium sulfide,

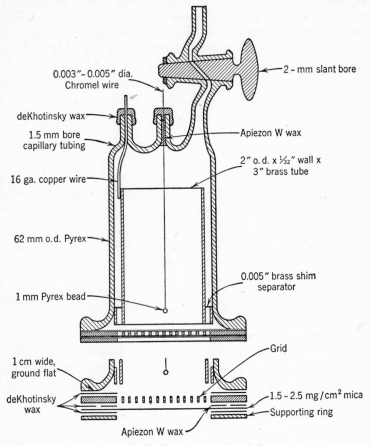

FIG. 22.   End-window counter tube.

produces counters which are virtually insensitive to light of a wide range of wavelengths and which have long plateaus. Shiny brass cathodes are somewhat photosensitive, a few counts per minute, when used with argon-alcohol mixture, but have greatly increased sensitivity with an aged neon-ether filling.

In another design of the end-window type, Fig. 22, the electrodes are supported inside a glass envelope.[10] If a filling at atmospheric pressure is used, the window can be made very large, but low pressure fillings necessitate a slit grid to support the window, usually of mica. In the example diagrammed, the mica window is waxed to the supporting grid, which is in turn sealed to the flange of the glass envelope. An outer support ring helps to prevent creeping of the mica and serves as a stand for the whole tube. In a typical counter the brass cathode had an inside diameter of 2 inches, was 3 inches long, and was lightly oxide coated by heating for a few seconds in a large flame; the anode was a 0.005-inch Chromel wire. The standard argon-alcohol filling was used, and the counter started at 850 volts; the lower end of the plateau was at 860 volts. Over the first 450 volts of the plateau, a slope of less than 0.4%/100 volts was obtained, after correcting for the change in coincidence correction with potential.[29]

Windows can be made of any material free from pinholes, strong enough to support itself at the desired operating pressure, stable to the counting gas, and thin enough to pass a good fraction of the incident radiation. Mica is probably the most common material because of its great strength, but aluminum and beryllium foils have also been found advantageous. If the instrument can be operated near atmospheric pressure, very thin windows can be made of rather delicate materials and the supporting grid can be eliminated. A mica window as thin as 1.25 mg/cm^2 will stand an atmosphere's pressure if properly mounted and supported and if less than 1½ inches in diameter; thinner windows are difficult to mount well enough to stand this treatment. However, mica as thin as 0.5 mg/cm^2 has been used with the helium-alcohol filling at atmospheric pressure in an unsupported 3-inch window.[30] Collodion windows as thin as 0.01 mg/cm^2 have been mounted in β spectrometers [31] and would be suitable for tracer work under special circumstances. Experiments in the authors' laboratories have shown that a properly prepared nylon film 0.04 mg/cm^2 thick can be used with the helium mixture, but the counter has a life of only a few days because the membrane is somewhat permeable to water vapor.

[29] Counters embodying an isolated supporting grid in their design pose an interesting problem—i.e., the effect on the characteristics of the counter because of the presence of a "floating" conductor not grounded in any way. The effect which one might expect is that the counter characteristics should change with use until the grid is charged up to an equilibrium potential. Some observers have found such an effect when thin collodion windows are used in β-ray spectrometer counting tubes. Actually no effects attributable to the presence of the grid have been noted even at very small grid-cathode separations in counter tubes of the design in Fig. 22.

[30] R. Loevinger and K. Scott, private communications. See also I. A. Bearden and C. L. Haines, *Phys. Rev.*, **40**, 1048 (1932).

[31] J. Backus, *Phys. Rev.*, **68**, 59 (1945).

2. Internal-Sample Counters

The Screen-Wall Counters. When the sample can be placed inside the counter, the observable activity is increased because of the elimination of the greater part of the absorbing layers between the sample and sensitive volume and because the geometric efficiency is ordinarily greatly increased; the geometric efficiency of ordinary end-window tubes is rarely better than 25% whereas that of internal sample counters can easily be made 45% or greater. Only one counter of this type is in use,

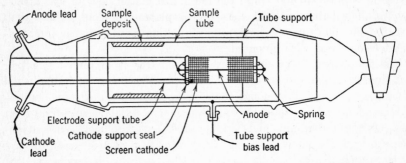

FIG. 23. Screen-wall counter. (A. A. Benson, after W. F. Libby.)

the screen-wall counter of Libby and Lee.[32] A modification of their design is shown in Fig. 23.[33]

The screen-wall counter is so named because its cathode (wall) is made of wire screen, usually about 10-mesh copper. The sample is placed on the inside surface of a tube coaxial with the sensitive volume; for samples very close to the screen and somewhat smaller than it in length, the geometric efficiency is very close to 50%. The counter is so arranged that the sample tube can be moved by tilting; the background is determined by removing the sample from over the sensitive volume by this procedure, while the relative sensitivity of a given counting mixture is determined by bringing up an external γ-ray standard.

Aside from a unique sample-preparation problem, the principal difficulty associated with the screen-wall counters is that the filling must be renewed for each sample. This entails prolonged pumping or flushing out of the tube so that good counter action will be achieved at the final filling; at best, this is a time-consuming feature. If the samples were changed in a "dry-box" filled with nitrogen or carbon dioxide, which

---

[32] W. F. Libby and D. D. Lee, *Phys. Rev.*, **55**, 245 (1939); O. Hahn and F. Strassmann, *Naturwissenschaften*, **30**, 256 (1942); K. E. Zimens, *Trans. Chalmers Univ. Technol. (Gothenburg)*, No. 54, p. 37 (1946); S. N. Naldrett and W. F. Libby, *Phys. Rev.*, **73**, 487 (1948).

[33] The counter tube shown in Fig. 23 was constructed by A. A. Benson.

could be later pumped out of the counter, the filling time could be greatly cut down since the sensitivity of all counters to small partial pressures of oxygen is intensified when the internal elements of the tube must be repeatedly exposed to air.[14] The screen-wall counter is not an instrument well suited for routine analysis, but there is often no faster way to measure the activity of a very small or very large amount of sample material of low radioactive strength.

The Windowless Counter. In Fig. 24 is shown a continuous-flow "windowless counter." The envelope is designed so that a continuous stream of helium saturated with ethanol or xylene can serve as the self-quenching filling. The sample mount is carried on a glass probe and is placed inside the cathode; because of scattering effects the geometric efficiency is greater than 50%. The instrument has not yet been improved to the point where it is satisfactory for routine measurement because of the time necessary to sweep out oxygen. When the flow system is sealed off, the operation is the same as that of the screen-wall counter and is somewhat more efficient for small samples. A similar apparatus

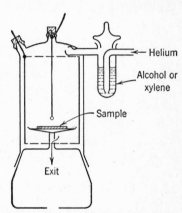

FIG. 24. Windowless counter.

with a slitted cathode [34] has been described. The sample is supported close to the slit.

The operation of atmospheric-pressure flow counters in the Geiger region is ordinarily difficult. A satisfactory solution to the high-geometry problem has been found when linear amplifiers are used instead of G-M circuits; one such device is commercially available under the name "Nucleometer." [35] It consists of a counter operated at a pressure slightly greater than 1 atmosphere; the pulses from the counter go to a linear amplifier and from there to a pulse-height equalizer. This latter circuit feeds a bridge circuit from which a vacuum-tube voltmeter is calibrated to read in counts per minute. The instrument is unusually stable and sensitive.[36]

Practically, it appears that the overall efficiency of the Nucleometer is almost 50% and that the sensitive volume extends almost to the surface of the sample. This situation is rather favorable for the measure-

[34] S. C. Brown, *Phys. Rev.*, **62**, 244 (1942).

[35] Manufactured by Radiation Counter Laboratories, Chicago, Ill.

[36] E. H. Wakefield, private communication.

ment of samples containing C^{14} because the results become less sensitive to small inhomogeneities in the thickness of the sample.

3. Integral-Sample Counters

Even with the internal sample counters, the isotope to be counted must be contained in some solid material. This prevents its dispersion within the sensitive volume, where geometric efficiencies greater than 50% could be obtained. The most delicate method for the determination of radioactivity is the introduction of the active material as a gas into the sensitive volume of the counter tube. The relative efficiency obtain-

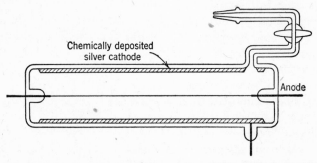

Fig. 25.   Counter tube for C^*O_2 samples.   (After R. B. Loftfield.)

able, for a series of such counters, is dependent upon the ratio of the sensitive and total volumes. For such measurements a tube similar to that shown in Fig. 20, but with thick walls, is suitable; but some investigators prefer "all-glass" counters of a design similar to that of the "finger" counter in Fig. 21 except that the reservoir is omitted. Such a counter is shown in Fig. 25. There are several modifications of the general procedure.

The first is the "additive" procedure of Libby, in which a standard argon-alcohol counting mixture is contaminated by the addition of a small pressure of radiocarbon dioxide.[37] The addition of diluent gas up to a pressure of 4 mm affects, but does not destroy, the properties of the original counting mixture. The method is as accurate as the pressure measurements involved, and the activity observed, when corrected for the extent of the insensitive volume of the counter tube, is very closely the absolute disintegration rate of the sample. Carbon dioxide reacts slowly with brass and other materials of which these tubes are quite often made; this results in a contamination of these surfaces with radioactivity, which activity is carried over to the next measurement. This phenomenon is known as memory and has been discussed on page 57.

[37] W. F. Libby, private communication.

Techniques showing even greater promise than that described above have been developed, based on the preparation of a counting mixture of which one component is a radioactive gas. The difference from the additive procedure is that the mixture left when the radioactive constituent is removed is not a satisfactory counting gas.

One such procedure, involving the use of radiomethane,[37] is especially suitable for very low specific activities, since the mixture employed results in relatively low starting voltages even when used to fill counters of large diameter. Methane alone is a good counting gas and serves as its own selfquenching agent; at pressures below 150 mm the filling can be used with no other quenching gas if electrical quenching is employed. A typical counter tube, 2 inches in diameter and 24 inches long, with a 0.003-inch anode wire, started at about 3,000 volts when filled with methane at 150 mm. The observed plateau was over 600 volts long and had a slope of less than 1%/100 volts; the resolving time of the tube was 10^{-3} second (coincidence correction about 2%/1,000 counts per minute).[38] Methane can be used up to 1 atmosphere pressure with a linear amplifier if only small ionization pulses are registered.[36]

Methane is prepared by the reduction of carbon dioxide with hydrogen over a ruthenium catalyst; [38] the procedure is described in detail on page 171. It is very important that the gas pumped into the counter tube be dry; it was found that a short trap cooled with Dry Ice-acetone mixture was not effective enough, but passage of the gas through a few centimeters of Drierite produced a satisfactory product.

Carbon dioxide alone is a poor counting gas, and its behavior is not improved by the addition of the usual quenching vapors such as alcohol or xylene. However, it has been discovered that the addition of carbon disulfide produces a mixture with good counting characteristics [39] and that at least one carbon dioxide-methane mixture is usable.[38]

At a carbon dioxide pressure of 20 cm, the addition of as little as 0.5 cm of disulfide produced a plateau 50 volts long where none existed before; disulfide pressures up to 10 cm were tried with this amount of dioxide, and all mixtures containing more than a few millimeters of disulfide produced satisfactory counters. At a constant 2 cm pressure of disulfide, satisfactory counter action is obtained if between 10 and 60 cm of carbon dioxide is used; the threshold voltage increases rapidly with the dioxide pressure. For example, a counter with a cathode 1.15 cm in diameter and a 0.006-inch anode was filled with 2 cm of disulfide; when 10 cm of dioxide was added, the counter started at 2,200 volts,

[38] G. R. Hennig, Atomic Energy Commission Report ANL-4080, AECD 1794.

[39] W. W. Miller, *Science*, **105**, 123 (1947); S. C. Brown and W. W. Miller, *Rev. Sci. Instruments*, **18**, 496 (1947).

but this rose to 4,700 volts when 54 cm of gas had been added. The use of this type of filling over the whole range of permissible carbon dioxide pressures necessitates specially constructed high-voltage supplies. Reliable tubes ranged in volume from 25 to 300 cc.

A vacuum filling system which has been designed for the mixture described above is shown in Fig. 26.[40] Barium carbonate is filtered and dried on the fritted disk funnel A; the funnel, or a small amount of any

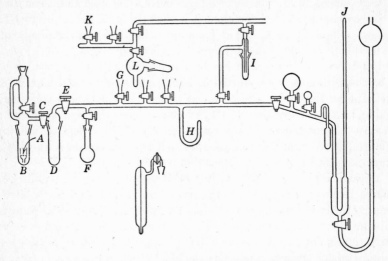

FIG. 26.   Vacuum system for the preparation of C^*O_2-CS_2 counter fillings.   (R. B. Loftfield.)

A	Sample	F	Carbon disulfide
B	Gas generation tube	J	Buret for measuring C^*O_2

organic compound, is placed in tube B, and the system is evacuated while trap I is frozen in liquid air. Stopcock C is then closed, and carbon dioxide is generated by rapid dropwise addition of a mixture of 80% H_2SO_4 (96%) and 20% fuming sulfuric acid, if barium carbonate is used, or of the Van Slyke-Folch wet combustion mixture (see page 93) if organic material is to be oxidized; no excessive foaming is noted. With stopcock E closed the moist carbon dioxide is transferred to trap D with liquid air; in the meantime a counter tube (see Fig. 25) is evacuated at G and filled with 2 cm of carbon disulfide from F, measured on manometer H. (Several counters may be evacuated and filled with disulfide at the same time.) Trap D is now warmed to room temperature, then cooled with Dry Ice-acetone; water-free carbon dioxide is then transferred to

[40] R. B. Loftfield, private communication. See also H. E. Skipper, C. E. Bryan, L. White, Jr., and O. S. Hutchison, *J. Biol. Chem.*, **173**, 371 (1948).

the gas buret J, measured, and put into the counter. After counting, the counter tube is attached to the system at K, the filling transferred to L with liquid air, and the carbon dioxide finally absorbed on Ascarite before disposal. A single complete analysis of a moderate activity takes 20–30 minutes.

A mixture of 10 cm carbon dioxide and 5 cm methane is a fair counting gas, with the single exception that counters filled with this formulation have resolving times which are longer than those ordinarily desired; a 1-liter counter tube so filled has a resolving time of 3×10^{-3} second.[38]

Photographic Methods

Nuclear radiations are capable of producing a photographic latent image, and the method known as radioautography is based upon this property. This technique is particularly valuable when it is desirable to know the distribution of radioactive material in a thin section of tissue or other type of sample, but it gives no information as to the chemical form of the radioactive substance. Radioautography has found extensive application in the visualization of tracer uptake by plant and animal tissues, but its use has been confined largely to work with isotopes emitting rather energetic α or β particles; [41] only three papers have been published which report experiments with C^{14}.[42] No such experimentation with C^{11} has been reported, though this isotope may be useful in the study of systems where information concerning short-term distribution processes is desired.

Radioautographs require high activities or long exposure; a total flux of $\sim 10^5$ β particles per square centimeter of film is necessary to produce a detectable blackening, and at least ten times this activity is needed to produce a satisfactory image.[43]

[41] J. G. Hamilton, M. H. Soley, and K. B. Eichhorn, *Univ. Calif. Pub. Pharmacol.*, I, 339 (1940); A. Lacassagne and J. S. Lattes, *Compt. rend. soc. biol.*, **90**, 352 (1924); D. I. Arnon, P. R. Stout, and F. Sipos, *Am. J. Botany*, **27**, 791 (1940); J. Gross and C. P. LeBlond, *McGill Med. J.*, **15**, No. 4, 1 (1946); J. G. Hamilton, *J. Applied Phys.*, **12**, 440 (1941). For details of various procedures see: L. F. Belanger and C. P. LeBlond, *Endocrinology*, **39**, 8 (1946); K. M. Endicott and H. Yagoda, *Proc. Soc. Exptl. Biol. Med.*, **64**, 170 (1947); T. C. Evans, *Proc. Soc. Exptl. Biol. Med.*, **64**, 313 (1947); P. Demers and V. Fredette, *Can. J. Research*, **A25**, 223 (1947); D. Axelrod and J. G. Hamilton, *U. S. Naval Med. Bull.*, **48**, No. 2, March-April, 1948, Supp., p. 122; A. M. MacDonald, J. Cobb, and A. K. Solomon, *Science*, **107**, 550 (1948).

[42] W. Bloom, H. J. Curtis, and F. C. McLean, *Science*, **105**, 45 (1947); A. V. Grosse and J. C. Snyder, *Science*, **105**, 240 (1947); A. M. MacDonald, J. Cobb, and A. K. Solomon, *Science*, **107**, 550 (1948).

[43] Many workers recommend No-Screen X-ray film. The Ansco product is said to be somewhat more sensitive than other brands.

Radioautograph technique has been successfully combined with filter-paper partition chromatography (see page 242) for use as an analytical tool in biological and photosynthesis studies.[44]

Shielding

The performance of most detectors is improved by proper shielding from local contamination, cosmic radiations, local electromagnetic disturbances, and often light. Lead, because of its availability and great density, is the most common material.

Small thicknesses of lead are ordinarily sufficient to eliminate the contribution to the background of most local sources of contamination; they are not sufficient if γ radiations or neutrons constitute an appreciable fraction of such contamination. In these situations extensive concrete shielding is required if counting must be carried out close to a powerful radiation source; and thicknesses of lead as great as $1\frac{1}{2}$ inches may be required even at distances of 100–200 yards. A 1-inch lead shield will actually increase the observed background because more energetic secondaries are produced than can be absorbed. A $1\frac{1}{2}$- to 2-inch lead shield with a $\frac{1}{4}$- to $\frac{3}{8}$-inch aluminum inner lining stops a large number of primary cosmic rays, almost all very energetic secondaries, and all secondaries with energies below 3 Mev.

A grounded shield, even of window screen, is sufficient protection against all but the most powerful electrical disturbances of local origin. Light protection of glass counter tubes is quite important because many tubes are either photosensitive or rapidly become so. The best insurance against light leaks is good machining of all openings in the shield; if even this is ineffective or if a counter must be operated in the light, the background from this source can be greatly reduced if the glass of the counter tube is painted with ceresin wax colored with a deep red dye.

Especially when end-window counter tubes are employed, the shield must contain the sample-carrying device. Various sample carriers have been described for placing all samples accurately in a standard position near the window of the counter tube. Some designs employ a sliding shield;[10] others, a locking device which necessitates opening the shield each time the sample is changed.[23] The only disadvantage of that procedure is that a light-induced background may take several minutes to decay. Usually, the sample-changing assembly must be designed to satisfy conditions imposed by the individual experimenter; for this reason, a detailed discussion cannot be included here.

[44] R. M. Fink and K. Fink, *Science*, **107**, 253 (1948); W. Stepka, A. A. Benson, and M. Calvin, *Science*, **108, 304**, (1948).

Chapter 6

SAMPLE PREPARATION I

1. Oxidation of Organic Substances

Isotope assay of materials labeled with carbon commonly involves their oxidation to carbon dioxide, which is sometimes measured directly and sometimes absorbed in alkali and converted to barium carbonate before assay. Conversion of the carbon dioxide to a solid, such as calcium carbonate or elementary carbon, with a molecular weight less than that of barium carbonate would substantially diminish self-absorption in mounted samples, since a given amount of carbon is contained in a smaller amount of material. So far, however, no information has been published on the use of such substances.

The oxidation procedures which have been used in tracer work include Liebig combustion, both on the macro and micro scale, sodium peroxide fusion, and wet oxidation by the persulfate and by the Van Slyke-Folch method. The choice of procedure depends on the time required for a determination, the nature and state of the substance, and the accuracy with which it is desired to obtain information concerning the amount of carbon in the specimen. Some common types of problems which arise in a tracer laboratory and the best ways of dealing with them will be considered before procedural details are discussed.

Pure Compounds. Pure compounds are obtained for assay in the course of studying the mechanisms of organic reactions and in biological work where metabolic interrelationships are being traced.

The determination of the isotope content of a pure compound may be approached in two ways. In the first, the specific activity of the organic sample is calculated with the aid of its empirical formula from the observed specific activity of the barium carbonate obtained by combustion. In the second, it is not necessary to know the empirical formula; the specific activity of the sample is calculated from the total activity of the barium carbonate (which is the total activity of the organic sample) by division by the sample weight.

In terms of laboratory operations, the first technique is characterized by the necessity for reduction of the blank in the combustion procedure to a very low value, since the *specific* activity of the barium carbonate is the experimentally observed datum on which the calculation of the specific activity of the organic compound is based, and it must not be lowered by adventitious carbon dioxide. The technique is also characterized by freedom from the necessity for measuring the amount of carbonate formed. With respect to this consideration, however, it will be noted that, to avoid the effect of selective burning, the combustion itself must be quantitative; the best way to make sure that a combustion has been properly performed is to measure the amount of carbon dioxide or precipitated carbonate obtained and establish that the value is reasonable.

If the isotope is C^{13}, assay of the combustion product in a mass spectrometer gives the atom per cent excess, in which form the isotope content of the organic sample is commonly expressed. If C^{14} is the tracer, assay gives the specific activity of the carbonate; the specific activity of the organic compound, expressed in standard units such as counts per minute per milligram, is calculated with the aid of the empirical formula.

In the second of the two combustion techniques, the requirements are the reverse of those just described in that the blank need not be eliminated but the *total amount* of carbonate obtained must be accurately measured. Again, the completeness of the combustion should be checked by comparison of the yield of carbonate with the expected quantity, and, in order that this requirement be met, the blank should be reasonably low and constant so that an approximate correction can be made.

Here, if the isotope is C^{14}, the specific activity of the sample is determined by first measuring the specific activity of the carbonate; then, multiplication by the total weight of carbonate obtained gives the total activity of the sample, and division by the weight of the sample gives its specific activity.

The second combustion procedure cannot be used to determine isotope per cent excess unless the blank is accurately known and constant so that a correction can be made for its effect. Instead of using a correction factor, however, it is better practice in this case to employ the first technique; that is, to take the precautions necessary to reduce the blank to negligible proportions. In work with C^{13}, a "specific activity" analogous to the specific activity of radioactive substances is not a quantity in common use, although its utility has been suggested (page 281).

In the foregoing discussion, the two variations of combustion technique have been described as separate procedures to indicate the fact that, when circumstances permit, the combustion operations can be simplified and time can thereby be saved. Nevertheless, where the highest accuracy is desired it is best to combine the two techniques, that is, to work with no blank and to determine accurately the amount of carbon dioxide obtained from the sample. By this means, one can check the value obtained for the specific activity of the organic compound. For a pure sample, the two methods must give the same result; but if impurities are present they may not. For instance, if a sample contains water, salt, or other non-carbonaceous impurities, the specific activity calculated by the second method will be low, because the total activity of the sample is divided by a number which is larger than the true weight of the labeled compound. A better value of the specific activity will be obtained by the first method, in which the specific activity of the substance is calculated from the observed specific activity of the barium carbonate, a quantity which is not changed by impurities of the type mentioned.

If the impurity contains carbon, it is still desirable to work under blank-free conditions, for then one may be able to detect the presence of such impurities; the ability to do this has great value in facilitating the discovery of the cause of specific activity values which are out of line with a trend, and even of insuring against drawing wrong conclusions from measurements. The possibility of obtaining analytical information on the percentage of carbon, as well as of hydrogen, in a sample is discussed more fully in the section on Liebig combustion.

In work with C^{14}, some samples of pure compounds will have a specific activity too high for a G-M counter to accommodate when a sample of ordinary size is prepared for assay. Such a situation is commonly encountered in compounds synthesized for biological use, where a very high specific activity is often chosen against the contingencies of biological dilution. Here, not only is it unnecessary to eliminate blank, but also inactive carrier must be added to dilute the active material. Rather large dilutions are often necessary, and the contribution of carbonate from the sample is so small that it may be impossible to measure the large amount of carrier accurately enough to permit its subtraction from the total weight of barium carbonate obtained to get the percentage of carbon in the sample. In such circumstances a combustion may be carried out by the first method to obtain the carbon-hydrogen analysis of the compound, and an aliquot of the barium carbonate diluted for counting. Dilution of barium carbonate (page 96) is a somewhat cumbersome operation, however, and time will be saved by abandoning the attempt to obtain analytical information and an activity determination from a single sample. As an alternative procedure, a standard carbon-hydrogen analysis can be performed on one sample, then a second sample can be burned for activity measurement by one of the rapid methods (peroxide fusion or wet oxidation). In the oxidation of the second sample, carrier is added, and the combustion product is used for the activity determination.

Tissues. Tissue specimens of almost any size may be encountered. In the mouse, the weights of whole organs and tissues range from less than a milligram to several grams. Tissues form a category of substances in which the carbon percentage has no particular significance, and it is for such specimens that the second modification of the combustion technique (page 80) finds its main application. Since the method for oxidizing the sample can be chosen without reference to the question of blank when this modification is used, any of the oxidation methods except the persulfate can be employed. Persulfate oxidation is not reliable for substances insoluble in water.

Biological Fluids. Aqueous solutions, such as urine or blood plasma, are conveniently oxidized by the "wet" persulfate method. The Van Slyke-Folch wet oxidation has also been used for this purpose.[22] Solutions can be burned in a standard combustion train if a quartz tube is employed.

Residues. After the synthesis of a compound labeled with C^{14}, there are left residues which may contain isotope in useful concentration; from these, carbon can be recovered by burning the material. Since the residues ordinarily amount to a gram or two, their combustion requires macro-scale apparatus.

Combustion in Oxygen

In a tracer laboratory, need will ordinarily arise to carry out combustions both on the macro and micro scale; wherever small amounts of materials can or must be worked with, operation on the micro scale is the method of choice. The nature of specimens requiring the highest order of accuracy will ordinarily dictate micro or semimicro operation, and the remarks in this section are directed to combustion on this scale. Their extension to larger apparatus does not require discussion.

The combustion train proper is the standard apparatus [1] with the exception of the packing in the combustion tube. When the carbon content of the specimen is determined by weighing barium carbonate, nitrogen does not interfere and lead peroxide need not be used in the tube. Although halogens do not interfere, silver wool is retained to hold back sulfur. If it is known that sulfur will not be encountered, the packing may be copper oxide alone, maintained at 550° or at 850° C. When the higher temperature is used, combustions can be carried out more rapidly and less residual activity remains adsorbed on the packing.

[1] F. Pregl and J. Grant, *Quantitative Organic Microanalysis*, 4th English Edition, Blakiston Co., Philadelphia, 1946, p. 34.

The combustion tube must be quartz if the higher temperature is to be used.

The carbon dioxide is absorbed in sodium hydroxide solution. A convenient absorber for the purpose is illustrated in Fig. 27. It consists of an outer body F, made from a 100-ml graduated Pyrex cylinder, cut off at the 70-ml mark and sealed to an inner 24/40 ground joint. The gas passes into the alkali through a fritted disperser, D,[2] to effect complete absorption. The reservoir B holds water for rinsing the inner tube and has a capacity of about 10 ml, or enough to fill the inner tube with water up to the dropper tip. Tube C is of such diameter that a rubber pressure bulb can be slipped over it to force rinse water through the disperser.

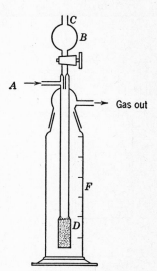

Fig. 27. Carbon dioxide absorber.

There are certain advantages in the use of carbonate-free alkali (page 81). A solution of sodium hydroxide whose carbonate content is negligible can be prepared from metallic sodium.[3] Thirty grams of c.p. sodium metal is weighed out in large pieces under oil. Each piece is carefully trimmed with scissors to remove all traces of crust, blotted with absorbent tissue, rinsed successively in two beakers of hexane, blotted again, and dropped into a flask containing 300 ml of alcohol which has been boiled to remove dissolved carbon dioxide. The preparation is performed in a hood because of the evolution of hydrogen. The operations are performed quickly, and no attempt is made to cool the alcohol; air is prevented from entering the flask by the vigorous emergent current of hydrogen and alcohol vapor. The reaction slows down before all the sodium is dissolved; as soon as the evolution of hydrogen slackens, boiled water is *cautiously* added to effect complete solution. A soda-lime tube is inserted in the mouth of the flask and the solution is cooled. Then

[2] Corning gas disperser tube with fritted cylinder No. 39533-C. This porosity gives a small enough pressure drop across the fritted area so that the suction of a Mariotte bottle plus the oxygen pressure maintained by a sulfuric acid pressure regulator will drive the gas through the system at the recommended rate of 5 cc/min and yet produce bubbles small enough that complete absorption of carbon dioxide occurs.

[3] F. P. Treadwell and W. T. Hall, *Analytical Chemistry*, 9th English Edition, John Wiley & Sons, New York, 1942, Vol. II, p. 490.

800 ml [4] of freshly boiled water is added; the solution, which is about 1 M in sodium hydroxide, is mixed and then is transferred to a siphon bottle (Fig. 28). This container is of all-glass construction, with a cap to protect the delivery tip and with a soda-lime tube in the air inlet. So stored, carefully prepared alkali will remain at least three months without developing a blank greater than 0.005 mg of barium carbonate per millimole of sodium hydroxide.

Sodium hydroxide with a fairly low carbonate content, for use in applications where the blank need not be eliminated entirely, can be

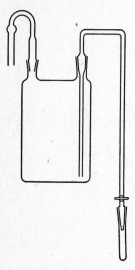

prepared conveniently by taking advantage of the low solubility of sodium carbonate in saturated sodium hydroxide. Water and sodium hydroxide are measured out and mixed in the proportion necessary to make a 50% solution. The sodium hydroxide dissolves in the water, which becomes hot, and on cooling some sodium hydroxide precipitates, along with most of the carbonate. The mixture is filtered and diluted with boiled water. The resulting solution has a blank of about 0.2 mg of barium carbonate per millimole of sodium hydroxide.

A convenient source of good-quality alkali is also to be found in the ampoules sold under the trade name "Acculute."

Combustion Procedure. A little alkali is run out of the delivery tip of the siphon and

Fig. 28. Siphon bottle for alkali storage.

discarded; then a quantity equal to five times the expected requirement is run into the cylinder F (Fig. 27) and is diluted with carbon dioxide-free water to a volume of 45 ml. The joint is greased lightly, the inner tube is put in place, and the assembly is attached at A to the outlet of the combustion tube. The suction of a Mariotte bottle with a long outlet arm is applied at the outlet of the absorber and adjusted until it is just sufficient to draw gas through the disperser when the mouth of the combustion tube is open. Then during the combustion the pressure supplied by a sulfuric acid pressure regulator is sufficient to maintain the current of oxygen, and the pressure in the combustion train is no higher than in the ordinary Pregl combustion. Thus there is no danger of leakage at the connection between the absorber and the

---

[4] When the quantities specified are used, the reagent has a composition which is near the point of incipient salting-out of the alcohol, and a slight turbidity is often observed. This disappears when the reagent is diluted in the absorber.

combustion tube. When the combustion is finished, the absorber is disconnected, the inner tube is raised until it is above the liquid in F, and its outer wall is washed with a fine stream of carbon dioxide-free water from a wash bottle fitted with a rubber pressure bulb. The reservoir B is filled, and the stopcock is opened to fill the inner tube with water, which is then forced through the fritted disperser by a pressure bulb applied at C. The grease is wiped off the ground joint, and the contents of the cylinder are rinsed into the precipitation flask shown in Fig. 29. An amount of ammonium chloride solution equivalent to the alkali used is added, followed by a twofold excess of barium chloride solution. The ground joint is then greased lightly, the cap is put on, the flask is swirled to mix its contents, and most of the air is removed from the flask by attaching it to a vacuum line and opening the stopcock momentarily.[5]

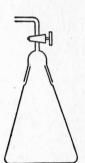

After standing for 15 minutes, the flask is opened and its contents are filtered through a weighed sintered-glass filter crucible of medium porosity. The crucible is covered during the operation with a watch glass to minimize exposure of its contents to atmospheric carbon dioxide. As an additional precaution against absorption of carbon dioxide during filtration, a crucible is selected large enough for the filtration to take place with reasonable rapidity. Satisfactory performance is obtained from a crucible whose disk is 1 mm in diameter for each 5 mg of barium carbonate to be filtered.

FIG. 29. Flask for precipitation of barium carbonate.

After being washed well with boiling water, the barium carbonate is dried at 120° C and weighed. The barium carbonate is then removed from the crucible. This operation is best performed by gently loosening the cake at three or four points around its perimeter with a small metal spatula; the barium carbonate comes cleanly away from the glass as a coherent disk. The small amount of carbonate adhering to the glass is ignored, since it is unnecessary to remove the carbonate quantitatively. The scraping necessary to obtain it contaminates the carbonate with as much as 5 mg of glass from the fritted disk; the presence of glass is

[5] The air is removed because it has been found that, in a small combustion room with a Bunsen burner going, the air in the free space above the solution contains enough carbon dioxide to give a blank of as much as 1 mg of barium carbonate.

The ammonium chloride is added in order to reduce the hydroxyl concentration sufficiently to avoid precipitation of barium hydroxide. Even if the alkali concentration is low enough so that there is no danger of precipitating barium hydroxide, ammonium chloride is added because it improves the mounting qualities of the barium carbonate precipitate.

undesirable because of the danger of unrepresentative sampling when a portion is taken for assay.

When all operations are performed carefully and alkali made from sodium is used, it is possible to fill the absorber with 50 ml of undiluted stock alkali, carry out a mock combustion (150 cc of oxygen), and obtain a blank less than 0.2 mg of barium carbonate. This makes it possible to analyze a substance for carbon at the same time it is being burned for isotope assay. The results of three determinations made on benzoic acid are given in Table XIII.

It should also be possible to obtain the hydrogen percentage by attaching a weighed Anhydrone tube for absorbing water to the end of

TABLE XIII

REPRODUCIBILITY OF GRAVIMETRIC ANALYSIS FOR CARBON

Weight Benzoic Acid	Weight $BaCO_3$	Theoretical Weight $BaCO_3$	Percentage of Theoretical
3.204 mg	36.4 mg	36.6 mg	99.45
10.350	117.2	117.0	100.17
10.540	118.7	119.5	99.49

the combustion tube. An unweighed guard tube of Anhydrone, followed by the carbon dioxide absorber, would complete the train.

Of course, many modifications can be made in the design of the carbon dioxide absorber. A bead tower (page 95) is a convenient device. Absorbers have also been made with a centrifuge tube as the outer member, a feature which permits the barium carbonate to be precipitated, washed, dried, and weighed without transfer. However, washing the precipitate by repeated centrifugation causes mechanical losses which are appreciable for small (0.1-gram) samples.[6]

When a material has a specific activity so high that dilution is necessary before assay is possible, the sample taken for combustion can be as small as can be accurately weighed on a microbalance. A boat containing benzoic acid is placed in the combustion tube behind the boat containing the sample. The sample is burned first, then the benzoic acid; by this procedure the packing of the combustion tube is flushed with inactive carbon dioxide. The flushing serves a dual purpose; it safeguards against a low value for the activity of the sample and against contamination of the next sample burned in the tube.

[6] D. Rittenberg, in *Preparation and Measurement of Isotopic Tracers*, Edwards Brothers, Ann Arbor, Mich., 1947, p. 41. Similar observations have been reported by other workers.

When small samples are taken, it is important to flush the tube in the manner described. This fact is illustrated by the data in Table XIV, which were obtained by two different methods of adding carrier.[7] In one, benzoic acid was burned after the sample; in the other, sodium carbonate was added to the absorber before precipitation of barium carbonate. The combustion tube was packed with copper oxide and maintained at 550° C. The total activities found when the tube was not flushed are 7 to 8% lower than those obtained by the flushing technique. This outcome indicates that there is adsorbed on the surface

TABLE XIV

EFFECT OF FLUSHING COMBUSTION TUBE ON RECOVERY OF ACTIVITY

Compound	Sample Weight, mg	Specific Activity of Compound, c/min/mg $(\times 10^5)$	Carrier
2-Naphthoic acid	1.180	1.00	Sodium carbonate
	1.451	1.07	26 mg benzoic acid
	1.181	1.08	31 mg benzoic acid
Dibenzanthracene	1.092	0.615	Sodium carbonate
	1.159	0.670	17 mg benzoic acid

of the packing a quantity of carbon dioxide equivalent to about 0.05 mg of carbon, which readily exchanges with gaseous carbon dioxide passing through the combustion tube. If a sample contains less than 5 mg of carbon and is burned without carrier, the total activity observed will be more than 1% low. Furthermore, if the succeeding sample is weakly active compared with that preceding, the total activity observed will be too high by a significant percentage. This error can be very great; if the second sample is 1% as active as the first, the observed total activity will be approximately 100% too high, if the same weight of carbon is burned in each combustion.

The figures tabulated in Table XIV are without doubt susceptible to considerable variation when experimental conditions, such as the time during which the combustion tube is swept with oxygen between determinations, are varied. Nevertheless, they show that it is advisable to burn carrier after any sample containing less than about 5 mg of carbon. They also show that it is inadvisable to use a single tube to cover too wide a range of activities; it is best to keep a tube separate for very active samples. When circumstances permit the use of a higher furnace

[7] C. Heidelberger, unpublished observations.

temperature, these nuisances are probably considerably abated, although there is no published experience pertinent to this point.

Sodium Peroxide Fusion

Fusion in a bomb with sodium peroxide has been in use for some time as a method for quantitatively oxidizing fuels to determine calorific value, and as an analytical method for determining sulfur,[8] phosphorus,[8] arsenic,[9] and halogens [10] in organic compounds. It has not found wide use as an analytical method for carbon for reasons which presumably stem in part from the fact that it is difficult to protect sodium peroxide in use from atmospheric carbon dioxide, and the blank is therefore fairly large and varies with the number of times the stock bottle has been opened. However, it has been mentioned earlier that in certain situations encountered in work with C^{14} the blank need not be known, and in these cases the technique recommends itself by the simplicity of the apparatus and operations, and by the speed with which a determination can be executed. The method is particularly adapted to applications where a large number of samples, such as the tissues from a group of animals, must be burned without the necessity of achieving the highest possible accuracy.

In the fusion, carbon is converted to sodium carbonate, from which it is recovered as barium carbonate. Elements in the sample other than carbon which form soluble barium salts have no interfering action. Sulfur and phosphorus cause precipitation of sulfate and phosphate along with barium carbonate. If the activity of the precipitate is measured by solid sample technique, the presence of phosphorus and sulfur introduces no appreciable error into the values for total activity [11] provided the radioactivity is uniformly distributed through the solid; this is true because the mass absorption coefficients for the β rays of C^{14} are very nearly the same for barium carbonate, sulfate, and phosphate. When the amounts of sulfate and phosphate are reasonably small, of the order of those found in tissue for instance, the error caused by inhomogeneity is inappreciable, but with large amounts the errors caused by inhomogeneity of the mounted sample and by unrepresentative sampling become significant.

[8] A. Elek and D. W. Hill, *J. Am. Chem. Soc.*, **55**, 3479 (1933).

[9] F. E. Beamish and H. L. Collins, *Ind. Eng. Chem.*, *Anal. Ed.*, **6**, 379 (1934).

[10] F. E. Beamish, *Ind. Eng. Chem.*, *Anal. Ed.*, **6**, 352 (1934).

[11] The specific activity of the solid is, of course, lowered by the presence of sulfate and phosphate, but, since the total weight is increased in the same proportion as the barium carbonate is diluted, the calculated values of the total and specific activity of the organic specimen are not affected.

If the activity measurement is made on gaseous carbon dioxide, the effect of sulfate or phosphate in the barium carbonate will depend on the technique used to fill the measuring chamber. If the carbon dioxide generated from the sample is swept quantitatively into the chamber (page 326), the total activity is obtained and the inactive impurities introduce no error.

If the technique described on page 327 is employed, the calculated total activity will be too high by a percentage equal to the percentage of the impurities in the barium carbonate used for filling the chamber. Since inactive barium carbonate must ordinarily be added to the active sample in order to furnish sufficient carbon dioxide to fill the chamber, the error is "diluted" by an amount dependent upon the quantity of inactive barium carbonate added. This amount is ordinarily considerable; consequently the presence of phosphorus and sulfur in amounts too low to cause a sampling error introduces no significant error into activity values determined on gaseous carbon dioxide by either of the methods of filling the assay chamber.

The peroxide fusion relies for success upon the attainment of a very high temperature, which insures complete oxidation of the sample. It is impractical to achieve this by intense heating of the bomb, because the metal would suffer extensive corrosion and the lead gasket which seals the bomb would melt. Instead, an oxidation mixture is used of such composition that it deflagrates when heat is applied, thereby attaining a high temperature. Since the flash occurs quickly, the bomb itself does not become hot enough to be endangered. In practice, these considerations require that the proportion in which the components of the charge are mixed be held fairly close to the optimum. In addition, the total amount of the charge must be approximately that which the bomb is designed to hold, for, if the charge is reduced, the thermal inertia of the bomb becomes relatively greater, and the flash does not establish a sufficiently high temperature for reliable combustion. Furthermore, particles of the charge are blown about if there is too much free volume in the bomb, and some of the sample may escape combustion.

The micro peroxide bomb 2302, supplied by the Parr Instrument Company, accommodates 75 mg of organic material, although samples as small as 60 mg can be reliably burned. When a sample weighs less than 60 mg, the difference is made up with sugar. The addition of sugar is not objectionable for very active samples or for those that are to be measured in an ionization chamber, for which purpose they will have to be diluted. However, for moderately active samples which are to be measured with a G-M counter, the dilution introduced by adding sugar increases the counting time seriously. Attempts to replace the sugar

with non-carbonaceous combustible materials, such as powdered magnesium, aluminum, zinc, and sodium hydride, to nourish the flash, fail
for various reasons and so a smaller version of the Parr bomb has been
found to be useful for handling small specimens. The design shown in
Fig. 30 accommodates 5 mg of sample; it is not commercially available.
Samples weighing less than this amount must be diluted to 5 mg with
sugar, but this is not a disadvantage, since very small samples must be
diluted in any event in order to ob-
tain enough barium carbonate to
manipulate.

Procedure with the Parr Bomb.[12]
Figure 30, which describes the
smaller bomb, serves equally well to
illustrate the operation of the Parr
bomb. The bomb is charged in the
standard way: [13] in the cup is placed
225 mg of powdered potassium nitrate or perchlorate, then the dry
sample, which is ground, [14] and powdered sugar if necessary to make 75
mg, and finally 1.5 grams of calorific grade sodium peroxide, which
must be in good condition. After
the bomb has been assembled, it is
thoroughly shaken to mix the con-

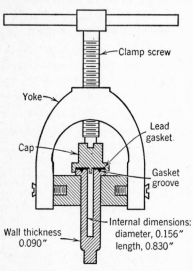

FIG. 30. Small peroxide bomb.

tents, then tapped sharply on the
bench top to compact them; the charge is ignited by holding the bomb
with tongs in the needle flame of an oxygen-gas burner, which is directed
on the bottom of the bomb. The bomb is heated until a slight jar is
felt (5 to 10 seconds), then 10 seconds longer; it is then allowed to cool
90 seconds in air, quenched in water, and dried with a towel. The use
of a small hot oxygen-gas flame gives more reliable fusion than a Bunsen
burner.

It is good practice to perform the ignition behind a safety glass shield.
As an additional precaution, fusion cups are thrown away when they
have lost 1% of their initial weight.

[12] J. C. Reid, unpublished work.

[13] Manual 116, Parr Instrument Company, Moline, Ill.

[14] If the sample is in chunks, the combustion is not reliable unless a considerable
part of the charge is made up of powdered sugar. In general, all the components
of the charge should be as finely divided as possible. It is also important to mix them
thoroughly before ignition.

The bomb is opened and placed on its side in a small beaker containing hot distilled water to dissolve the melt. The beaker is provided with a cover glass to catch spray carried up by the bubbles of oxygen which form as excess peroxide reacts with the water. About 5 minutes is required for the melt to dissolve completely. The solution obtained contains a small quantity of coarse black flakes of nickelic oxide, which are removed by filtering the mixture through a small coarse sintered-glass funnel into a 125-ml Erlenmeyer flask. This is conveniently done in about 2 minutes with the aid of a bell-jar vacuum filtration apparatus. The bomb, its cover, and the watch glass are carefully rinsed with hot distilled water. To the filtered solution, which should not be appreciably warm, is added 15 ml of 40% formalin [15] to reduce excess peroxide. This is necessary to prevent precipitation of barium peroxide when barium chloride is added. The flask is stoppered loosely, since hydrogen is evolved. After 15 minutes, 2.5 ml of ammonium chloride solution (300 g/l) and 5 ml of barium chloride (300 g/l) are added. The barium carbonate is then collected on a weighed sintered-glass filter, where it is washed, dried, and weighed.

Procedure with the Smaller Bomb. In the bomb are placed in turn 15 mg of powdered potassium nitrate or perchlorate, 5 mg of ground organic sample,[16] or sample and sugar, and 150 mg of calorific grade sodium peroxide. The bomb is placed in the clamp, and after the contents have been mixed and compacted they are ignited in a small hot oxygen-gas flame. The bomb is held so that the flame plays on the solid projection at the bottom; if it is heated higher up the lead gasket may melt. Since it is impossible to feel any disturbance when the ignition occurs, a standard heating schedule is adopted:

0 seconds	In flame.
10	Fusion should have occurred.
13	Bottom of bomb bright red; remove from flame.
20	Return to flame.
25	Bottom of bomb bright red; remove from flame.
90	Quench under tap.

A good fusion is indicated by a large decrease in the volume of the charge and the absence of granules of unchanged sodium peroxide.

[15] The formaldehyde is oxidized to formic acid. Under the conditions specified, there is little or no conversion of formate to carbonate.

[16] It is particularly important to grind the sample and to mix the charge well when the small bomb is used.

Barium carbonate is obtained from the melt in the same way as for the larger bomb, using 1.5 ml of formalin. Representative values obtained on various compounds containing C^{14} are listed in Table XV.

TABLE XV

REPRODUCIBILITY OF ACTIVITY DETERMINATIONS OBTAINED BY PEROXIDE FUSION

Compound	Specific Activity, c/min/mg	Mean Deviation as Percentage of Mean	Carbon Recovery as Percentage of Theoretical
Small bomb			
$CH_3C*OONa$	317		115
	325	1.3	120 †
$C*H_3COONa$	5,290		121
	5,210	0.86	120
Melanin *	20.0		126
	19.8	0.50	118
Large bomb			
H_2NCH_2C*OOH	375,000		...
	379,000	0.48	‡
⬡—$C*H_2CH(NH_2)COOH$ OH (with OH)	180,000		...
	181,000	0.28	‡
⬡$C*OOH$	211		118
	227 §	3.6	123

† The values are high by an amount which is ordinarily a little higher than the amount of carbonate found in blank determinations.

‡ Theoretical carbon recovery not calculated because sugar, which was weighed only roughly, was added.

§ These values represent the maximum spread in a series of seven determinations.

Van Slyke-Folch Wet Oxidation

Wet oxidation is in use in many tracer laboratories as a convenient way to oxidize samples for isotope assay. Of the various oxidizing reagents that have been proposed, the Van Slyke-Folch mixture is considered [17] to be the closest approach to an ideal universal reagent. It has been found to give excellent analytical values for carbon when used

[17] F. Pregl and J. Grant, *Quantitative Organic Microanalysis*, 4th English Edition, Blakiston Co., Philadelphia, 1946, p. 62.

in conjunction with a gasometric apparatus for measuring evolved carbon dioxide [18] or with a weighed absorption tube arrangement.[19]

The reagent is made by placing in a 1-liter Erlenmeyer flask provided with a ground-glass stopper 25 grams of chromium trioxide, 5 grams of pulverized potassium iodate, 167 ml of phosphoric acid (density 1.7, made by boiling 85% phosphoric acid), and 333 ml of fuming sulfuric acid containing 20% free sulfur trioxide. The mixture is heated, with occasional rotation of the flask to accelerate solution of the solids. When the temperature of the solution reaches 150° C, the heating is discontinued and a beaker is inverted over the mouth of the flask while the solution cools. The ground stopper is then inserted, and a beaker is inverted over it to keep out dust. An apparatus for filling assay chambers with carbon dioxide directly from a wet oxidation is described on page 145.

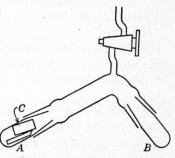

A convenient apparatus for carrying out small-scale oxidations when it is desired to collect barium carbonate is shown in Fig. 31.[20] The sample to be oxidized, containing 5 to 10 mg

Fig. 31.   Apparatus for Van Slyke-Folch oxidation.   (H. A. Barker.)

of carbon, is placed in cup A, and the small beaker C is filled with 3 to 6 ml of oxidant. Cup B receives 4 ml of 0.25 N barium hydroxide. The apparatus is assembled and evacuated through the stopcock with an oil pump. The operation is performed by opening the stopcock momentarily, then closing it; this action is repeated several times, so that all the air will be swept out of the apparatus by the water vapor which arises from the barium hydroxide solution. The stopcock is manipulated cautiously, so that the barium hydroxide solution does not foam up. The stopcock is finally closed and the apparatus is disconnected from the pump. The assembly is shaken carefully to mix the contents of A; the mixture is then boiled gently with a small flame for 10 to 15 minutes. The assembly is allowed to stand 5 minutes longer to insure complete diffusion of carbon dioxide into the alkali. The barium carbonate is then collected on a weighed filter.

When this apparatus is used, potassium iodate is omitted from the oxidizing reagent, since the oxygen given off when it is present interferes

[18] D. D. Van Slyke and J. Folch, *J. Biol. Chem.*, **136**, 509 (1940).

[19] R. M. McCready and W. Z. Hassid, *Ind. Eng. Chem., Anal. Ed.*, **14**, 525 (1942).

[20] H. A. Barker, private communication.

with the diffusion of carbon dioxide; when this is done, however, the recovery of carbon tends to be a little low (2 to 5%). If the oxidation is carried out as specified, with a small flame, there is no appreciable blank from sulfur trioxide.

For samples containing no nitrogen or halogen, the amount of carbon dioxide formed can be determined by using a measured amount of barium hydroxide of accurately known normality in B and titrating the excess with standardized hydrochloric acid, using phenolphthalein indicator.[21] This can easily be done without dissolving any barium carbonate. After the amount of carbonate has been determined, it can be collected by centrifugation, since it is unnecessary to collect it quantitatively.

If it is desired to oxidize larger samples, an oxidation vessel of the type illustrated in Fig. 58 can be used, and the carbon dioxide swept into an absorber.[22]

Persulfate Oxidation

The method to be described is an adaptation [23] of a procedure [24] which was not originally developed for tracer work.

The oxidation apparatus is shown in Fig. 32. The reaction vessel is a 100-ml flask, A, carrying a side arm through which a tube extends to the bottom of the flask. Through the tube is admitted a current of air, freed of carbon dioxide by passage through Ascarite and 1 M sodium hydroxide in the purifier-bubble counter C. The absorber B consists of a tower packed with 3-mm glass beads resting on a mat of glass wool; an extension of the tower extends to the bottom of a 125-ml Erlenmeyer flask. The absorber is connected to A through the reflux condenser D.

To carry out a combustion, a sample containing about 5 mg of carbon is placed in flask A with 36 ml of carbon-free water [25] and 1 gram of finely ground potassium persulfate.[26] The flask is rotated to dissolve as much of the reagent as possible, 1 ml of 4% silver nitrate solution

[21] F. P. Treadwell and W. T. Hall, *Analytical Chemistry*, 9th English Edition, John Wiley & Sons, New York, 1942, Vol. II, p. 498.

[22] H. E. Skipper, C. E. Bryan, L. White, Jr., and O. S. Hutchison, *J. Biol. Chem.*, **173**, 371 (1948).

[23] S. Weinhouse, private communication.

[24] O. L. Osburn and C. H. Werkman, *Ind. Eng. Chem., Anal. Ed.*, **4**, 421 (1932).

[25] Carbon-free water is prepared by refluxing for 1 hour a mixture of 1 liter of distilled water, 10 grams of potassium persulfate, and 10 ml of 4% silver nitrate. Ten per cent of the water is then distilled and discarded; the remainder is distilled and collected, with precautions to exclude atmospheric carbon dioxide.

[26] The solubility of potassium persulfate is 5.3 grams per 100 ml at room temperature. If it is not all in solution, liberation of oxygen takes place at crystal surfaces and the oxidizing efficiency is lowered.

is added, and the flask is attached to the reflux condenser. In the Erlenmeyer flask is placed 10 ml of 0.5 N sodium hydroxide solution, and the bead tower is set firmly in place. Vacuum sufficient to draw 1 bubble of air per second through the apparatus is applied at the outlet of the bead tower, and flask A is warmed to 70° or 80° C by a bath of warm water. When the mixture has darkened and the evolution of gas has ceased (15 to 25 minutes), the water bath is removed, the air

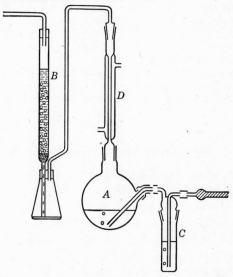

FIG. 32. Apparatus for persulfate oxidation. (S. Weinhouse.)

flow is increased to 3–4 bubbles per second, and the flask contents are refluxed gently for 10 minutes. A small flame is used, since there is danger of incomplete oxidation if the oxidant is decomposed too rapidly.

The absorber is disconnected, and the glass beads are washed with three 10-ml portions of boiled water; the washings are allowed to fall into the Erlenmeyer flask. Barium carbonate is then precipitated in this flask. The carbonate is collected on a weighed sintered-glass funnel. In washing the beads and in the filtration, atmospheric carbon dioxide is excluded by placing over the apparatus a large inverted funnel through which a slow stream of tank nitrogen is passing. When the alkali solution used in the absorber is made by diluting filtered 50% sodium hydroxide (page 84), the blank is 1.5 to 2 mg of barium carbonate. Of this, about 0.3 mg comes from the reagents used in the combustion mixture and the rest is from the alkali. The persulfate oxidation is reliable only for substances soluble in water. Typical results obtained [23] by the procedure described are given in Table XVI.

TABLE XVI

RESULTS OF ANALYSES BY THE PERSULFATE METHOD

Compound	Sample Weight, mg	Carbon Recovery as Percentage of Theoretical
Glucose	9.9	101
Succinic acid	10.6	101
Acetanilide	7.1	99.2
Acetone	6.3	101
Potassium hydrogen phthalate	10.9	101
S-Benzylthiourea hydrochloride	12.2	102
Silver citrate	28.4	101

2. Dilution of Very Active Specimens

It has been mentioned earlier that compounds containing radiocarbon are sometimes prepared with an activity too high to be measured directly by the instruments available when a sample of ordinary size is taken for assay; such material must be diluted. The dilution can be performed when the sample is burned, but for various reasons it is sometimes desired to dilute the material without burning it. This is done by adding to the active compound a suitable amount of the inactive compound. The weight of each is measured so that the dilution ratio is known; the specific activity of the original material can then be calculated by multiplying the specific activity of the diluted sample by the dilution ratio.

The mixed sample is homogenized before assay. With soluble compounds, this is accomplished by dissolving the mixture in a suitable solvent; the homogenized sample is then recovered by crystallization. The recovery need not be quantitative, since the dilution ratio is known.

The homogenization of heterogeneous samples is more often required for barium carbonate than for any other compound. This operation requires discussion because it cannot be carried out by a simple recrystallization. Instead, carbon dioxide is generated and absorbed in sodium hydroxide solution, where homogenization occurs. Barium carbonate is then precipitated from the solution by the addition of barium chloride.

To carry out the operation, an apparatus similar to that shown in Fig. 33 is useful. The absorber, bubbler 2, is filled with a 50% excess of $1 N$ sodium hydroxide; to bubbler 1, the generator, is added the weighed, inactive barium carbonate. The active material is weighed out in a platinum or porcelain boat and carefully placed in the generator. The walls of this bubbler are washed down with 25 to 50 ml of distilled water, and the top is put on. With stopcocks B, C, and D closed, the system is evacuated through A with an aspirator; A is then closed. Through C, dilute hydrochloric acid is added slowly to the barium carbonate. When the pressure in the bubblers approaches atmospheric

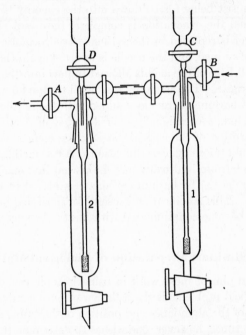

Fig. 33. Apparatus for homogenization of barium carbonate.

(acid is sucked in more slowly), a slight vacuum is applied to the outlet of the second bubbler and nitrogen is admitted to the first through the stopcock B. The vacuum is so adjusted that no appreciable pressure is necessary to force the current of nitrogen through the system. The addition of hydrochloric acid is continued until the carbonate is completely dissolved; then the system is swept with nitrogen for about 20 minutes. The absorber is emptied and rinsed, and barium carbonate is precipitated from the solution so obtained.

Often it is desired to dilute a small amount of carbonate, and the technique just described, even on a small scale, is time-consuming. A method has been devised [27] whereby all the necessary steps can be carried out in a small centrifuge cone. A total of less than 100 mg of barium

[27] A. A. Benson, private communication.

carbonate is placed in a 15-ml centrifuge cone, which is then stoppered with a rubber cap of the type used for sealing bottles containing sterile liquids. A drop of glycerin is placed on the cap, and a hypodermic needle attached by sealing wax to a glass syringe from which the plunger has been removed is inserted through the drop; the cone is evacuated with an oil pump through the syringe. The rubber cap must be at least $\frac{1}{16}$ inch thick to resist being forced down into the cone by the atmospheric pressure. When the evacuation is complete, the needle is removed [28] and the plunger is replaced in the syringe. Hydrochloric acid (1 M) is drawn into the syringe, and the needle is inserted again through the cap. All but about 0.1 ml of the acid is allowed to flow into the cone, and the needle is withdrawn. The assembly is allowed to stand 5 minutes, then a slight excess of barium hydroxide is added with the needle. The assembly is gently shaken occasionally over a period of 5 minutes to effect complete absorption of the carbon dioxide; the homogenized carbonate can then be obtained by centrifugation. As a modification of this technique, the barium hydroxide may be placed in a small cone placed inside a larger one. The barium carbonate is placed in the bottom of the outer cone. This modification is useful for purifying barium carbonate which has become contaminated with inert substances.

3. Preliminary Preparation of Biological Materials

The ultimate aim of most work in using isotopic carbon as a tracer to solve biological problems is the isolation of pure compounds and the determination of the abundance and position of the tracer atoms in their molecules. At times, however, one wishes to determine the gross tracer content of biological materials without carrying out isolation work. This situation arises, for example, in survey experiments with a newly labeled compound where one wishes to get a general idea of which tissues are the most immediately interesting. If C^{13} is the tracer, the samples must be burned to carbon dioxide, except for the occasional few which are volatile and which lend themselves to direct assay in a mass spectrometer. With the radioactive carbon isotopes the possibility of making measurements directly on the material is open, but with C^{14} the best accuracy is generally obtained by counting carbon dioxide or barium carbonate, particularly if one wishes to relate to each other the activities of several substances of diverse properties, such as soft tissue, bone, and the administered compound.

Whole Tissues. Tissues may be burned either fresh or dry. If fresh tissue is burned, its specific activity is obtained on a wet-weight basis,

---

[28] The hole in the rubber closes and the vacuum is maintained. The glycerine assists in preventing leakage.

and comparison of a tissue with a relatively high water content, such as lung, with one containing less water, such as bone, will make the latter appear more active metabolically than it actually is, unless the water content of each tissue is determined in a separate experiment and specific activities converted to a dry-weight basis. However, very small organs, such as the thyroid glands of mice, dry rapidly and lose a significant percentage of their water before they are brought to the balance; this behavior makes the determination of water content difficult. When comparisons between such specimens are involved, it is best to dry all tissues before burning them.

Since a certain amount of time usually must elapse between dissection and combustion, fresh tissues should be stored at a temperature low enough to prevent enzymatic and bacterial action, which might form gases and volatile compounds, with consequent escape of tracer. Loss of tracer also can occur in the tissue-drying operation if the labeled compounds present are volatile under the conditions of desiccation. The best procedure is to dry tissues 24 hours under vacuum at a temperature below 60° C. Under these conditions, the water is completely removed yet the temperature is low enough to avoid chemical breakdown of the components of the tissues. Little information is available concerning the problem of activity loss during desiccation, and it is good practice to collect the tissue water in a trap and determine its activity. It has been observed that the water from the tissues of mice to which had been administered radioactive tyrosine [29] contained less than 0.1% of the total after being dried 18 hours at 60° C under oil pump vacuum. If it is necessary to avoid protein denaturation, the milder lyophilization, or "freeze-drying" technique, can be used, and if even this procedure causes loss of a biological activity under investigation it will be necessary to work with fresh tissue.

Dry tissue may be burned by any of the combustion methods except the persulfate; fresh tissue can be reliably burned in a combustion furnace. A quartz combustion tube must be used or water from the tissue will crack the tube by suddenly running onto a heated area of the glass. The Van Slyke-Folch procedure has also been used [22] as a method of oxidizing fresh tissue.

When the gross specific activity of whole organs is to be determined, attention must be paid to sampling technique, since it has been found that heterogeneity in the distribution of radioactivity through tissue can be pronounced, especially in bone.[29, 30] Small organs can be burned *in toto* in order to eliminate this effect, but it is not convenient to take the time required to burn large amounts of tissue. Moreover, it is very

[29] J. C. Reid and H. B. Jones, *J. Biol. Chem.*, **174**, 427 (1948).
[30] W. Bloom, H. J. Curtis, and F. C. McLean, *Science*, **105**, 45 (1947).

commonly desired to determine the total activity of the specimen by burning an aliquot and to use the rest for other operations. In all such cases, it is important to grind the tissue, if dry, before sampling or to homogenize well if fresh.

Excreta. Loss of tracer in drying excreta from mice given radio-tyrosine is somewhat greater than the loss from tissues, particularly if bacterial action has commenced. The loss from combined excreta is about 1% of the total; individual values have not been determined for urine and feces separately. This loss is small, but if it must be avoided the excreta must be oxidized without drying. Care must be exercised to homogenize feces well before sampling, particularly specimens taken at short intervals after the administration of tracer, since the initial rate of change of activity is often very great, and successive increments of feces will differ widely in tracer content.

It will rarely be necessary to dry samples of urine and other fluids; the activity will be determined by persulfate oxidation of an aliquot of the liquid.

Chapter 7

SAMPLE PREPARATION II

The preliminary sample-preparation operations convert active materials derived from research into forms more suitable for isotope assay. Samples to be analyzed for C^{13} are usually burned to carbon dioxide, though a few investigators have used samples of methane. Materials containing the radioactive tracer isotopes of carbon may be "counted" as gases, liquids, or solids, depending upon the nature of the isotope, the amount and specific activity of the radioactive material, and the time available for the activity measurement.

Here, as with the problem of basic instrumentation, it must be emphasized that the situations encountered in routine application of the tracer technique are such that the investigator should have at his command several methods for preparing samples to be submitted for assay if he is to cope with any eventuality. There are certain methods of sample preparation which are fast and fairly accurate; other techniques are demanding of time but involve errors far smaller than even the ordinarily moderate experimental errors other than counting error. In this chapter we shall not try to present all the methods for sample preparation which have been proposed but rather shall attempt to explain a number of techniques which involve the widest possible range of sample weights, activities, and chemical forms; the advantages and limitations of each method will be pointed out wherever possible.

Detectors have been described which are capable of operation with gaseous, liquid, or solid samples. No experimental details have been published concerning the measurement of gaseous samples of carbon 11, of liquid samples of carbon 14, or of other than gaseous carbon 13 compounds, but the other combinations are widely encountered.

Preparation of Gaseous and Liquid Samples

Gaseous samples containing carbon 13 or 14 are prepared by the combustion of tissues, cell suspensions, extracts, or pure compounds. The carbon dioxide which results is usually either trapped at a low temperature or absorbed as carbonate for later precipitation and regeneration. Some investigators have carried out wet combustions and have filled their assay chambers with the purified carbon dioxide, using a single apparatus. Such a technique has been described briefly on page 76. The combustion of organic materials and the absorption of the dioxide and its precipitation as barium carbonate have been discussed in the preceding chapter, pages 82–96; the generation of carbon dioxide from barium carbonate is discussed in the sections on the synthesis of one-carbon compounds, pages 153–154, and in the description of a high-vacuum system for routine filling of ionization chambers, pages 143–146. A few investigators have used methane in gas-filled counter tubes;[1] carbon dioxide is reduced according to the procedure described on page 171.

Choice of Sample Form and Material

Carbon 13 samples are nearly always analyzed in the form of carbon dioxide gas, and a number of brief guides to proper techniques are available;[2] much of this material is discussed in sections on vacuum operations and need not be repeated here. In experimentation carried out with radioactive tracers, gaseous sample materials are advantageous when very weak activities must be determined with accuracy and where large amounts of sample are obtained. Instruments and detectors of several kinds are suitable for this purpose. The "additive" type of counter filling, in which a standard counting mixture is contaminated with a small partial pressure of active carbon dioxide (see page 74), requires only a small fraction of a millimole of gas when counters of moderate size (200–300 cc) are used. The reproducibility of measurements performed with such a counter is largely that with which the rather delicate pressure measurements can be made. Counter tubes operating with active carbon dioxide-disulfide or methane fillings (pages 75 and 76) require only a few millimoles of active material, and the results obtained are not severely affected by problems of pressure measurement since the active components are always present at partial pressures of at least a few centimeters. Ionization chambers require rather large amounts of active material, from 1 or 2 to 60 or 70 mmoles of gas. In many cases a small sample is diluted with inactive material in order that the chamber be filled to the proper operating pressure, and in others the large amount of sample is directly available from

---

[1] For example: E. C. Anderson, W. F. Libby, S. Weinhouse, A. F. Reid, A. D. Kirschenbaum, and A. V. Grosse, *Science*, **105**, 576 (1947); *Phys. Rev.*, **72**, 931 (1947). See page 75.

[2] D. Rittenberg and S. Weinhouse, in *Preparation and Measurement of Isotopic Tracers*, J. W. Edwards, Ann Arbor, Mich., 1947, pp. 31–42, 43–50.

experiment. Results obtained with ion chambers of moderate volume (100–300 cc) are relatively insensitive to ordinary errors in pressure measurement. A problem common to all methods dependent upon a sample-filled detector is presented by "memory," which is usually a source of error more serious than any other.

Solutions can usually be prepared quite rapidly and with little difficulty. It is therefore quite logical to assume that the measurement of liquid samples would be a particularly simple and accurate method for radioactivity determination, especially since volumes of solutions can be measured with great accuracy in a short time. Liquid samples are advantageous in many situations, particularly when samples of carbon 11 are analyzed. One can dilute the activity by adding solvent; contamination of the measuring instruments is easily avoided or corrected; the chemical constitution of the original material need not be altered; and reproducibility of results is largely an instrumental problem.

C^{14}-containing samples are not easily measured in solution since the β particles of maximum range can penetrate only 0.28 mm of water. C^{11} is easily detectable because of its energetic positrons, which produce γ radiation during the annihilation process; both radiations are sufficiently penetrating that this isotope has been counted often in solution. A very useful counter tube for experiments involving liquid samples has been described on page 68.

Liquid-sample preparation sometimes requires combustion of carbonaceous material; the carbon dioxide formed is absorbed in alkali, and an aliquot of this solution is counted. Liquid samples are especially convenient where several chemical operations must be rapidly carried out on an experimentally derived extract or sample, and it is desired to check the activity of various parts of the sample at different stages in the process. For example, it may be desirable to measure the activities of the ethereal, alcoholic, acid, and alkaline extracts of a certain tissue and yet not destroy the chemical identity of the active substances. After the radioactivity measurements have been finished, further chemical treatment can be carried out. When C^{11} is used, it must be possible to perform all the operations in rather brief intervals since a 20-minute half-life permits of no time-consuming techniques. Some of the early photosynthesis work [3] demonstrates how a series of separations can be made quite rapidly if the experiments are ingeniously devised.

Liquid samples can be introduced into annular spaces surrounding thin-walled counters, or they can be pipetted into shallow dishes which are then placed in a standard position near a counter tube or in or near an ion chamber. The latter technique has been used with samples of

[3] S. Ruben, W. Z. Hassid, and M. D. Kamen, *J. Am. Chem. Soc.*, **61**, 661 (1939).

carbonate in normal potassium hydroxide.[4] Four milliliters of solution was pipetted into a circular hard-rubber dish 4.5 cm in diameter and 0.5 cm deep. The dish was placed close to the detector, in this case a pressure ion chamber; the results obtained were sensitive to the uniformity of the liquid surface. In order that the surface be reproducibly level, it was necessary to prevent creeping at the edge by coating the liquid with a thin film of olive oil. The edge of the dish was touched with a wire which had been barely moistened with oil; the completed sample was then covered with aluminum foil so that the results would be unaffected by evaporation of the solvent. The accuracy of such a method can be made quite high, different samples of the same active material yielding specific activities with a mean deviation from the mean of less than 4%; the accuracy is somewhat improved if a detergent is used to increase the wetting power of the solution, especially if the sample dishes are of metal (see page 113).

Preparation of Solid Samples

Solid samples fall into two main categories: (1) those prepared by the evaporation of solutions, and (2) those for which the starting point is a slurry of insoluble material.

Tracer radiations, especially those of C^{14}, are appreciably absorbed in thin layers of solid-sample materials. In order that accurate correction be made for this self-absorption effect, it is necessary that the sample deposit be of as uniform thickness as possible. The difficulties associated with most of the known sample-preparation techniques are engendered by this necessity. It is theoretically possible to prepare a uniform sample of almost any material; however, knowledge in this field is rather limited, and one can conclude only that a great deal of work would be necessary to formulate a general procedure or procedures which could be applied to any one of a large number of compounds. The experiments that have been performed have been limited by the nature of the problems to which they were applied; thus, most of the samples falling in the first category have been prepared from materials which occur at some stage of the photosynthetic process, or which are derived from certain metabolism studies, while the second category is dominated by samples of a single compound, barium carbonate, obtained by combustion from many sources.

Available activities can be most efficiently utilized if the material of which the samples for counting are made contains a high percentage of

4 J. H. C. Smith and D. B. Cowie, *Plant Physiol.*, **16**, 257 (1941); *J. Applied Phys.*, **12**, 78 (1941).

carbon. This is clearly not the case with barium carbonate, which is widely used because it agglomerates well when precipitated and therefore can be filtered rapidly and easily. Carbonates of the lighter metals, such as calcium and zinc, would be preferable because of their higher relative carbon content, but they are nearly always difficult to handle because of the presence of a large fraction of very fine particles. The only road open for investigations involving the light-metal carbonates

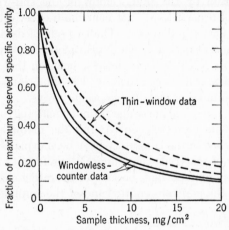

Fig. 34. Self-absorption correction curves for barium carbonate (upper curve in each pair) and ceresin wax (lower curve in each pair). The thin-window counter data were obtained at ∼30% geometry through 2.3 mg/cm² equivalent of mica and air; the windowless counter (Nucleometer) data were obtained at ∼50% geometry.

is that which will result in the discovery of conditions of precipitation which yield a more easily handled product.

Most crystalline organic materials which have been used for counting samples contain a large percentage of carbon, and through their use large self-absorption corrections can be avoided. The best possible sample material from this point of view would be elemental carbon, and some workers have experimented with its preparation for counting sample use by reducing active carbon dioxide with metallic calcium and magnesium at high temperature.

Self-absorption correction curves are functions of the scattering and absorbing powers of the sample, mounting materials, and any absorbing layers between the sample and the sensitive volume of the detector, and of the geometric arrangement of the detection system. In practice all carbon compounds that do not contain atoms of high atomic number require practically identical correction at any given surface density, all other variables being the same. The magnitude of the discrepancy be-

tween correction curves for two different types of sample material and
the effect of an interposed absorbing layer (counter window) are illustrated by the two pairs of curves in Fig. 34, where results obtained with
samples of barium carbonate are compared with those observed when
active wax samples were used.[5]

The great difference between the end-window and windowless counter
data is due to the complete absorption of the low-energy end of the C^{14}
β-particle spectrum by the thin window of the end-window counter.
These very weak β particles do not contribute effectively to the measurable flux of reflected radiations. The two sets of data were collected
at different geometries; that of the Nucleometer is virtually 50%, but
reference to Table XXXIV leads to the conclusion that the increase in
observed reflection will be considerably less important than the large
increase in the number of measurable primary rays.

The frequent use of a particular sample material necessitates the
determination of its correction curve, and the methods whereby this
can be accomplished in the laboratory have been explained on pages 27–
31. In the case of materials containing C^{11}, uniformity of thin samples
may be relatively unimportant, because of the rather considerable penetrating power of the positrons emitted and of the annihilation radiation.

Use of Auxiliary Porous Media

Samples of solutions and suspensions containing carbon 11 in non-
volatile form have been prepared for analysis by evaporating small
volumes on pieces of blotting paper.[3] One or two milliliters of the solution or suspension were pipetted dropwise onto a piece of thin blotter
about 5 by 8 cm; the paper was warmed on a hot plate while this was
done, and the temperature of the blotter was so regulated that the individual drops dried in 5 to 10 seconds without spattering. The whole
surface was covered with the active material so that different samples
would have approximately the same geometry when counted. When all
the sample had been deposited on or in the paper and dried, the blotter
was covered with cellophane and wrapped around a thin-walled counter
tube of the type shown on page 67. A large number of samples prepared by this method will give results, say specific activity of a solution,
for which the mean deviation from the mean is about 4%. The activities
of suspensions cannot be measured and compared so accurately since
very small particles are drawn into the pores of the blotter by capillarity,
while larger particles remain on the surface; it is practically impossible
to duplicate these distribution conditions in going from sample to

⁵ P. E. Yankwich and J. W. Weigl, *Science*, **107**, 651 (1948). See also pages 108
and 311.

sample, especially when there is little uniformity in particle size. Experiments made by one of the authors led to values for the total scatter of 4-6% for very uniform samples, solutions, and most crystalline precipitates, and 6-10% for relatively inhomogeneous solid deposits such as macerated tissues.

A modification of this method useful in work with carbon 14 has been proposed by several workers; [6, 7] the technique is limited to the use of solutions. Samples are prepared in dishes of thick aluminum foil 2 or 3 mm deep; the dish diameter is always less than that of the counter window, but diameters from 2.5 to 3.5 cm seem to be convenient. From 0.1 to 0.2 cc of the solution is placed in the center of the dish, and the drop thus formed is covered with a disk of lens-cleaning tissue which is slightly smaller than the bottom of the dish (see Fig. 35). Usually the

FIG. 35. Use of lens tissue in sample preparation (schematic). (E. W. Fager.)

liquid wets the paper rapidly and spreads out quite uniformly; however, acidic aqueous solutions do not spread well, and the addition of a drop of acetone or ethanol has been found to facilitate the process. The contents of the dish may be dried in a vacuum desiccator or in an oven at 105°. As little as 0.15 mg/cm^2 of organic material is sufficient to cause the paper disk to adhere to the bottom of the dish. (The present authors find that 0.02 mg/cm^2 of collodion will serve as a good adhesive.) Where the amount or nature of the dissolved material is such that the paper curls off the bottom (this happens much more often when the solutions are oven dried than when desiccator dried) 1 or 2 drops of a 10% sucrose solution serve to weight the paper. A similar technique has been independently developed and successfully applied to the preparation of samples from pure fats and petroleum-ether solutions of fats. [8]

Self-Absorption Corrections and Reproducibility. The self-absorption corrections for evaporated solution samples prepared by these methods are made assuming that the active material is uniformly dispersed throughout the paper. The apparent sample thickness is the total weight of sample and paper divided by the area of the disk. The self-absorption correction factor for this thickness is used to compute the activity at zero (or other standard) thickness. Only the actual weight of the active material is considered when aliquot calculations are made. At least one

[6] W. B. Leslie, *Experimental Use of C^{14}*, Atomic Energy Commission, MDDC 674.

[7] E. W. Fager, in *Report of a Symposium on the Use of Isotopes in Biological Research, Chicago, March 3-4, 1947.*

[8] C. Entenman and S. Lerner, private communication.

author [7] has found that the barium carbonate correction curve can be used with fair accuracy for the handling of results obtained from samples prepared by this method. However, the barium carbonate curve cannot ordinarily be used for accurate work with wholly organic samples heavier than 4–6 mg/cm^2 because of backscattering effects. Addition of more solvent to even up an initially uneven deposit must be avoided, as must addition of solvent to a disk not yet dried, since both processes wash the paper in a manner such that the activity is no longer uniformly dispersed throughout its bulk. The error in reproducibility is increased

TABLE XVII

REPRODUCIBILITY OF SAMPLES ON LENS TISSUE [7]

Total Apparent Thickness, mg/cm^2	Percentage Deviation from Average Computed Specific Activity	Total Apparent Thickness, mg/cm^2	Percentage Deviation from Average Computed Specific Activity
1.22	5.4	3.07	0.3
1.37	1.8	3.88	2.4
1.42	0.8	4.78	3.1
1.94	1.4	5.73	0.4
2.47	0.5	6.88	0.6

somewhat if the drop is added to the paper rather than the paper to the drop.

The error in reproducibility of this method can be made small in comparison with many other experimental errors if sufficient care is taken. Especially in biological work, the counting sample reproducibility error is often smaller than that inherent in many tissue-preparation operations on a single subject. Some experiments by the present authors lead them to believe that the mean variation in specific-activity determinations of several deposits of a single active material will ordinarily be about 3% for amounts of sample sufficient to produce an actual sample density of more than 0.5 mg/cm^2.

In Table XVII are collected figures indicative of the results obtained with a series of ten samples prepared by this technique; varying amounts of a sucrose solution were added to 0.1 ml of an active sodium carbonate solution. The specific activities at zero thickness were computed with the aid of the barium carbonate correction curve.

Evaporation onto Non-Porous Mounts

As it is often undesirable to let the active material soak into the mounting, techniques must be developed for evaporating solutions or suspensions of the active material onto non-porous materials such as metal or glass. These mounts are usually either flat disks, for use with end-window counter tubes, or cylinders about an inch in diameter, which are used with the screen-wall counter.

The preparation on the inside surface of a cylinder of uniform samples of constant area is an extremely difficult problem, one for which there is yet no satisfactory solution. The best general technique involves the evaporation of a slurry or solution of the sample material onto the surface of the cylinder, which is warmed with hot air and kept turning while the sample is added from a controllable pipet. The solvent and solute rules are similar to those that will be developed below for flat samples on glass and metal disks.

Successful methods are known for the preparation of deposits of many pure soluble substances, and these techniques will be discussed before the preparation of counting samples from extracts or suspensions is considered.

Samples of Pure Soluble Substances. It will be shown later that uniform deposits of barium carbonate can be made over a rather wide range of sample thicknesses; techniques similar to that used in the preparation of such samples can be and have been devised for other precipitates (for example, formaldehyde 2,4-dinitrophenylhydrazone). Deposits, or "plates," [9] of active phenylhydrazone which are of other than very slight thickness must be corrected for self-absorption losses, and in general the correction curve would have to be obtained by a method such as one described on pages 27–31; however, a large amount of experimentation has shown that the absorbing and scattering powers of many organic materials are very nearly the same, as mentioned on page 105, and are also approximately that of barium carbonate up to about 4 mg/cm^2. This near-equality has been demonstrated by various workers for sample thicknesses as great as 10 mg/cm^2, with substances such as silver cyanide (which gives very poor "plates"), formaldehyde 2,4-dinitrophenylhydrazone, glycogen,[10] palmitic acid,[8] and several protein homogenates. For accurate work with substances which are constantly encountered in experimentation it is best to determine the self-absorption curve, which, if it should be identical with that for barium carbonate or some other material, will at least serve as a check on the method of sample preparation.

Satisfactory mounting conditions have been determined for a number of pure substances.[11] In all cases to be discussed here, the deposits were

[9] The word "plate" as used throughout this book means a uniform, usually thin, deposit of radioactive material on an impermeable mount such as aluminum or glass. No reference will be made to techniques of electrodeposition, and the word "plating" means the operation involved in preparing a "plate" as defined above.

[10] A. B. Hastings and A. K. Solomon, private communication.

[11] A. A. Benson, S. Aronoff, and A. G. Hall, unpublished experiments; see also reference 14.

made on disks with a covered area of 11.5 cm^2, and the sample thicknesses were nearly always less than 0.5 mg/cm^2. The self-absorption loss is usually ignored when counting such very thin samples (more accurate activities being determined by counting later barium carbonate derived from combustion of the active material), but sample uniformity is necessary because the efficiency with which the radiations from a small area are counted depends upon its position relative to the counter window (see Fig. 95).

These compounds are plated out of solution since settling techniques usually fail at such small surface densities because of the powerful effects of surface tension on the distribution of the small particles which would be used. The choice of a solvent is regulated by the nature of the compound, the amount to be plated, and the nature of the mount.

The solvents chosen for work at low surface densities, less than 1.0 mg/cm^2, are those in which the solute has a high solubility. If the solubility is low, a portion of the deposit may be formed while other parts are still in solution; the plate then grows from this "point," and there is a rapid and uneven migration of the precipitated particles to the regions in which agglomeration is occurring. When good solvents are used, the crystallization takes place slowly over the whole covered area; of course, the exact behavior noted is dependent upon the drying conditions. If a moderate amount of sample is to be used, about 1.0 to 4.0 mg/cm^2, the best deposits are produced when the substance is moderately soluble in the solvent; there is little migration of the sample particles which cannot be controlled by manual agitation of the plating assembly, and the small crystals formed during relatively rapid evaporation of the solvent serve to bind and even up the whole deposit.

The plates are usually made on disks of photographic-plate glass or thin aluminum. Plates thicker than 3.0–3.5 mg/cm^2 are more easily made by the settling technique used for barium carbonate, which is described below. Thinner deposits require a greater amount of attention, and their preparation can be greatly simplified if they are made on a turntable assembly like that sketched in Fig. 36. The aluminum disks are stamped from 2S, ¾-hard sheet with one polished face, flat strip rolled. The sheet used in the authors' laboratories is approximately 0.006 inch thick. The glass disks [12] are ground and shaped to

[12] Glass disks with a lightly ground surface are often useful when aqueous solutions are to be evaporated. The capillarity of the ground surface reduces the effect of the the high surface tension of water and thus helps the solution to spread. Conversely, when organic solvents are used the action of this surface is usually detrimental to the best results because the spreading becomes so rapid that the operator cannot exercise proper control over the evaporation. A smooth surface, the ungrooved back of the disk, is satisfactory for those organic solvents which are less volatile than acetone.

the form shown in Fig. 37. The samples made on these disks are confined to a definite area by the small groove, because the solution will not turn the sharp corner. When metal disks are used this problem

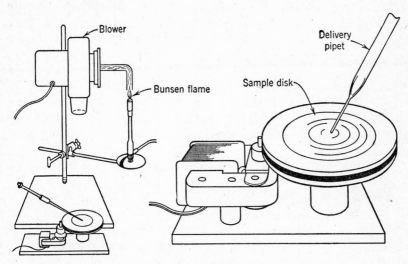

FIG. 36. . Turntable apparatus. (A. A. Benson.)

must be solved by manual control. The velocity of the hot air stream is regulated by controlling the speed of the blower and is usually kept low enough so that the surface of the solution will not be greatly agitated.

The choice of mount depends upon the particular compound and the amount to be deposited. Samples thicker than 4 mg/cm^2 are usually plated on aluminum in a cup of the type shown in Fig. 42 by settling technique. Samples of medium thickness, 1.0 to 4.0 mg/cm^2, are more often plated on aluminum but glass must be used in certain cases; these samples can be made in the evaporation cup if the mounts are aluminum but must be made on the turntable when glass mounts are necessary, since the glass is so inflexible that it is impossible to make a solvent-tight seal with the sleeve of the plate maker. Thin samples, up to 1.0 mg/cm^2, are made on either mount but almost always on the turntable. Plates

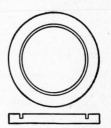

FIG. 37. Glass sample mounting disk; overall diameter 4.5 cm. (A. A. Benson.)

are relatively easy to make on either kind of disk, but it is easier to see a small amount of material on the aluminum surface. When the optimum uniformity is necessary, and if the solution spreads unevenly,

TABLE XVIII [11]

PLATING DATA FOR CERTAIN PURE SUBSTANCES

Compound	Solvent
Acids	
phenylacetic	Ether or ethyl acetate
N-benzoylalanine ⎫ fumaric ⎪ malic ⎬ methylmalonic ⎪ succinic ⎭	Glacial acetic acid
acetic (barium or sodium salt) ⎫ asparagine ⎪ citric (monohydrate) ⎪ lactic (sodium salt) ⎬ oxalic ⎪ 3-phosphoglyceric (barium salt) ⎪ phosphoserine (barium salt) ⎭	Water
aspartic ⎫ glutamic ⎭	Water, then add piperidine
alanine ⎫ glycine ⎬ serine ⎭	Water, V if on Al
Carbohydrates	
fructose ⎫ glucose ⎬ sucrose ⎭	Water with V
2,4-Dinitrophenylhydrazones	
acetaldehyde ⎫ formaldehyde ⎪ oxalacetic acid ⎬ pyruvic acid ⎭	Pyridine
Ethylenediamine-dihydrochloride or dihydrobromide	Water, G
N-benzoylalanine ⎫ p-bromophenacylglycerate ⎪ N-carbobenzoxyalanine ⎪ Glucose phenylosazone ⎬ Iodoform (volatile) ⎪ p-phenylphenacylacetate ⎪ Serine ⎭	Pyridine

the addition of a small amount of a detergent, about 0.05 mg in 1 drop of water, has been found to help the spreading of the sample.[13]

In Table XVIII are collected plating data for a number of pure substances. In the solvent column the letter V indicates that the detergent must be added, while Al or G indicates that good plates have been made only on aluminum or glass, as the case may be.

It has been mentioned that the self-absorption correction is ignored in most cases where the sample is thinner than 0.5 mg/cm^2. At this thickness about 7% of the observable activity is absorbed in the sample material, and this practice can be indulged only when such inaccuracies are unimportant. Actually the specific activities of several samples in this range will check within 3–4% since all suffer about the same absorption loss, but proper self-absorption corrections must be applied to all samples, regardless of thickness, if the reproducibility of these methods is to be evaluated. Extensive experimentation in the authors' laboratories has shown that the expected mean deviation of the computed mean corrected specific activity of a large number of samples prepared from pure soluble substances is 3 to 5% in the 0 to 1.0 mg/cm^2 range, 1.5–4.0% in the 1.0 to 4.0 mg/cm^2 region, and 1.5–2.5% in the range 4.0 to 10 mg/cm^2. Of course, these techniques are subjective, and a certain amount of practice is necessary.

Methods like these, especially when small amounts of material are involved, lend themselves nicely to the preparation of samples of many complex substances. For example, some workers [14] have prepared plates in the "thin" range of chlorophyll, carotenes, and other plant pigments, from ether, proteins from water, and cellulose homogenate from ethanol-water mixtures; very light deposits of whole plant cells, algae, yeast protein, and cholesterol have been made from aqueous suspensions.

Plating of Extracts. Very often it is desirable to prepare for radioactivity analysis samples of extracts or of solutions in which the amount of active material is very small. This situation is frequently encountered in metabolism studies where the main part of a given sample must be saved for further chemical treatment but a small amount can be checked for activity. It has been found that the best plates are prepared by evaporating small volumes of the desired solution onto either aluminum

---

[13] The detergent used by the authors is Colgate-Palmolive-Peet Co.'s VEL. The usual concentration is approximately 10 mg detergent in 10–15 ml of water. One drop is sufficient to cause a large decrease in the surface tension of a small amount of most aqueous solutions.

[14] A. Benson and M. Calvin, *Science*, **105**, 648 (1947); S. Aronoff, A. Benson, W. Z. Hassid, and M. Calvin, *Science*, **105**, 664 (1947); S. Aronoff, H. A. Barker, and M. Calvin, *J. Biol. Chem.*, **169**, 459 (1947).

or glass in the form of a thin spiral line.[15]   The turntable is used, and the hot air stream is regulated so that the evaporation of the solvent is practically instantaneous.   The solution is added from a micropipet controlled by a syringe; the form of the deposit is shown in Fig. 38.

FIG. 38.   Form of spiral line sample (before spreading).

Mouse bile and urine as well as many tissue extracts have been plated by this method.   Some of the media used are water, dilute sodium hydroxide solution, ethyl acetate, methyl and ethyl alcohols, ether, pyridine, acetic acid, carbon tetrachloride, chloroform, and benzene; benzene produces exceptionally good deposits on both glass and aluminum.   The weight of material deposited in preparing these samples is usually less than 1 mg, which corresponds to a surface density of the order of 0.1 mg/cm^2.   The self-absorption loss is inappreciable, but the activity observed is different from that found when the samples are burned and counted as barium carbonate, because of slight spattering and because it is difficult to achieve the same distribution of point-detector geometries possessed by an extended solid source (see Fig. 94).

Preparation of Samples from Suspensions

The most accurate activity determinations involving the use of solid samples are made using barium carbonate, and there are several reliable methods for preparing uniform samples of almost any thickness.   The organic material is burned to carbon dioxide by one of the methods described on pages 82–96, absorbed in alkali, and precipitated as barium carbonate.

The conditions of the precipitation and drying have a great effect on the particle size.   Carbonate-free 1 N sodium hydroxide is the usual absorbing medium, but samples precipitated from this solution by the direct addition of barium chloride solution are grainy and difficult to grind fine enough to make good thin plates.   Thicker deposits, say above 3.5 mg/cm^2, are relatively easily made even with rather coarsely ground carbonate.   The addition of a small excess of ammonium chloride or ammonium nitrate decreases the rate at which the solution absorbs inactive carbon dioxide from the air and results in the precipitation of finer particles.   However, the solids thrown down are sensitive to the drying temperature, 130° C being a safe maximum; above this temperature the particles grow rapidly in the hot, wet mass.   Many of these difficulties can be avoided by a preliminary drying with acetone followed

15 A. Benson and C. Heidelberger, unpublished experiments.

by ether; washing with alcohol invariably produces hard, granular precipitates.

Plates of barium carbonate and other slightly soluble compounds can be made by filtration, evaporation, or centrifugation methods. These will be discussed in turn.

Filtration Techniques. The simplicity of the filtration process has appealed to many investigators as a rather convenient solution to the problems involved in the preparation of uniform sample deposits. Several variations of the method have been devised.

Sample retaining filter

In one of these [16] the sample is prepared in a brass Büchner-type funnel shown in Fig. 39. The Büchner funnel is set on the ground rim of a glass funnel, of the same outer diameter, which is connected to a suction flask; the vacuum is supplied by a water aspirator. A circle of heavy qualitative filter paper is cut to fit into the funnel and placed over the bottom on the inside. This filter paper later serves to prevent gross deformation of the sample layer near the holes drilled in the bottom of the filter. A sheet of high-wet-strength filter paper (such as Schleicher and Schuell No. 589 or Munktell's No. OK) is pressed into the funnel with a plastic cylinder about 1 inch in diameter; the paper projecting over the edge is trimmed off with a sharp scalpel. Strong suction is applied, and the papers are wet with water; the paper is pressed onto the bottom and wall of the funnel with a flattened thick stirring rod or a small vial. After the paper has dried, its cut edge is attached to the rim of the funnel with molten paraffin (this serves to prevent air leaks

Base filter (paper)

Brass cup

FIG. 39a.   Büchner-type filter assembly.

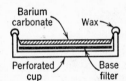

FIG. 39b.   Completed sample. (W. D. Armstrong and J. Schubert.)

around the paper which greatly retard the speed of filtration). The funnel and paper are washed with acetone and ether, and air-dried to constant weight. The barium carbonate is added in small portions from either an aqueous or alcoholic suspension, or from the original precipitation solution, in which case the whole sample precipitated is counted. Gentle intermittent suction is applied until the paper is covered with a thin layer of carbonate, after which stronger suction is used. The precipitate is washed with water, acetone, and ether and dried to constant weight by drawing air through the filter for 15 or

16 W. D. Armstrong and J. Schubert, *Anal. Chem.*, **20**, 270 (1948).

20 minutes. The whole filter is placed under a thin-window tube for counting.

The activity-thickness curves obtained by these investigators yield (as would any set of data obtained under reproducible conditions with a given experimental arrangement) a self-consistent set of self-absorption

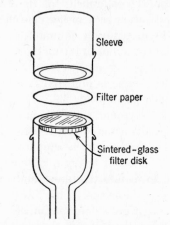

FIG. 40.   Glass filter assembly.

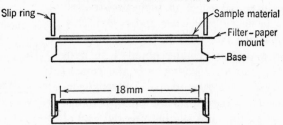

FIG. 41.   Mounting ring and base.   (F. C. Henriques, Jr., et al.)

correction factors. A graph of these figures does not correspond to similar data obtained by other authors, but this is not important in routine relative activity measurements. The total observable variation in specific activity measurements carried out on samples prepared as above is estimated to be about 1.5–2.5%.

A filtration method originally developed for use with benzidine sulfate containing S^{35} [17] has been applied by a few investigators to barium carbonate precipitates and shows considerable promise. The equipment is diagrammed in Figs. 40 and 41. The filter assembly, used with a water aspirator, consists of a Corning filter disk of coarse porosity and a sleeve

[17] F. C. Henriques, Jr., G. B. Kistiakowsky, C. Margnetti, and W. G. Schneider, *Ind. Eng. Chem., Anal. Ed.*, **18**, 349 (1946).

that can be held down with rubber bands. A tared filter circle, prepared from Munktell's No. OK paper, is placed over the filter disk and wet with water; suction is applied; the glass sleeve is then clamped on. An aqueous or alcoholic suspension of barium carbonate is washed into the sleeve and filtered rapidly. The precipitate is rinsed with acetone and ether and dried by suction. Since the glass cylinder covers part of the paper, the sample must then be dried in a desiccator. The paper and precipitate, when dried and weighed, are mounted on the disk shown in Fig. 41. In the original work the sample deposits were approximately 18 mm in diameter, and this seems to be a convenient size. No reproducibility data are available for barium carbonate, but the mean deviation of the computed mean specific activity of a large number of benzidine sulfate samples was about 2.5%; that for barium carbonate is probably somewhat higher, especially for samples less than 5 mg/cm^2 in thickness. The apparatus is similar to that used in an earlier research with S^{35}.[18]

A third filtration method has been devised for use in a completely self-contained system.[19] In a single complex unit a sample is combusted and precipitated. The amount of original sample used is so determined that a saturation or "infinite" thickness of barium carbonate is obtained; this eliminates the need for self-absorption corrections, the activity observed being a linear function of the specific activity of the precipitate.

A technique similar to the second described above has been used to prepare samples of radioactive mouse protein.[20] The protein is prepared as follows: About 100 mg of fresh tissue is homogenized with 5 ml of 10% trichloroacetic acid in a glass macerator; the homogenate is then centrifuged. The precipitate is suspended once in 5 ml of 5% trichloroacetic acid and centrifuged. In the same manner the precipitate is washed three times with 5 ml of acetone; it is filtered onto paper from the last wash. The samples seldom weigh more than 50–60 mg.

Evaporation Procedures. Nearly all evaporation methods are identical except for the diameter of the sample prepared. Most workers prefer samples 1.5 to 2.5 cm in diameter; but several laboratories, including the authors', have standardized on samples 4 cm in diameter. Advantages are claimed for both the small and large samples, but the choice is not influenced by any important factor other than personal

[18] H. Tarver and C. L. A. Schmidt, *J. Biol. Chem.*, **130**, 67 (1939).

[19] J. D. Roberts, W. Bennett, E. W. Holroyd, and C. H. Fugitt, *Anal. Chem.*, in press (1948).

[20] T. Winnick, F. Friedberg, and D. M. Greenberg, *Arch. Biochem.*, **15**, 160 (1947); *J. Biol. Chem.*, **173**, 189 (1948). These authors have found that the filtration procedure here described is not altogether satisfactory and now evaporate acetone suspensions of the protein onto aluminum disks.

convenience. In general, the sample deposit is prepared by evaporating, under controlled conditions, the liquid from a suspension of barium carbonate or other insoluble salt. The solid material must be free of lumps and is usually ground in a mortar under the suspending medium before being transferred to the sample cup.

Some laboratories make use of shallow dishes pressed from aluminum foil or machined from stainless steel.[10] In a representative case a barium carbonate sample weighing 5 to 25 mg is precipitated and washed (with alcohol) in a 15-ml centrifuge cone; the precipitate is then suspended in 0.2 to 0.4 ml of water and transferred by micropipet to a stainless-steel cup 0.1 cm deep and 1.4 cm in diameter. The cup is warmed on a hot plate kept at 40°–60°, and the suspension is stirred with a thin glass rod as the evaporation proceeds. Eight identical measurements gave results reproducible to ~1.5% including counting error, when more than 5 mg of barium carbonate was used. Several investigators, by methods similar to this, have prepared saturation ("infinite") thicknesses of sample materials, thus eliminating the need for self-absorption corrections.

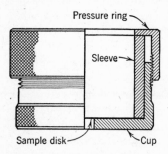

FIG. 42. Slurry evaporation assembly.

A number of groups use techniques which deposit the barium carbonate on thin aluminum disks. A typical mounting assembly is shown in Fig. 42.[21] The disk and the thick concentric sleeve form a cup into which the slurry can be poured; a tight seal is effected by the pressure ring. The whole assembly is heated on a hot plate for a few seconds and then placed under a heat lamp; under these conditions good samples as thin as 0.5 mg/cm^2 can be prepared because a relatively large volume of suspending medium is used and there is opportunity to smooth out the deposit by various manual agitations of the cup assembly while the liquid is evaporating. The shallow dish preparation technique uses rather pasty slurries of material which result in very uniform thick samples, but thin deposits require manipulation of the precipitate with a stirring rod since the volume of suspending medium is usually too small to permit useful manual agitation of the whole dish. A choice between the two methods can be made only in the light of the problems to be encountered by the individual investigator.

[21] P. E. Yankwich, G. K. Rollefson, and T. H. Norris, J. Chem. Phys., 14, 131 (1946); W. G. Dauben, J. C. Reid, and P. E. Yankwich, Anal. Chem., 19, 828 (1947). See also R. H. Hendricks, L. C. Bryner, M. D. Thomas, and O. Ivie, J. Phys. Chem., 47, 469 (1943). See also R. E. Smith, Science, 107, 603 (1948).

To a great extent, the degree of excellence obtainable in the preparation of thin samples is dependent upon the particle size in the carbonate. Thick plates can be made with relatively coarse particles, but thin ones require a finely ground precipitate. A convenient solution is found when the approximate amount of carbonate to be plated is ground under a few milliliters of 95% ethanol in a small mortar. After a few minutes' grinding the suspension is allowed to settle for a few seconds and the major portion of the slurry quickly poured or pipetted into the "plate-making" cup. The short settling time allows any pieces of grit to fall to the bottom of the mortar where they will not be caught up and transferred to the plate maker.

Various suspension media have been tried; investigations have been made of the quality of plates deposited from the following: methanol, ethanol, ether, acetone, water, ethyl acetate, water with various wetting agents added, n-propanol, isopropanol, carbon tetrachloride, and benzene.[22] Of these the most uniform deposits at all thicknesses are produced by the alcohols; methanol is ruled out, however, because of the toxicity of its vapor. Ordinary 95% ethanol is the medium upon which the authors have standardized their procedures.

The evaporation is actually a somewhat more complicated process than it may appear to be, especially when thin samples are to be made. Samples above 2.5 mg/cm^2 can usually be prepared with little difficulty if the precipitate has been well ground, regardless of the conditions under which the precipitation was made. Lighter samples are more sensitive to particle-size distribution because surface-tension effects near the dry stage are quite powerful. The usual observation, at the 0.7–1.0 mg/cm^2 level for example, when no special precautions are taken, is that the particles tend to concentrate at the edge and center of the disk, just as the deposit approaches dryness, to such an extent that certain areas of the mount are not covered. The problem can be overcome by using only finely ground carbonate, carefully cleaning the mount before the tare weighing, carrying out the evaporation under a heat lamp without preliminary boiling of the suspension on a hot plate, and protecting the surface of the liquid from air currents. Agitation of the plating assembly is often used to break down the concentration of solid particles in the edge and near the center when plates heavier than 1.5 mg/cm^2 are prepared. In this thickness range a technique consisting in tapping the cup assembly on the bench top, and swirling and agitating the suspension by shaking, is usually very successful. In the preparation of thinner samples such machinations are sometimes more detrimental than beneficial. It must be emphasized that these directions are only suggestions

22 P. E. Yankwich, unpublished experiments; T. H. Norris, private communication.

since the problems of each individual research will, in general, require somewhat different handling of the experimental details.

When the precipitate has been thoroughly dried under the heat lamp, the sample plate is removed from the cup (a simple device is shown in Fig. 43) and put on a hot plate at around 140° for 10 or 15 seconds to remove the last traces of volatile material. The sample is then weighed and is ready for counting.

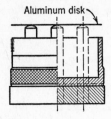

Aluminum disk

FIG. 43.   Disk remover.

In Table XIX are collected some results obtained from samples of various thicknesses prepared by the method just described. No attempt was made to select particularly excellent plates for counting.[23] The mean deviation of the samples in the series was 1.7%, and the standard deviation was 0.4%.

The barium carbonate deposits prepared by the method described above adhere to the aluminum mounts remarkably well. If it is desired to prepare a sample for use as a permanent standard the usual tenacity of the precipitate should not be relied upon. A simple method for preparing permanent samples is to bind the carbonate by adding to the original

TABLE XIX

REPRODUCIBILITY OF SAMPLES PREPARED BY SLURRY EVAPORATION [23]

Weight $BaCO_3$, mg	Thickness, mg/cm²	Corrected Specific Activity, c/min/mg	Percentage Deviation from Mean of 41 Samples
5.2	0.45	138.1	3.9
7.2	0.63	144.4	0.3
19.5	1.69	146.7	1.9
35.2	3.06	141.4	1.7
44.5	3.87	142.7	0.8
76.6	6.65	144.3	0.3
127.1	11.0	142.1	1.5
178.9	15.5	145.7	0.9
232.0	20.1	144.8	0.3

slurry 1 drop of diluted shellac solution for every 20 mg of barium carbonate. (The shellac solution is prepared by diluting 1 part of prepared orange shellac with 4 parts of ethanol.) The evaporation of the alcohol is carried out in the usual manner, but the high-temperature

[23] The plates used were picked from a series of 41 samples mounted by B. A. Fries as a test of the simplicity and reliability of the method.

drying is omitted. Samples thus prepared cannot be compared accurately with each other or with samples made up without shellac. They are useful only as secondary standards.

A Centrifugation Method. Uniform layers of finely divided solids can be made by centrifuging a suspension in a flat-bottomed container, and this operation has been applied to the preparation of radioactive sample plates.[24] The special centrifuge cup which is used is shown in Fig. 44; it is basically the same as that shown in Fig. 42. In the original design the precipitation and all washings were carried out in the cup with a tared aluminum sample disk in place. If this is inconvenient the grinding technique of the evaporation method can be substituted. After the final centrifugation, the supernatant liquid is removed by decantation and the sample is carefully placed in a drying oven or vacuum desiccator. Considerable care must be exercised in the drying operation because the precipitate is very wet and the sudden application of high temperature or high vacuum will cause spattering, which makes the plate useless. No data have been published regarding the reproducibility obtainable with this method, but the variation in specific activities is about that obtainable with evaporation technique.[25]

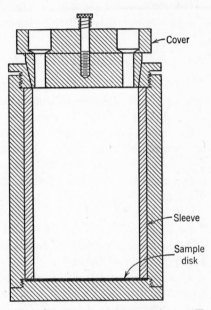

FIG. 44. Special centrifuge cup. (H. E. Silberstein.)

Samples of Compacted Powders

By almost any of these preparative techniques samples of effectively "infinite" thickness can be made, i.e., of such thickness that the radiations from the bottom layers are completely absorbed in the sample and do not contribute to the measured activity. The principal advantage associated with the use of these very thick plates is that no self-absorption corrections need be made; the observed activities are determined

[24] The apparatus described here was developed by Miss Hannah E. Silberstein in the Department of Radiology, University of Rochester.

[25] W. H. Langham, private communication.

only by the relative strengths of the various samples, provided that a constant geometry is maintained. A few workers have prepared these infinitely thick samples by filling shallow dishes, like those pictured in Fig. 35, with finely divided solid. A stiff spatula is used to compact the precipitate and level the surface with the edge of the dish. A disadvantage of this procedure is that a large amount of active sample is required; this makes for inflexibility in routine operations since small samples are often encountered and it is usually a time-consuming process to increase the sample size by dilution with inactive material.

Loss of Radioactivity from Solid Samples

Some degradation schemes yield samples of iodoform which must be counted; such a determination is often difficult because iodoform sublimes rapidly at room temperature and an appreciable fraction of the solid material is lost while the activity measurements and associated weighings are being made. Although most substances of which solid samples for counting are made have relatively low vapor pressures at room temperature, some of them can lose activity by exchange with atmospheric carbon dioxide, others by reaction with moisture, etc. Studies designed to elucidate these loss mechanisms have been carried out only on sodium bicarbonate and barium carbonate.

Some investigators have found it convenient to prepare extremely active samples of barium carbonate for counting by treatment of the solid with acid, followed by absorption of the carbon dioxide in dilute sodium hydroxide; an aliquot of the carbonate-bicarbonate solution is then evaporated to dryness. The bicarbonate in these samples can be thermally decomposed at moderate temperatures and one might expect some loss from this process; both the carbonate and bicarbonate can lose activity, conceivably, by exchange with the carbon dioxide in the air. In an experiment designed to demonstrate the relative importance of the two modes of activity loss, a small amount of sodium bicarbonate solution at pH 8.8 was evaporated onto a sample mount and counted; the residue was dissolved and evaporated to dryness several times, a count being made at the end of each cycle. The results are shown in Table XX. It is apparent that even the relatively small concentration of carbon dioxide in laboratory air can bring about very serious exchange losses when sodium bicarbonate solutions are evaporated; it was found that the addition to such samples of a small amount of sodium hydroxide solution prevented activity loss; i.e., sodium carbonate solutions do not lose appreciable amounts of activity when evaporated.

Most C^{14} radioactivity determinations of solid samples are made on barium carbonate, and it is to be expected that this solid can lose activity by exchange with carbon dioxide through carbonic acid and its ions. The rate of this exchange should be inappreciable in the absence of water. Though several estimates have been made as to the rate of loss from barium carbonate precipitates, only a few experiments have been reported, and these are only indicative.

In one study,[26] thick deposits of solid were prepared by a technique already discussed,[16] see page 115; these were placed in a desiccator and

TABLE XX

Loss of Activity from NaHCO$_3$ on Evaporation [6]

Procedure	Sample Activity, c/min
Original sample evaporated	23,400
Residue dissolved in H$_2$O, evaporated in laboratory air	12,700
Residue dissolved in H$_2$O, evaporated in laboratory air	5,890
Residue dissolved in CO$_2$-free H$_2$O, evaporated in CO$_2$-free air	5,700
Residue dissolved in CO$_2$-free H$_2$O, evaporated in CO$_2$-free air	5,440
Residue dissolved in CO$_2$-free H$_2$O, evaporated in laboratory air	4,640
Residue dissolved in CO$_2$-free H$_2$O, evaporated in laboratory air	3,580
Residue dissolved in H$_2$O, evaporated in laboratory air	2,690

allowed to stand in atmospheres of (1) moist carbon dioxide, (2) moist carbon dioxide-free nitrogen, and (3) dry carbon dioxide. Exchange was observed only in (1); after 65 hours, 37.4% of the activity had disappeared from the solid and was recoverable from the confined gas space. The air was kept moist by a layer of acidified water on the bottom of the desiccator, which was evacuated with a water pump before the carbon dioxide was admitted.

Somewhat different results have been obtained with samples prepared by evaporation-settling, using aluminum mounts.[27] Four different types of experiment were performed, the first of which was a repeat of part of the work just described. Two plates, 3.7 and 5.6 mg/cm^2 thick, were stored in a sealed desiccator, the bottom of which was covered with distilled water; the gas space was swept with a moderate stream of tank carbon dioxide for 15 minutes before the vessel was sealed. After 172 hours, the plates were removed and counted; the activity loss in both cases was $0.9 \pm 1.0\%$. Concentrated hydrochloric acid was added to the water layer in an amount necessary to produce an approximately 3 N solution; the samples were put back into the vessel, which was swept again with carbon dioxide and sealed. The samples were removed after 150 hours and their radioactivities determined; the lighter sample

[26] W. D. Armstrong and J. Schubert, *Science*, **106**, 403 (1947).
[27] P. E. Yankwich, *Science*, **107**, 681 (1948).

lost an additional $1.2 \pm 1.0\%$ of its original activity, whereas the heavier plate apparently gained $0.2 \pm 1.0\%$. The atmosphere in the vessel during the second part of this experiment was sufficiently acid to etch the exposed portions of the aluminum disks.

These experiments were repeated with samples prepared by filtration technique [16] which were about 8 mg/cm² thick. In carbon dioxide moistened by distilled water one sample lost $33.0 \pm 1.1\%$ of its activity in 56 hours. A similar sample prepared from the same batch of barium carbonate lost 36% of its activity when stored in carbon dioxide mois-

TABLE XXI

ACTIVITY LOSS FROM $BaCO_3$ PLATES—REPEATED LIQUID EVAPORATION [27]

	Typical Result			
Liquid	Thickness, mg/cm²	Liquid Volume, ml	Activity Loss, %	Dependence on Sample Thickness
95%-ethanol	4.65	11.0	0.0 ± 0.6	None observed
Distilled H_2O	0.42	15.0	0.79 ± 0.1 per ml liquid	Loss per milliliter decreases with increasing thickness
95%-ethanol + CO_2	4.82	21.0	0.2 ± 0.5	None observed
Distilled H_2O + CO_2	0.41	9.1	0.88 ± 0.1 per ml liquid	Loss per milliliter decreases with increasing thickness

tened by acidified water for 56 hours. During 56-hour "acid" storage, similar samples prepared from batches of barium carbonate which were precipitated under various other conditions lost amounts of their original activities which varied from 5 to 40%, all losses occurring without important changes in sample weight.

An experiment was performed to give information on the exchange rate when the heat-dried solid was in contact with two solvent media. Two plates, both 4.65 mg/cm² thick, were carefully freed of loose particles and placed in shallow dishes; one was covered with 95% ethanol saturated with carbon dioxide and the other with distilled water, also saturated with carbon dioxide (this gas is about 3 times as soluble in ethanol as in water). After 28 hours the samples were carefully removed from the dishes and dried in air at 100°. Radioactivity determinations showed that both samples had lost only $0.3 \pm 1.0\%$ of their activity in this time.

In a third test, small portions of carbon dioxide-saturated ethanol and water; and carbon dioxide-free ethanol and water, were evaporated repeatedly from heat-dried barium carbonate plates of various thicknesses. The plate was freed of loose particles and wet with 0.25 ml of the solvent or solution to be investigated, then dried in air at 100°. The plate was then cooled, another portion of liquid added, and the cycle repeated; at suitable intervals the sample radioactivities were measured. The results are summarized in Table XXI. The small difference in rate of loss between the two aqueous media probably is due to very rapid loss

TABLE XXII

LONG-TERM LOSS OF ACTIVITY FROM $BaCO_3$ SAMPLES [27]

Conditions of Storage	Plate Thicknesses, mg/cm^2	Mean Percentage Loss (9 Weeks); Error Includes Counting Error and Sensitivity Loss
Uranium glass	......	1.2 ± 1.2
BaCO$_3$-shellac bound	......	1.0 ± 1.2
Covered Petri dishes	1.65, 2.20	2.9 ± 2.0
Office-type room	0.53, 3.06	2.6 ± 1.2
Outdoors (protected only from rain)	1.07, 2.90	15.2 ± 4.2
Stream of wet outdoor air	0.63, 3.29	3.6 ± 1.3
Drying oven at 130° (air)	1.35, 2.14	3.6 ± 1.3
Stream of wet CO$_2$	1.75, 2.87	8.0 ± 1.4
Organic synthesis laboratory low CO$_2$, relatively acid air	1.03, 2.77	6.01 ± 1.3
Combustion room, high CO$_2$, relatively acid air	0.66, 1.88	12.1 ± 1.6
Sample storage book; somewhat better sealed than Petri dishes	1.25, 2.86, 3.10	1.7 ± 1.3 (20 weeks)

of dissolved carbon dioxide from the evaporating solution of carbon dioxide in water; the rate of loss with this solution would probably be considerably higher if the evaporation were carried out under a constant pressure of carbon dioxide.

In one paper [26] a loss of 2.7% in 6 days is reported for a sample stored in a covered Petri dish. A fourth set of experiments [27] has been performed to shed more light on this long-term exchange loss. Pairs of heat-dried barium carbonate plates of different thicknesses were stored over a period of 9 weeks in different controlled and uncontrollable atmospheres. At intervals of 10 to 14 days, the plates were collected and their radioactive strengths determined; at the end of the test the samples were reweighed, but no significant weight change was observed. The sensitivity of the counter was checked with standards of uranium glass and of shellac-bound barium carbonate (see page 120). The data obtained are collected in Table XXII. It is apparent from them that some barium carbonate samples, at least those which are heat dried, can be stored for long periods without serious loss of activity. Exchange may not be a trivial matter with samples prepared by any other method, because of particle-size distribution, particle-surface condition, etc.; each circumstance requires at least observation of active samples for long periods.

Chapter 8

VACUUM TECHNIQUES
IN ORGANIC CHEMISTRY

In many phases of the work described in this book it is desirable to employ vacuum lines (closed systems) because almost any operation which involves transfer and storage of small quantities of volatile materials can be carried out with greater efficiency and safety by means of a closed system than by any other method. In this chapter methods and practical information for the construction and operation of vacuum systems are outlined; particular emphasis has been given to application of closed systems to problems in organic synthesis. (For more detailed information on the subject of vacua, reference should be made to the numerous textbooks [1] and papers on this subject.)

Uses of Vacuum Systems

Several types of operation can be advantageously carried out in a closed system; distillations, separations, and transfers of volatile compounds are rapid, quantitative, and safe. For example, the losses involved when 0.5 ml of methyl iodide is measured or transferred by ordi-

[1] S. Jnanananda, *High Vacua*, D. Van Nostrand Co., New York, 1947.

Strong et al., *Procedures in Experimental Physics*, Prentice-Hall, New York, 1943.

A. Farkas and H. W. Melville, *Experimental Methods in Gas Reactions*, Macmillan and Co., London, 1939.

J. Yarwood, *High Vacuum Technique*, John Wiley & Sons, New York, 2nd Ed., 1945.

G. W. C. Kaye, *High Vacua*, Longmans, Green and Co., London, 1927.

L. Dunoyer, *Vacuum Practice*, D. Van Nostrand Co., New York, 1926.

G. Monch, *Vakuumtechnik in Laboratorium*, R. Wagner Sohn, Weimar, 1937. Reproduced by Edwards Bros., Ann Arbor, Mich., 1944.

W. Espe and M. Knoll, *Werkstoffkunde der Hochvakuum-technik*, Julius Springer, Berlin, 1936. Reproduced by Edwards Bros., Ann Arbor, Mich., 1944.

A. Klemenc, *Die Behandlung und Reindarstellung von Gasen*, Akademische Verlagsgesellschaft, M. B. H., Leipzig, 1938. Reproduced by Edwards Bros., Ann Arbor, Mich., 1943.

A very useful source of practical information is advertising literature of the companies which manufacture vacuum equipment.
127

nary methods are considerable. However, this same amount of material represents 685 cc of gas at 20 cm pressure and 20° C; the pressure of this quantity of gas can be measured easily to 0.1% and, by condensation of the gas in traps cooled in a refrigerant such as Dry Ice, 99.9% of the methyl iodide can be transferred in a few minutes.

When radioactive compounds are used, there may be a considerable health hazard because of the danger of inhalation of active material. If, however, volatile compounds are handled and stored in a closed system at a pressure of less than 1 atmosphere, these dangers are minimized.

A vacuum system need be neither elaborate nor expensive for organic synthetic work. A water aspirator with a cold trap (Dry Ice) often produces a sufficiently low pressure for simple transfers and distillations. Mechanical pumps are readily available which produce working vacua of about 10 microns (1 micron = 10^{-3} mm mercury) when part of a small static system; a pressure of a few microns is as low as is needed for most organic work.

In the following section some of the problems involved in the design and operation of a closed system are outlined by reference to certain standard manipulations. These procedures can be extended to many different types of problems, because the basic techniques are the same for most complex vacuum operations.

Distillation Transfer

A fundamental operation, conveniently performed on vacuum lines, is the quantitative transfer of a compound by distillation. An example of the technique is the drying of 0.5 ml of methanol with 1 gram of mag-

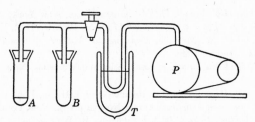

Fig. 45.   Simple vacuum line: T, Dry Ice- or liquid-air-cooled trap; P, mechanical pump.

nesium sulfate. In Fig. 45 is shown the basic system that is required for this transfer, a vacuum line which involves a minimum of equipment: one stopcock, a vacuum pump, some glass tubing, rubber stoppers, and a Dry Ice-acetone bath.

The procedure is as follows: The test tube containing the methanol-magnesium sulfate mixture is connected to the system and is cooled in a Dry Ice bath (the vapor pressure of methanol at this temperature is only a few microns). The line including test tube B is then pumped to a pressure as low as the mechanical pump will produce (about 100 microns), and the stopcock on the line is closed. The Dry Ice bath at A is transferred to test tube B, and test tube A is warmed to about 40° C. If there are no leaks, not more than 5 to 10 minutes should be required to distil most of the methanol from A to B. The test tube containing

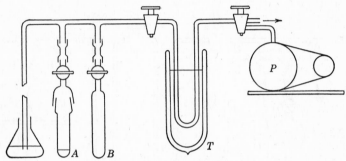

FIG. 46. Improved vacuum line: T, Dry Ice- or liquid-air-cooled trap; P, mechanical pump.

the purified methanol can then be removed from the line, stoppered, and stored for future use. The separation and transfer should be 95 to 99% complete, depending on the condition of the vacuum pump, the tightness of the rubber stoppers, and the surface nature of the drying agent.

The transfer equipment just described is sufficient for many purposes, but if it is necessary to repeat a process often, or if very active material is being handled, several improvements are indicated. When the dried and purified methanol is removed from the line for storage, it is necessary to open the test tube to the air in order to stopper it. If the test tube is cold, moisture will be condensed on it, and if warm, losses of methanol by vaporization will occur. One way to solve these problems is to connect the container for the methanol to the line through a stopcock and a short rubber or plastic tube; the glass tube containing the drying agent can be made from a standard taper joint (see Fig. 46). When the stopcock on the receiver tube is closed after the transfer, the product is stored in the closed container. If this improvement is made, and a simple manometer is added, the system shown in Fig. 46 results; this manifold will give as good results on a simple transfer as can be obtained without the use of liquid air or diffusion pumps.

Separation by Vacuum Distillation

A second basic operation which may be performed by means of vacuum systems is the separation of compounds through differences in their vapor pressures. It is possible to achieve nearly quantitative separation where there is a differential of about 10^3 in the vapor pressures of the compounds, but with substances whose boiling points are close together a distillation column or chemical method of separation is necessary. Vacuum separations may involve either the condensation of the less-volatile component or the selective evaporation of the more-volatile

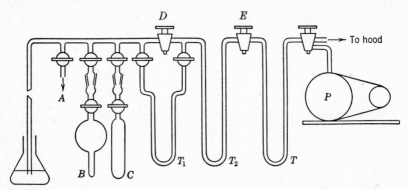

FIG. 47.   Vacuum line for separation of compounds by distillation: T, liquid-air-cooled trap; P, mechanical pump.

substance.   (In general, the former procedure will give the better purification.)

It is necessary to perform this type of separation after the high-pressure hydrogenation of carbon dioxide to methanol, where it is desired to separate the reduction products, water (0.5 ml) and methanol (0.5 ml), from the remaining carbon dioxide (20 cc at NTP), after the removal of these substances from the hydrogen (70 to 80 liters at NTP) and the catalyst used in the reduction.   These operations can be carried out in the system shown in Fig. 47; eight stopcocks, glass tubing, and a vacuum pump are needed for the construction of this line.   The pump should be capable of producing a working vacuum of 10 to 20 microns; standard taper joints, instead of short pieces of tubing, for the attachment of removable vessels to manifolds are desirable.

The mechanical manipulations for these separations are as follows: Traps T_1 and T_2 (Fig. 47) are connected in series and cooled with liquid air.   The gases from the bomb, which is connected at A, are passed through the traps at a very slow rate, and the hydrogen (none of which is condensed) is vented into a hood.   When the pressure in the bomb reaches 1 atmosphere, the bomb is warmed and pumped until all the methanol and water is distilled into the traps; the stopcock connecting the bomb to the line is then closed. Trap T_1 is warmed, and its contents are distilled into trap T_2. The reduction products and carbon dioxide have now been separated from the catalyst and hydrogen and have been transferred from the bomb to the vacuum system. The line and container B (a small storage bulb for carbon dioxide with an appendage tube for condensing the gas) are evacuated; stopcocks D and E are closed, and trap T_1 is cooled in a Dry Ice-acetone bath. The liquid air bath is then transferred from trap T_2 to the appendage on bulb B. As the carbon dioxide distils from the trap T_2 to the bulb, the water-methanol mixture is condensed in the Dry Ice trap T_1. When the transfer is complete, as shown by pressure measurements, the carbon dioxide storage bulb is closed from the rest of the system. The water-methanol mixture may be conveniently distilled into the storage vessel C. (If a leak should develop in the system at any time during the transfers, the entire product may be redistilled into trap T_2 while the system is being pumped, and after the leak is stopped the original procedure may be continued or repeated.)

Vacuum-Line Equipment

The construction of manifolds for more extensive and varied work in organic syntheses will be described later in this chapter. In the following section some of the more important components of such lines will be discussed.

Vacuum Pumps

Pumps for the production of vacuum are usually divided into two classes: (a) mechanical pumps that can operate against atmospheric pressure and are used for the production of moderate vacuums; (b) diffusion pumps, which require a fore pump and are used for the production of high or medium vacuums in systems requiring high evacuation rates.

Mechanical Pumps. A number of suitable mechanical pumps are commercially available.[2] The pump chosen should be capable of maintaining a satisfactory vacuum in spite of small leaks and outgassing, and should be capable of evacuating the system to the desired operating pressure in a reasonable length of time. Thus a mechanical pump should have a pumping speed of several liters per minute at the lowest pressure at which it is expected to be used.

[2] Duo-Seal pumps, W. M. Welch Manufacturing Co., Chicago, Ill.; Cenco pumps, Central Scientific Co., Chicago, Ill.; Kinney pumps, Kinney Manufacturing Co., Boston, Mass.

A good way to compare several pumps is to examine the graphs of their pumping rates vs. pressure (this information is supplied by most manufacturers of vacuum equipment on request). Thus, if a choice is to be made of several mechanical pumps for a fore vacuum, a comparison should be made of their pumping speeds at the necessary backing pressure (this is usually about 10 to 50 microns for oil diffusion pumps). In addition to having a satisfactory pumping rate, a mechanical vacuum pump should be rugged and resistant to corrosion, it should use a small volume of oil to reduce degassing time, and it should be quiet. (Noisy pumps may sometimes be quieted by connection to an external vacuum system such as a house vacuum line.)

Diffusion Pumps. Diffusion pumps not only produce a better vacuum than mechanical pumps, but also increase the capacity or pumping rate of mechanical pumps, especially at lower pressures. Glass pumps can be constructed by an expert glass blower, and both glass and metal pumps are commercially available.[3] Either mercury or high-boiling oils are used in diffusion pumps; there are advantages to each of these fluids, but the present trend is toward the use of oil. The principal disadvantage of mercury is its high vapor pressure at room temperature; a system employing a mercury pump requires the use of a trap to prevent diffusion of mercury vapor into the system. These traps increase the volume of the system and offer additional gas-flow resistance. At high vacuums, mercury vapor from a diffusion pump acts as a choke and prevents the diffusion of gases from the line to the pump. Mercury vapors are toxic, and the breaking of a hot mercury diffusion pump creates not only a serious health hazard but also a difficult clean-up job. On the other hand, mercury diffusion pumps are less easily fouled by contamination and oxidation of the pumping fluid than oil pumps, but large amounts of air should not be passed through either type of pump.

Since the vapor pressure of a diffusion pump oil is usually 10^{-5} to 10^{-6} mm at room temperature, a trap is not required to protect the working manifold except at very low pressures. A trap is still needed to protect oil and mechanical pumps from corrosive or organic vapors. Oil diffusion pumps are faster than mercury diffusion pumps of a comparable physical size.

Traps

Where traps are to be used with medium or high vacuums, it is necessary that they be made of large tubing and that constrictions be avoided (Fig. 48). It is not necessary to have a long condensation path, for the

---

[3] Distillation Products, Inc., Rochester, N. Y.; Ace Glass, Inc., Vineland, N. J.; Central Scientific Co., Chicago, Ill.

efficiency of such a trap is very high at low pressures even when the flow rate is large. At low pressures (less than 1 mm) the mean free path of the molecules (see Appendix VII) is so large that the gas will have a very high probability of being cooled and condensed on the walls of the

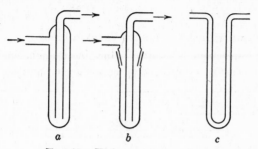

FIG. 48. High-vacuum-type traps.

vessel. Under these conditions there is almost no cooling of gases through conduction by non-condensible gases, and therefore there is no tendency to form fogs or smokes. Traps used to condense mercury may be of the permanent type, but if a trap is used to condense organic material, it is desirable to construct it from a large ground joint so that it can be disassembled and cleaned (Fig. 48, b).

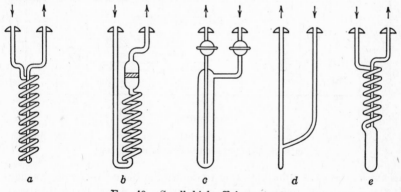

FIG. 49. Small, high-efficiency traps.

For pressures of above 1 cm, it is necessary to use small flow rates and traps with relatively long cold paths and small bore, in order to obtain efficient contact between the gas and the wall of the trap; even so, care must be taken to insure that temperature equilibrium is reached and smokes and fogs do not develop. These small-bore traps cannot be used for high-vacuum work as they have too large a pressure drop.

In Fig. 49 several of these small traps are shown: trap a is a simple spiral trap; trap c is a removable storage trap; and trap e is a special spiral trap used when a gas is liquefied but not solidified. In operations where fogs or smokes are encountered, trap *b* may be used; in this trap the gas first is chilled in a spiral and then is passed through a sintered-glass disk (medium porosity and also chilled) where the fog or smoke is caught.

Pressure-Measuring Instruments for Vacuum Lines

Pressure measurement is used to determine the efficiency of vacuum transfers, to measure quantities of compounds handled as gases, to

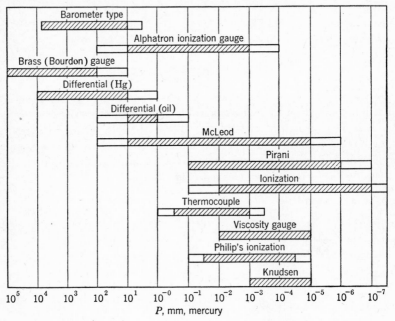

FIG. 50. Ranges of pressure-measuring instruments. Shaded areas represent ranges of optimum accuracy for a given gauge.

locate leaks in vacuum lines, and to determine the condition of mechanical and diffusion pumps. In the synthetic work described in this book, contamination of gauges with volatile compounds is an important problem; vacuum gauges should therefore be easily disconnected from the line and cleaned. It is convenient to connect gauges to vacuum lines with a single ball-and-socket joint. Gauges should have small surface areas, and metal surfaces which are slower to degas than glass surfaces and should be avoided if possible. Gauges should have high corrosion resistance so that they may be used without deterioration in the presence of acid vapors; they should not burn out when exposed to air or otherwise be harmed by a sudden inrush of air; they should be continuous reading; and, last, they should not be too expensive, because it is often desirable to use several gauges on a single vacuum system.

In Fig. 50 the approximate useful pressure ranges of some of the more common gauges are shown; in Appendix VIII a number of these gauges are described and their application to organic work is discussed.

Vacuum Transfer Efficiency. When *in vacuo* transfers are made or equipment is designed for this work, it is desirable to know how low a final pressure in the system is needed to give a certain percent transfer, and how low an initial pressure is needed to give this desired final pressure in a reasonable amount of time. This discussion does not consider flow rates (see Appendix VII) but instead is concerned with a phenomenon in which a non-condensible gas is carried by condensible material and fills the line and condensing tube so that further flow of condensible material from the original container is essentially stopped. If there are one or more small-bore stopcocks and an appreciable length of tubing connecting the two containers, there will be very little back diffusion of these non-condensible gases, and the system will soon come to a point where further transfer of gas is very slow.

The extent to which this phenomenon may occur is illustrated by the following sample calculations on the efficiency of a vacuum transfer: bulb A of 2,000-cc capacity (20° C) is connected through a small stopcock to a condensing tube, B, of 40-cc volume (Fig. 51). The system is filled with carbon dioxide at 100 mm pressure in which there is 100 microns (0.1 mm) *of non-condensible gas* (air); half the condensing tube (20 cc) is then cooled with liquid nitrogen (90° K). If it is assumed that the gas above the liquid nitrogen level in the condensing tube is at room temperature, that the ideal gas laws hold, and that there is *no back diffusion* of non-condensible gases through the stopcock, equation 1 can be set up for the final pressure, P (in millimeters, in the system. At this final pressure the gas in B will be entirely

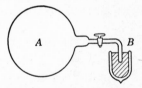

Fig. 51. Transfer of gases *in vacuo.*

air, for all the carbon dioxide will be condensed out, and the gas in bulb A will be the original mixture. Under these conditions the quantity of air in B less the air originally in it will be equal to the air removed from A. When viscous flow ceases,

$$P \text{ in } A = P \text{ in } B$$

$$(20)(293/90)P + 20P - 40(0.1/100) = (2,000)(0.1)(100 - P/100) \qquad (1)$$

$$P = 2.33 \text{ mm Hg}$$

Thus 2.33% of the carbon dioxide would not be transferred although the inert gas represents only 0.1% of the carbon dioxide. If the initial pressure of the inert gas in this same system were 10 microns, the final pressure would be 0.234 mm and only 0.23% would not be transferred. At 1 micron inert gas pressure in the carbon dioxide, the final pressure would be 0.0235 mm, or 0.02% would not transfer. This is an extreme case, but it does show how important the phenomenon may be.

This effect, i.e., the slowing down of vacuum transfers in a static system because of the accumulation in the condenser of non-condensible gases, can be reduced or eliminated by several means. One of the simplest ways to improve such distillations is to use a double transfer; the compound is first distilled from its container to a large trap on the line with simultaneous pumping. Thus the air is pumped off and the transfer goes to completion. The first container is closed from the line, and the trap is closed from the pumping system; the contents of the trap are then distilled into a new container. This technique is particularly useful when the compounds have been standing in a closed evacuated container, for small leaks around the stopcock and slow degassing from the walls are difficult to prevent.

Large-bore tubing and short distillation paths will reduce the effect of poor vacuum transfer because the non-condensible gases can diffuse back into the original container. If a liquid is being transferred, small containers can be used to decrease the final losses; non-condensible gas dissolved in the liquid often increases such loss. Solid drying agents tend to adsorb air and may give considerable trouble. In both of these cases the double transfer is very useful. It is also sometimes possible to avoid vacuum transfers completely, merely sweeping the compound from one container to another with an inert gas. This procedure works well except when the formation of fogs and smokes is encountered.

Treatment of Stopcocks and Joints

Almost every worker who uses vacuum equipment has favorite greases for lubricating stopcocks.[4] Different sizes of stopcocks, however, require different types of lubricants. Thus, high-vacuum stopcocks and large traps should be lubricated with a heavy grease; smaller stopcocks require a sticky lubricant, one that does not tend to striate when the stopcock is turned.

Stopcocks should be greased in lines (Fig. 52); as the plug is pushed into the barrel of the stopcock, the air is forced out by the advancing grease and no striations or air bubbles are left on the stopcock. This procedure is recommended for greasing all stopcocks, standard taper joints, and ball joints (put a circle of grease on the ball in this case) which are to be used for vacuum work. Old grease should be cleaned from a stopcock or joint before regreasing. Lubricants made of silicone [4]

---

[4] Some commercially available lubricants are: Lubriseal, distributed by A. H. Thomas Co., Philadelphia, Pa.; Apiezon greases L, M, and N, Technical Products Ltd., England; High-vacuum-type Silicone grease, Dow Corning Corp., Midland, Mich.; Celvacene vacuum grease, Distillation Products, Inc., Rochester, N. Y.

are very useful in many phases of synthetic organic work, since they may be heated without loss of sealing property and are inert toward reactive chemicals.

It is desirable to "grind-in" all stopcocks to be used in vacuum systems. A simple procedure for grinding a stopcock is as follows: The plug is moistened with a paste of 400-mesh silicon carbide in 80% glycerin + 20% water and ground into the barrel by moving the plug back and forth while it is slowly rotated. Final grinding is carried out with 600-mesh carbide and glycerin after the 400-mesh carbide is washed

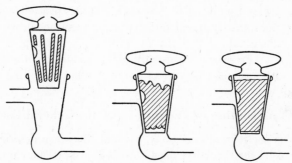

Fig. 52. High-vacuum-type stopcock. A method for application of grease to prevent striation is shown.

off. Water is undesirable as a lubricant for grinding-in a stopcock because the stopcock tends to stick. If the stopcock plug is marked with several heavy pencil lines, it is possible to tell when grinding is complete and to detect poorly matched plugs and barrels.

It is sometimes convenient to lubricate joints with a low-melting wax such as commercial sealing wax or a heavy hydrocarbon wax. When these joints are cool and the wax is hardened, a very strong joint results which will not develop leaks, yet the line can be disassembled by heating the joint with a "cool" flame. These semi-permanent waxed joints, particularly when made with ball-and-socket connections, are very useful in the construction of a vacuum system, for they permit fabrication of the line in small units and easy alignment in assembly.

Non-Condensible Gases—Toepler Pumps

By cooling traps with liquid nitrogen, all volatile carbon compounds except carbon monoxide (b.p. $-190°$, m.p. $-207°$), methane (b.p. $-161.5°$, m.p. $-184°$), and carbon tetrafluoride (b.p. $-128°$, m.p. $-184°$) may be distilled in vacuum. If liquid air is not available, a number of organic compounds must be handled as non-condensible gases. For isotopic carbon work, the most important of these compounds is carbon dioxide. If the system can be so designed and a suitable reaction is available, generation and utilization of the gaseous compound can be accomplished in the same system without the need for a vacuum distillation. A good example of this type of reaction is the Grignard reaction using labeled carbon dioxide (page 179). In many reactions such a simplification is not possible, and a Toepler pump is necessary for transferring the gas. Essentially, a Toepler pump consists of a bulb connected to a mercury reservoir and to two parts of a vacuum system with a two-way stopcock (Fig. 59). Gas from one side of the line is drawn into the bulb by lowering the mercury and is then forced into the other side of the system by raising the reservoir. If this process is repeated a number of times, nearly quantitative transfers can be effected. Small-bore or capillary tubing is useful in systems of this type to decrease losses in lines. Pressures are usually high enough and the work slow enough in such systems that rate of gas flow is not a limiting factor.

Construction of Vacuum Lines for General Use

In various sections of this book, vacuum lines are described which have been used for special problems, such as a particular organic synthesis or filling counter tubes. In the discussion of these systems specific information as to the nature of the frames on which these systems are mounted, or how the pumping system is constructed, has not been presented. In the use of vacuum systems many such technicalities must be considered, and it is the purpose of the following section to discuss some of them and to give practical examples of such equipment. (The vacuum lines described here are certainly not the only systems on which the desired manipulations can be performed.)

If a considerable amount of vacuum work is to be done in a laboratory, the construction of a semi-permanent vacuum line is desirable. It may be considered to consist of three parts: the frame or grill work, the pumping system, and the working manifold. The design of the last component will vary with the work to be done, but the grill and pumping system may be standardized.

Frame

A very satisfactory grill to support a vacuum system can be fabricated from ½-inch cold-rolled iron rod welded into a lattice (see Fig. 53). Although not necessary, it is convenient if the wooden or metal frame that supports the grill work is made an integral part of a low table of such a height (about 20 inches) that mechanical pumps and other accessories can slide under the table. The rods in the metal grill should not be spaced too closely, for it is then difficult to work on the back of the line. A convenient spacing is: vertical rods, 11 to 12 inches apart; horizontal rods, 15 inches apart. It is possible to purchase complete frames or component parts.

Various service facilities are needed for a vacuum system, depending on the extent of the work to be done. A few common ones are: (1) electricity for pumps, gauges, and hot plates; (2) water for cooling diffusion pumps and condensers; (3) gas and oxygen for glass blowing (the oxygen

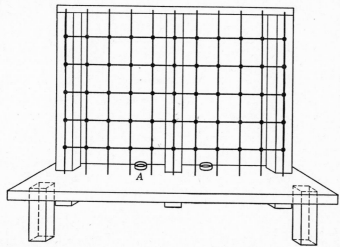

FIG. 53. Grill and frame for use with vacuum systems: *A*, water drains.

can be supplied from a portable tank). If radioactive gases are being handled, some means should be available to flush out the line when work is finished. This flushing may be accomplished by means of a low-pressure air line; the residual gases are blown outdoors or into a hood. Alternatively, these gases may be drawn into a house vacuum line if the house pump vents into a suitable stack. (This house vacuum may also be used to evacuate large systems rapidly, to avoid pumping large amounts of gas through the high-vacuum system.)

Pumping System

In the construction of small vacuum systems, the estimation of the sizes of stopcocks and lines that will permit full utilization of the pumping speed of the mechanical and diffusion pumps is mostly a matter of experience. However, considerable technology has been developed on this subject, which cannot be presented here. (In Appendix VII a short discussion of the nature of flow in vacuum systems is presented, together with some equations that permit calculation of the conductance of simple systems.) The easiest procedure for the organic chemist is to construct the system with pumps and line larger than needed for the given work; a system which is able to produce a vacuum ten times better than the anticipated need and which has a satisfactorily high pumping speed is desired.

The pumping system shown in Figs. 54 and 55 consists of the following parts: a mechanical pump, a diffusion pump, a suitable bypass system,

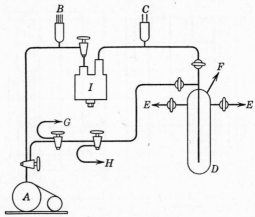

FIG. 54. Schematic diagram of pump manifold: *A*, mechanical pump; *B*, vacuum thermocouple gauge; *C*, Philip's ion gauge; *D*, trap; *E* and *F*, outlets to manifolds; *G*, exhaust line; *H*, glass-blowing and air-inlet connection; *I*, diffusion pump.

vacuum gauges, and cold traps. It can be located close to the working manifold and is compactly and sturdily constructed of large-bore tubing to reduce unnecessary volume and flow resistance. A bypass is included in order to avoid passing large amounts of air through the diffusion pump and to provide an exhaust from the line. A trap is provided for the condensation of corrosive or volatile material that might harm either the pumps or the operator. High-vacuum-type stopcocks are used; these (see Fig. 52) have far less tendency to leak than ordinary stopcocks. (High-vacuum stopcocks should be placed so that the stopcock will remain seated, i.e., atmospheric pressure will hold the plug in, when the outer parts of the system are let down to air pressure.) A high-vacuum-type right-angle stopcock is placed above the low-vacuum outlet of the diffusion pump, so that it is possible to change the oil in the diffusion pump (see Fig. 55). After the old oil has been drained and cleaned from the pump, new oil is added through the stopcock barrel.

Two gauges are recommended for use on the main manifold if much vacuum work is to be carried out: a thermocouple vacuum gauge on the high-pressure side of the diffusion pump to show the condition of the fore pump, and a Philips ionization gauge on the high-vacuum side of the pump to show the condition of the diffusion pump and to aid in leak detection. This Philips gauge has been placed between the diffusion pump and the trap, rather than after the trap, to conserve space. For

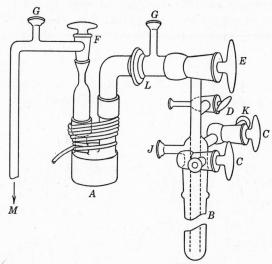

Fig. 55. Detail of general-purpose pump manifold: A, diffusion pump; B, trap, 40 cm long, 45/50 joint, outside shell 50 mm o.d., inside tube 20 mm o.d.; C, manifold stopcocks, 8-mm bore; D, bypass stopcock, 4-mm bore; E, main stopcock, 15-mm bore; F, stopcock, 6-mm bore; G, vacuum gauge connections, 28/12 socket; J, interline connection outlet, 28/12 socket; K, manifold connection, 28/12 socket; L, 50/30 ball and socket; M, line to mechanical pump, 15 mm o.d.

the reasons for the choice of these two gauges, see Appendix VIII on vacuum gauges.

The unit shown can evacuate a clean degassed 500-cc-volume manifold to a vacuum of 1 micron in 2 minutes. The mechanical pump [5] used for the system has a free air capacity of 58 l/min and a pumping speed of 27 l/min at 20 microns. The all-metal diffusion pump [6] has a pumping speed of 10 l/sec at 10^{-4} mm. The pumping system can produce a vacuum of about 10^{-5} mm without a cold trap.

[5] W. M. Welch Manufacturing Co., Chicago, Ill. (cost about $150–160), Model 1405B. Any large-capacity mechanical pump which can maintain a pressure of 30–50 microns in the backing up system is satisfactory. Quiet operation is highly desirable.

[6] Distillations Products, Inc., Oil Diffusion Pump VM10W (cost about $75). This pump was modified by adding additional cooling coils and a cup arrangement (also cooled) to connect the metal to the glass.

This pumping system should be mounted with the diffusion pump and bypass network behind the grill work, thus keeping the front of the grill clear for manifolds, cold traps, etc.

If a manifold is to be evacuated with this pumping system, the procedure is as follows: The manifold is first evacuated with the house vacuum, if available, and then is pumped down with the mechanical pump to about 1 mm pressure. The bypass is closed off, and the diffusion pump is opened to the system.

Manifolds

Manifold for Organic Synthesis. In Fig. 56 a general-purpose manifold for organic work is shown. Except for procedures involving Toepler

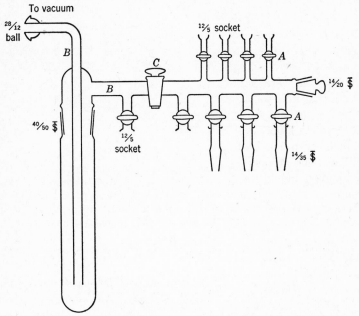

Fɪɢ. 56. General-purpose manifold for synthetic organic chemistry: *A*, 3-mm slant bore stopcocks; *B*, 15-mm o.d. tubing; *C*, 6-mm stopcock.

pumps most of the isotopic syntheses described in this book which require a vacuum line can be carried out on this manifold.

The large trap on the manifold is used for rapid handling of compounds in high vacuum; it is not a protective trap because the main pumping system should include such a unit and leave this trap free for transfer of compounds. Immediately following this trap are two small ball joint connections for a removable trap that may be bypassed (see Fig.

49 for illustrations of such traps); these units are used for drying gases, separating components of mixtures by distillation, etc.

The four outlets on the top of the line are for making connections to pressure-measuring units and gas bulbs. A sample arrangement would be: a low-pressure gauge (for example, a vacuum thermocouple gauge, see Appendix VIII), a high-pressure range gauge (brass vacuum or mercury manometer gauge), an aliquoting bulb for measuring gas samples, and a gas storage bulb for carbon dioxide. If these bulbs are constructed with an appendage, condensible gases can be transferred to them quantitatively by vacuum distillation. The three outlets on the lower side of the line are for making connections to the manifold. It is convenient to have all the storage bulbs and pressure-measuring units above or behind the line so that the lower side of the line will be completely clear for reaction units.

The size of the stopcocks on the line is not critical except that they should be large enough to give adequate flow rates. Three-millimeter-bore stopcocks on the line taps are about as small a stopcock as will be satisfactory if a working vacuum of 10–20 microns is desired. Slant-bore stopcocks will give less trouble with leaks than straight-bore ones. The stopcock on the line itself should be a minimum of about 6-mm bore, but here a straight stopcock will work satisfactorily since there is usually a vacuum on both sides of the plug. At the end of the line a 14/20 standard taper joint and stopper is installed to facilitate cleaning the manifold. The manifold should be supported by one extension clamp placed near the outer end and by a ball-and-socket joint clamp on the other.

Manifolds Used to Fill Ion Chambers. Ion chambers and certain of the techniques involved in the measurement of active carbon by this means have been discussed on page 72 f. A manifold which is used to fill ion chambers may include any or all of the following: carbon dioxide storage bulbs (for standards of active and inactive carbon dioxide), apparatus to generate and purify carbon dioxide, apparatus to fill the ion chamber to a given pressure, manometers, vacuum gauges, traps, and aliquoting bulbs.

It is possible to fill ion chambers with carbon dioxide by means of Toepler pumps, or by the use of liquid air in a standard vacuum transfer operation. In Fig. 57 a manifold is shown which has been designed [7] for use with liquid air. In order to use this manifold without liquid air, it would be necessary to remove trap 2 and put in place of trap 1 a Toepler pump which is then connected directly to the horizontal manifold.

[7] C. D. Janney and B. J. Moyer, Atomic Energy Commission, MDDC 1303, July 31, 1947.

One of the requirements in this work is the need to fill ion chambers with a definite quantity of carbon dioxide; since the temperature of the chamber is not conveniently regulated, the exact pressure of the filling will be dependent on the chamber temperature. It is easy to control the pressure of the carbon dioxide put in chambers when they are filled with Toepler pumps, but when liquid air is used to effect the transfer careful

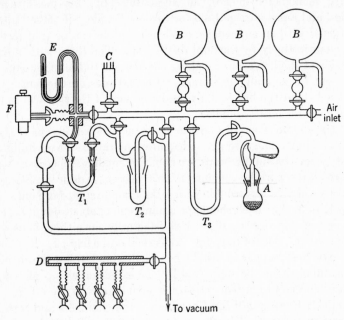

Fig. 57. Manifold used to fill ion chambers: A, carbon dioxide generator; B, carbon dioxide storage and aliquoting bulbs; C, vacuum thermocouple gauge; D, manifold used to evacuate ion chambers; E, mercury manometer; F, ion chamber, T_3, Dry Ice-cooled trap. (C. D. Janney and B. J. Moyer.)

manual control is necessary. In addition, active carbon dioxide must be used in the measurement of the pressure in the chamber. Thus, it is desirable that this system be as small as is convenient. In the system shown in Fig. 57, capillary tubing is used for the pressure-measurement section of the manifold.

The manipulations involved in the filling of an ion chamber with the system shown in Fig. 57 will be described in some detail. As an example a 100-cc-volume chamber will be used. Approximately 1 gram of barium carbonate is converted to carbon dioxide in apparatus A. If the original unknown weighs less than 1 gram, sufficient inactive barium carbonate is added to bring the total to that weight (this dilution must

must then be taken into consideration in the interpretation of the results of the determination). The carbon dioxide generator, arranged so that the sulfuric acid can be added to the barium carbonate a drop at a time, employs a wad of glass wool to stop the carbonate spattered by the

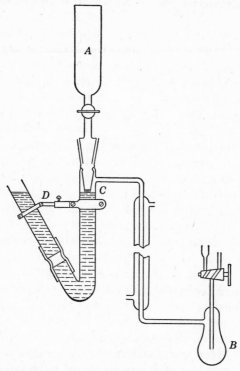

FIG. 58. Unit used to introduce carbon dioxide directly from a combustion to an ionization chamber: *A*, ion chamber; *B*, wet combustion vessel; *C*, sintered-glass disk sealed with mercury column; *D*, adjustment arm for mercury column. (W. B. Leslie.)

sudden evolution of gas; any powder is there reacted with additional sulfuric acid which comes through the vent hole.

The ion chamber and generator are first evacuated to a pressure of about 10 microns. The carbon dioxide is then generated (water vapor is at least partially removed in the Dry Ice-cooled trap—a spiral trap, Fig. 49a would be better) and frozen into trap T_1 with liquid air. Any air released from the surface of the barium carbonate (approximately equal to 0.1 to 0.5% of the total volume of carbon dioxide in a typical case) is pumped out through trap T_2 which may be cooled as a safety trap if desired. Trap T_1 and the stainless-steel manifold are closed from the rest of the system, and the carbon dioxide is allowed to vaporize until the pressure has reached the desired value; the three-way stopcock is turned, and the excess carbon dioxide passes into the bulb provided. The chamber valve is closed and the residual gas is discharged, in this case through the mechanical pump which is vented into the house vacuum line.

As shown in Fig. 57, flexible metal bellows and machined metal ball-and-socket joints can be used to make connections to the ion chambers if the chambers are of a heavy construction (see page 144).

When organic material is analyzed for radio carbon content with an ionization chamber it is often desirable to combust a sample and to introduce the carbon dioxide formed directly into the measuring chamber. In Fig. 58 is shown a pressure-regulating device designed to facilitate such a process.[8] The sample is placed in the reaction bulb and is treated with an oxidizing solution (such as Van Slyke's mixture, see page 92 f.). A slow current of carbon dioxide slowly sweeps the generated carbon dioxide into the ionization chamber, A; the automatic mercury control is so set that when the pressure in the system exceeds 1 atmosphere the mercury is pushed away from the sintered-glass disk and carbon dioxide is drawn into the evacuated ionization chamber.

If hot copper oxide and oxygen are used to burn the sample the procedure is similar, but the calibration of the ionization chamber will be somewhat different because of the oxygen in the carbon dioxide. However, if the chamber is larger than the critical size for maximum absorption of the carbon β rays, this effect will not be very large; the specific ionization of carbon dioxide and oxygen is about the same.

Manifolds for Mass Spectrometers.[9,10]   A mass spectrometer system usually requires two manifolds, one to evacuate the tube and a second to deliver the sample. The first system, a high-speed, high-efficiency pumping unit, consists of a good mechanical and diffusion pump and a high-vacuum trap cooled with liquid air or Dry Ice slush. This system must be capable of maintaining a vacuum of 10^{-6} to 10^{-7} mm in the spectrometer tube in spite of the introduction into the tube of material to be analyzed. Both oil and mercury diffusion pumps have been used.

The design of the delivery system is dependent on the nature and number of samples to be analyzed. When the carbon isotope ratio of carbon dioxide is to be determined this manifold usually consists of a

[8] W. B. Leslie, private communication.

[9] A. O. Nier, in *Preparation and Measurement of Isotopic Tracers, A Symposium*, J. W. Edwards, Ann Arbor, Mich., 1946.

[10] A. O. Nier, in *A Symposium on the Use of Isotopes in Biological Research, University of Chicago, March 3–4, 1947*.

manometer, a simple gas-handling system which uses liquid air or Toepler pumps to effect transfers, and a capillary leak. The leak system should permit delivery of gas to the spectrometer tube at a rate of about 0.05 cc (NTP) per hour.

The generation of the carbon dioxide is often carried out on a separate manifold to eliminate the danger of spray or dust contamination to the spectrometer system. A bulb with a stopcock and ground joint connection may be used to transfer the generated carbon dioxide to the spectrometer manifold.

Chapter 9

SYNTHESIS OF
CARBON-LABELED COMPOUNDS

With the exception of those for the preparation of the one-carbon compounds, all syntheses that involve the introduction of isotopic carbon into a molecule necessitate the formation of a new carbon-to-carbon bond. A considerable number of reactions that are standard practice in synthetic organic chemistry can be and have been used for this purpose. Most of these reactions have been modified in order to increase the yields and decrease the scale on which the necessary manipulations must be carried out. Some completely new methods have been devised in order to conserve the labeling isotope, and the previous chapter on specialized vacuum techniques serves to illustrate some significant advances in synthetic operations that arose from the exigencies of working with isotopes and that may materially affect the classical procedures employed in the field of synthetic organic chemistry.

In devising a synthetic route to a desired compound, it is advisable to choose a scheme in which, if possible, the label is introduced near the end of a sequence of reactions, so as to maintain as high an overall yield based on the isotopic starting materials as possible. It is also necessary to choose a reaction for the introduction of the isotope that is most compatible with the starting materials available. At present, the small number of these starting materials has made this choice an extremely limited one. However, because of the projected availability of some simple isotopic synthetic intermediates, the scope of reactions may be greatly increased, so that it is possible that, in the foreseeable future, the organic chemist concerned with the preparation of labeled substances may have at his disposal a considerable array of starting materials. These will not be as common and inexpensive as ordinary "side-shelf reagents," but they may serve to cut down the number of steps involved in a given synthesis and may even limit it to one or two critical reactions. Thus there is good reason to suppose that eventually synthetic organic chemists should be able to prepare almost any carbon-labeled compound without much specialized experience or equipment.

Before the synthesis of a labeled compound is carried out, one should calculate the concentration of isotope that is necessary for the intended experiments, and this value must be reconciled with the amount of starting material available. In this way it is possible to decide the scale on which the synthesis will be performed. It is then strongly advisable to carry out at least one and preferably several practice runs on this scale, so that the manipulations can be perfected, unforeseen difficulties can be resolved, and the highest possible yield can be realized. Before the actual isotopic synthesis is begun, all apparatus should be scrupulously cleaned and set up in the hood so that adequate health protection is provided.

Of the numerous reactions that result in the formation of a new carbon-carbon bond, only a very few have found wide application for the initial introduction of isotopic carbon into a molecule, and the discussion that follows will be limited to these reactions.

Carbonation of the Grignard Reagent

$$RMgX + CO_2 \rightarrow RCOOMgX + H_2O \rightarrow RCOOH + MgOHX$$

This reaction, involving the addition of a halomagnesium compound to carbon dioxide, first discovered by Grignard,[1] offers almost unlimited possibilities for the synthesis of carboxylic acids. With some highly hindered or aromatic halides, the Grignard reagent may be replaced by the lithium derivative to increase the yields of products resulting from the carbonation reaction. Since one of the most important starting materials available for the preparation of compounds containing isotopic carbon is carbon dioxide (in the form of barium carbonate), this reaction gave promise of being an extremely useful method of incorporating isotope into organic molecules. However, the classical procedure for carrying out the reaction consisted in treatment of the Grignard reagent with a considerable excess of carbon dioxide, either by passing it as a gas [2] into the reaction mixture or by pouring the Grignard reagent onto Dry Ice.[3] The yields obtained by these methods are usually 50–85% based on the Grignard reagent, and are generally unsatisfactory for the conservation of valuable labeled carbon dioxide. Considerable experimentation has been carried out in order to improve the yields in this reaction and to avoid the use of excess carbon dioxide. Several improve-

[1] V. Grignard, *Ann. univ. Lyon*, **6**, 1 (1901); *Chem. Zentr.*, 1901, II, 622; *Comp. rend.*, **138**, 1048 (1904).

[2] H. Gilman and R. H. Kirby, *Org. Syntheses, Coll. Vol. I*, John Wiley & Sons, New York, 1944, p. 361.

[3] L. F. Fieser, *Experiments in Organic Chem.*, D. C. Heath and Co., Boston, 1935, p. 73.

ments have been effected, and a considerable number of acids have been prepared in high yields based on carbon dioxide. One of the earliest and most successful syntheses in which isotopic carbon was used is in a preparation [4] of acetic acid in which a mixture of methyl magnesium iodide in ether solution and labeled carbon dioxide are shaken to give carboxyl-labeled acetic acid in 85–95% yields. In a later paper the synthesis of carboxyl-labeled octanoic acid in 81% yield was reported [5] in which the carbonation reaction was conducted in a high-vacuum system; since that time a large number of other carboxylic acids have been prepared.

The advantages of carrying out the reaction in a vacuum system are many. The moisture and oxygen present in the air are absent; the gas is contained in a closed system and cannot escape; the uptake of carbon dioxide may easily be followed by means of a manometer; the low temperature at which the reaction can be made to take place under these conditions minimizes the formation of ketonic and other by-products; and the use of liquid air or nitrogen enables one to distil quantitatively the carbon dioxide from one container to another. The reaction flask may be shaken or stirred with an induction stirrer (see Appendix IX).

A general procedure that has been successful in the preparation of a considerable number of carboxylic acids [6] will be described in considerable detail on page 178; and a further discussion of important factors in the reaction will be given. Thus, the carbonation of the Grignard reagent is an extremely important and successful method for the introduction of labeled carbon into organic molecules because of the high yields obtained in most cases, the ready availability of the starting material, and the reactivity of carboxylic acids which may be conveniently converted into a variety of other compounds.

Reactions Involving Cyanide

Next to barium carbonate, the most readily available starting material is potassium cyanide. This compound can be obtained commercially, enriched in the heavier stable isotope, C^{13}. It can be prepared from barium carbonate, until recently the only synthetic source of C^{14}, but is now available containing C^{14} from Tracerlab, Inc., upon application through the Isotopes Branch of the Atomic Energy Commission.

Nitriles, obtained from the displacement reaction of potassium cyanide with alkyl halides, may be hydrolyzed to the corresponding carboxylic acids; this method of synthesis has been applied to the preparation of

[4] S. Ruben, M. B. Allen, and P. Nahinsky, *J. Am. Chem. Soc.*, **64**, 3050 (1942).

[5] S. Weinhouse, G. Medes, and N. F. Floyd, *J. Biol. Chem.*, **155**, 143 (1944).

[6] W. G. Dauben, J. C. Reid, and P. E. Yankwich, *Anal. Chem.*, **19**, 828 (1947); C. Heidelberger, P. Brewer, and W. G. Dauben, *J. Am. Chem. Soc.*, **69**, 1389 (1947).

isotopic succinic acid [7] and acetic acid [8] and to the direct hydrolysis to formic acid.[9]

The addition of hydrogen cyanide to carbonyl compounds has been utilized for the preparation of several isotopic compounds. The earliest use in this connection was in the synthesis of lactic acid containing C^{11}.[10] In this case isotopic acetaldehyde was allowed to react with non-isotopic potassium cyanide to give the cyanhydrin from which the α,β-labeled lactic acid was obtained by hydrolysis. The carboxyl-labeled lactic acid was prepared in the same manner from non-isotopic acetaldehyde and isotopic cyanide.

The cyanhydrin addition reaction has also been carried out on acet-aldehyde in the presence of ammonia, and the resulting nitrile was hydrolyzed to dl-alanine.[11]

These reactions, then, have been extensively used for the introduction of isotopic carbon into a wide variety of compounds which may then undergo a number of other reactions to create new carbon-to-carbon bonds and a host of other compounds.

Acetylene

Acetylene is a useful and reactive substance that is available from barium carbonate as described on page 204. Its ready hydration to acetaldehyde has made acetylene a useful intermediate in several syntheses involving isotopic carbon, particularly those for lactic acid.[10, 12] A whole series of reactions of acetylene has emerged from the work of Reppe which makes possible new compounds that may be synthesized from labeled acetylene. At present the techniques are rather specialized, and more experimental information must become available before these reactions can be generally attempted on a laboratory scale. A sum-mary [13] of these reactions indicates some of the possibilities for new types of syntheses.

1. One-Carbon Compounds

In organic chemistry it is often possible to discuss the chemical behavior and preparation of compounds as members of a homologous

[7] M. B. Allen and S. Ruben, *J. Am. Chem. Soc.*, **64**, 948 (1942).

[8] S. Weinhouse, G. Medes, and N. F. Floyd, *J. Biol. Chem.*, **158**, 411 (1945).

[9] S. Gurin, in *Report of a Symposium on Use of Isotopes in Biological Research, University of Chicago, March 3–4, 1947*, p. 12.

[10] R. D. Cramer and G. B. Kistiakowsky, *J. Biol. Chem.*, **137**, 549 (1941).

[11] S. Gurin and D. W. Wilson, *Federation Proc.*, **1**, 114 (1942); R. B. Loftfield, *Nucleonics*, **1**, No. 3, 54 (1947).

[12] W. Sakami, W. E. Evans, and S. Gurin, *J. Am. Chem. Soc.*, **69**, 1110 (1947).

[13] M. H. Bigelow, *Chem. Eng. News*, **25**, 1038 (1947).

series; however, the first members of these series may differ considerably from the others, and special attention is usually given to them. This is particularly true in the preparation of labeled substances where the synthesis of one-carbon compounds involves a preparative chemistry which differs from that of many other compounds in that no new carbon-

TABLE XXIII

PREPARATIONS OF ONE-CARBON COMPOUNDS AND YIELDS (BASED ON CARBON DIOXIDE)

Compound	Prepared from:	Best Percentage Yield (Based on Carbon Dioxide)	See page
Na_2CO_3	CO_2	~100	155
$NaHCO_3$	CO_2	~100	155
$COCl_2$	CO	95	156
$CO(NH_2)_2$	$\begin{cases} CO_2 \\ COCl_2 \end{cases}$	$\begin{cases} 80 \\ 90 \end{cases}$	157 / 158
$ClCN$	$AgCN$	72	158
$BaNCN$	$BaCO_3$	. .	158
$(H_2N)_2C{=}NH_2Cl$	$BaNCN$	61	159
$H_2NCOOC_2H_5$	$CO(NH_2)_2$	36	160
CO	$\begin{cases} CO_2 \\ CaCO_3 \end{cases}$	$\begin{cases} \sim100 \\ 99 \end{cases}$	163 / 163
CHI_3	CH_3COCH_3	. .	248
HCO_2K	$NaHCO_3$	90	165
HCO_2CH_3	HCO_2K	~100	165
KCN	$\begin{cases} CO_2 \\ BaCO_3 \end{cases}$	$\begin{cases} 80 \\ 78 \end{cases}$	160 / 161
$AgCN$	HCN	80	160
HCN	KCN	80	162
$HCHO$	CH_3OH	45	166
CH_3OH	$\begin{cases} CO_2 \\ HCOOCH_3 \end{cases}$	$\begin{cases} 90 \\ 80 \end{cases}$	167 f. / 168
CH_3I	CH_3OH	85	169
CH_4	CO_2	~100	171

to-carbon bonds are established. Different techniques are required for the preparation of each of these compounds.

The need for high yields in the synthesis of one-carbon compounds is important, for, although they are of limited interest as possible tracers, these substances are often needed in the syntheses of other compounds. The preparation of a more complicated molecule may involve a large number of steps, and as good a yield as possible in every step is necessary if any appreciable amount of the final material is to be obtained. Considerable work has been done on the development of high-yield one-carbon syntheses; numerous specialized techniques and preparations have been developed to expedite this work. Thus it will be noted that many of these preparations have been carried out in vacuum systems. If a number of these preparations have to be carried out, time may well be spent on the construction of a suitable vacuum line; but, if only a few preparations are to be made, even the most complicated of these syntheses can be carried out with little more than standard laboratory equipment. Some of these one-carbon compounds are becoming commercially available as the field of tracer research is developed.

Most of these syntheses have been carried out with C^{14} or C^{11} as the tracer isotope; these preparations have been started with barium carbonate or carbon dioxide and have been worked out on a small scale, usually in the millimole range. On the other hand, only a few preparations of one-carbon compounds have been made with C^{13}, because cyanide, in which form this isotope has been obtained, undergoes a sufficient number of reactions that its incorporation into more complicated molecules is relatively simple. These syntheses with carbon 13 have usually been executed on about a 0.1 mole scale.

. In Table XXIII the one-carbon compounds are listed with maximum yields based on preparation from carbon dioxide.

Preparation of Carbon Dioxide from Barium Carbonate

Carbon dioxide has been generated from barium carbonate by two methods: roasting of the salt and treatment of the carbonate with an acid. The acids used for this purpose have included sulfuric, hydrochloric, perchloric, and phosphoric acids. On pages 177–179 several types of acid generators for carbon dioxide are shown.

The generation of carbon dioxide by roasting [1] is carried out in a quartz tube at about 1100° C. The yield of carbon dioxide obtained by this method is not quantitative on a large scale and the technique finds most of its application in physical experiments, such as mass ratio determinations, where it is particularly useful because the procedure is simple and the evolved carbon dioxide needs no purification. In a study of the isotopic concentrations of several fractions of carbon dioxide generated by heating barium carbonate, it has been found that the first hundredth of the sample evolved has an isotopic composition somewhere between that of the rest of the sample and that of normal carbon. This effect may be due to carbon dioxide adsorbed on the surface of the barium carbonate and is a source of error in isotope concentration determinations

[1] M. G. Inghram, *Mass Spectrometric Observation of C^{14}*, Atomic Energy Commission MDDC 60, June 1946.

which use carbon dioxide when only small fractions of the samples are decomposed.

The several methods of releasing carbon dioxide from barium carbonate by acidification are about equivalent in yield, but, depending on the acid used, there are some differences in the amounts of acid impurities and water found in the product, and in the ease with which these impurities are removed. There is no perfect acid for the generation of carbon dioxide; each one has some undesirable features.

The use of hydrochloric acid yields a soluble barium salt but is undesirable in that the product is contaminated with water and traces of hydrogen chloride. Over $2 N$ hydrochloric acid, the vapor pressure of water is 21.8 mm and that of the hydrogen chloride is 0.0013 mm (at $25°$ C); over $6 N$ hydrochloric acid the vapor pressure of water is 15.4 mm and that of the hydrogen chloride is 0.148 mm (also at $25°$ C). The solubility of carbon dioxide in such solutions is not very different from that in water, about 0.8 cc/ml of water at 1 atmosphere carbon dioxide pressure.

In dilute solutions perchloric acid is excellent for generation of carbon dioxide if the presence of water vapor in the gas is not objectionable. The vapor pressure of the acid in such solutions is negligible, and barium perchlorate is soluble in water. The solubility of carbon dioxide in such solutions probably is not very different from that in water.

For generation of carbon dioxide, orthophosphoric and sulfuric acids are similar, although sulfuric acid is somewhat better. The vapor pressure of water over 85% phosphoric acid is 2.2 mm whereas it is considerably less than a micron (10^{-3} mm) over 95% sulfuric acid at room temperature. Both barium phosphate and sulfate are insoluble, but in excess sulfuric acid barium sulfate may be redissolved, especially if the solution is warmed. (The solubility of carbon dioxide in sulfuric and dilute phosphoric acid solutions is about the same as it is in water.) When concentrated sulfuric acid is used to generate carbon dioxide, drying agents are not needed. If other acids are used and drying agents are required, solid (porous) material should be selected carefully, because finely divided solids such as phosphorus pentoxide and magnesium sulfate invariably adsorb some carbon dioxide. A good drying agent for carbon dioxide is a spiral trap (see Fig. 49) cooled in Dry Ice; the vapor pressure of water at Dry Ice temperature ($-78°$ C) is 0.6 micron. This drying procedure should also be followed with caution, for at fast flow rates the efficiency of a spiral trap is low, and at high carbon dioxide pressures the solubility of the gas in ice is appreciable.

Alkali Carbonates and Bicarbonates—C^{14}. $NaHC*O_3$, Na_2C*O_3,[2] $KHC*O_3$[3]

$$C*O_2 + NaOH \rightarrow NaHC*O_3$$
$$C*O_2 + 2NaOH \rightarrow Na_2C*O_3 + H_2O$$

A labeled alkali carbonate or bicarbonate is prepared by absorption of carbon dioxide in a stoichiometric or excess amount of carbonate-free alkali hydroxide. In the latter case the alkaline solution is back-titrated with dilute acid; this procedure is usable only if the presence of salts is not undesirable.

The equipment and techniques employed in the preparation of such a carbonate or bicarbonate are the same as those in the carbonation of Grignard reagents (see page 179 and Figs. 70 and 72); the solution of alkali is substituted for the Grignard solution, and the absorption of the carbon dioxide proceeds as usual. The apparatus for the homogenization of mixed, solid barium carbonate can also be used for these preparations (see page 96 f.). Carbonate-free hydroxide is sometimes conveniently prepared by slow solution of the pure alkali metal in water; a simple way to do this involves the use of a vacuum desiccator. The bottom is covered with a layer of water, and a beaker containing the clean metal is set on a raised frame. The unit is then connected to the water aspirator and pumped; when the metal has been converted to a solution, the reaction is complete. It is, of course, possible to dissolve the alkali metal in alcohol, but the presence of the alcohol is sometimes undesirable in later reactions of the carbonate.

When solutions of sodium bicarbonate are evaporated in air, there may be a considerable loss of activity due to exchange of the labeled bicarbonate with carbon dioxide of the atmosphere. Thus it has been found [2] that samples of sodium bicarbonate lose about one-half of their activity when evaporated to dryness in the laboratory atmosphere. The problem of activity loss from solids has been discussed (see page 122).

Phosgene—C^{11}, C^{14}. $C*OCl_2$ [4]

$$C*O + Cl_2 \rightarrow C*OCl_2$$

Phosgene (*Caution: highly toxic!*) is the diacid chloride of carbonic acid and as such shows most of the typical reactions of acid chlorides; it has been used in the preparation of labeled urea and associated derivatives by reaction with ammonia or amines.

[2] W. B. Leslie, *Experimental Use of C^{14}*, Atomic Energy Commission, MDDC 674, June 15, 1947.

[3] D. B. Melville, J. R. Rachele, and E. B. Keller, *J. Biol. Chem.*, **169**, 419 (1947).

[4] J. L. Huston and T. H. Norris, *J. Am. Chem. Soc.*, **70**, 1968 (1948).

Phosgene is prepared in high yield by the photochemical reaction of labeled carbon monoxide and chlorine; in this reaction an activated chlorine molecule combines with carbon monoxide. If a light source rich in ultraviolet is used (a quartz mercury lamp, for instance) the absorption of energy by the phosgene will promote a reverse reaction with accompanying reduction in the yield of product; the quantities of phosgene and carbon monoxide will depend on the ratio of visible to ultraviolet light.

A vacuum system for the conversion of carbon monoxide to phosgene is shown in Fig. 59. Bulb F is filled on the non-capillary section of the line with an excess of chlorine purified by the same procedure as that by which carbon dioxide is purified

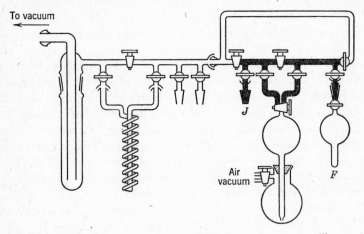

FIG. 59.   Manifold with Toepler pump.   Solid lines represent capillary tubing.

for carbonation reactions (see page 194). The bulb is then transferred to the capillary section of the line, and the generator or storage bulb containing the carbon monoxide is connected at J. After the connecting lines are evacuated through the large-bore tubing, the chlorine is frozen into the reaction bulb (F) with liquid air; the carbon monoxide is transferred by means of a Toepler pump to the same bulb. The reaction vessel is then removed from the line, and the gases are warmed, mixed, and irradiated with strong visible light (for example, sunlight). The irradiation time varies with the particular light source, but about an hour is usually sufficient with artificial light. Bulb F is then connected to the main line at D, and the unreacted carbon monoxide is removed when the mixture of gases is pumped through a spiral trap cooled with liquid air; the phosgene and excess chlorine condense in the trap but carbon monoxide is pumped off. Excess chlorine is removed from the phosgene when the gas is shaken at room temperature with antimony or amalgamated copper in the reaction vessel shown in Fig. 61. The yield based on carbon monoxide is usually 90 to 95% but with proper illumination may be higher.

Urea—C^{14},[5, 6] C^{11}.[7]   H$_2$NC*ONH$_2$

Carbon-labeled urea has been prepared by two methods: by the direct reaction of radioactive carbon dioxide with ammonia at high pressures and by the reaction of phosgene with ammonia.

$$C*O_2 + 2NH_3 \rightarrow H_2NC*ONH_2 + H_2O$$

$$C*OCl_2 + 2NH_3 \rightarrow H_2NC*ONH_2 + 2HCl$$

Preparation by High-Pressure Reaction. In the preparation of urea by the high-temperature reaction of carbon dioxide and ammonia [5] the sample is prepared on a vacuum line (see Fig. 56); dry carbon dioxide (41.7 mmoles) is vacuum-distilled into a heavy-walled glass tube (11 mm i.d., 36 cm long) which is constricted 27 cm from the bottom; this leaves a free volume of 25 cc below the constriction. Ten milliliters of liquid ammonia is then distilled into the tube (care should be taken during this distillation to condense the first few milliliters of ammonia in the bottom of the tube and gradually raise the cooling bath as the condensation proceeds; otherwise a plug may be formed halfway up the tube which makes distillation of all the ammonia impossible). When the ammonia has been distilled, the tube is sealed at the constriction.

While the tube is heated, it is subjected to an external atmosphere of nitrogen such that the pressure outside the tube is always larger than that inside. To accomplish this, the tube is placed in a hydrogenation type bomb which is then filled with nitrogen to a pressure of 2,800 psi; the bomb is then heated at 200° C for 3–4 hours. After the tube has cooled to room temperature, it is removed from the bomb, cooled in a Dry Ice bath, and opened. The ammonia is allowed to evaporate, and the contents of the tube are transferred to a flask by the use of hot alcohol. The product is dried over phosphorus pentoxide *in vacuo*. The yield is found to be 80% (2.0 grams) based on carbon dioxide.

Preparation by Medium-Pressure Reaction. In another procedure [6] ammonium carbamate is produced first from a few milliliters of labeled carbon dioxide and ammonia according to the reaction

$$C*O_2 + 2NH_3 \rightarrow H_2NC* \overset{\displaystyle O}{\underset{\displaystyle ONH_4}{\big\Vert}}$$

Crystals of solid ammonium carbamate are produced in a thick-walled capillary-glass tube immersed in liquid air. After it has been warmed to 0° C the tube is sealed off at such a volume that the total pressure will be about 35 atmospheres when the tube is heated. The tube and crystals are heated at 135° to 150° C for 3 days to give a 40% yield of urea based on carbon dioxide. (Suitable safety precautions must be taken.) The tube is cooled and opened, and the material which has not reacted and the urea are warmed to drive out the ammonia and carbon dioxide; these gases are passed through a trap or absorber so that active carbon dioxide can be removed.

[5] C. E. Bryan, Atomic Energy Commission, Isotopes Division Circular, C-8, September 1947.

[6] A. L. Myerson and F. Daniels, University of Wisconsin, private communication.

[7] P. E. Yankwich, unpublished experiments.

Preparation from Phosgene. If ammonia is bubbled through a solution of labeled phosgene in toluene, a quantitative conversion to urea can be achieved.[7] This type of reaction is universal for any primary or secondary amine and thus makes possible the preparation of many substituted urea derivatives. The urea precipitates from the toluene and may be filtered, and dried *in vacuo*. Phosgene is very soluble in toluene, and solutions can be prepared on the vacuum line or by bubbling the phosgene through the toluene.

Cyanogen Chloride—C^{11}. ClC*N [8]

This very poisonous gas has been prepared by the reaction of chlorine and slightly moist silver cyanide.

$$AgC*N + Cl_2 \rightarrow ClC* \equiv N + AgCl$$

To a solution of 1 mmole of labeled alkali cyanide buffered with sodium bicarbonate, a slight excess of dilute silver nitrate solution is added to form a silver cyanide precipitate. After the solution has stood a few minutes the carbonate is decomposed with 0.1 N nitric acid. A pad of "Filteraid" [9] which weighs 10 to 25 mg is prepared in a sintered-glass crucible, and the silver cyanide is filtered on this mat. (Silver cyanide would stick to the sintered disk if this step were omitted. The use of a Büchner funnel and paper filter is permissible if Filteraid is employed.) By means of an aspirator, air is forced through the pad for about 5 minutes to dry the precipitate partially. The pad and cyanide are then carefully transferred to the reaction vessel, a small tube of 30-cc volume. The air is quickly pumped out of the reactor so that the minimum of water will be lost, and 2 mmoles of chlorine is frozen in. The reactor, which is fitted with a stopcock, is then closed, removed from the system, and immersed for 10 minutes in brine at $-5°$ C.

The reaction tube is allowed to warm to room temperature, and the mixed reagent and product gases are distilled through phosphorus pentoxide and frozen into a tube containing 5 grams of 10-mesh antimony. The antimony tube is closed off from the system and shaken manually for 5 minutes to insure reaction of the chlorine with antimony. More complete removal of the excess chlorine can be achieved if, instead of antimony, one uses copper turnings that have been partly amalgamated by immersion in mercurous nitrate solution. The yield of cyanogen chloride is at least 80% based on the amount of silver cyanide used.

Barium Cyanamide and Guanidine Hydrochloride—C^{14}. BaNC*N, $(H_2N)_2C* = NH \cdot HCl$ [10]

Labeled guanidine hydrochloride has been prepared as follows:

$$BaC*O_3 + 2NH_3 \rightarrow BaNC*N + 3H_2O$$

[8] C. N. Rice and P. E. Yankwich, unpublished experiments.

[9] Johns-Manville Co., New York, N. Y.

[10] N. H. Marsh, L. C. Lane, and D. J. Salley, American Cyanamid Co., private communication.

$$BaNC^*N + 3NH_4NO_3 \rightarrow$$

$$(H_2N)_2C^*\!\!=\!\!NH \cdot HNO_3 + Ba(NO_3)_2 + 2NH_3$$

$$(H_2N)_2C^*\!\!=\!\!NH \cdot HNO_3 + (NO_2)_3C_6H_2ONH_4 \rightarrow$$

$$(H_2N)_2C^*\!\!=\!\!NH \cdot HOC_6H_2(NO_2)_3 + NH_4NO_3$$

$$(H_2N)_2C^*\!\!=\!\!NH \cdot HOC_6H_2(NO_2)_3 + HCl \rightarrow$$

$$(H_2N)_2C^*\!\!=\!\!NH \cdot HCl \downarrow + HOC_6H_2(NO_2)_3$$

Barium carbonate is converted to barium cyanamide by high-temperature reaction with ammonia. Apparatus for the conversion consists of a quartz tube (46 cm long and 1.4 cm i.d.) equipped with a centered outlet tube (8 mm i.d. and 16 cm long) at one end and a side-arm inlet tube (4 mm i.d.) at the other. Into the open end of the fore part of the tube is fitted an inner standard taper plug carrying a centered quartz thermowell (7 mm o.d.) which extends in a centered position along the axis 25.5 cm into the reaction tube. Anhydrous ammonia is supplied to the reaction tube from an upright (for vapor delivery) cylinder equipped with a needle valve for regulation of flow rate. Between the cylinder and reactor the ammonia passes through a glass manifold carrying suitable vent valves and a mercury-filled safety trap. After leaving the reactor the ammonia passes through a safety trap, an absorber filled with aqueous ammonia saturated with barium hydroxide to catch any radio carbon dioxide that may be evolved, and a calibrated capillary-manometer flowmeter filled with dibutyl phthalate and then is vented to the hood. The reactor tube is heated in a high-temperature furnace; the temperature is measured with a thermocouple which extends to the end of the thermowell. A quartz boat containing 138 mg of barium carbonate (0.7 mmole) is placed in the reactor just downstream from the thermowell, and ammonia is passed through the tube at a rate of 6 l/hr. The quartz tube is heated to 800° C during 1 hour, and the temperature is maintained at that level for 5 hours. While the furnace is allowed to cool, the ammonia flow is maintained.

The barium cyanamide is heated with a 50% excess of ammonium nitrate for 30 minutes at 165° C, thus producing guanidine nitrate. The fused mixture is stirred in a thick-walled centrifuge tube with a stirring rod which is kept with the material for the rest of the reaction (this eliminates transfer losses on the stirring rod). The fusion mixture is cooled to 80° C, and 22.2 ml of 1.4% aqueous ammonium picrate solution is added dropwise to the centrifuge tube in which the solution is stirred. The tube is cooled to 25° C, and the picrate is allowed to crystallize for 1 hour. The tube (with rod) is centrifuged, and the supernatant liquid is siphoned off. The precipitate is washed with 10 ml of 0.8% ammonium picrate solution and again centrifuged; the supernatant liquid is siphoned off. This step is repeated, and then the precipitate is washed similarly with 10 ml of water. The precipitate is dried *in vacuo* over anhydrous calcium chloride.

The guanidine picrate, still in the centrifuge tube, is suspended in anhydrous ether, and the suspension is saturated with hydrogen chloride gas. The precipitate of guanidine hydrochloride is washed three times with ethereal hydrogen chloride solution and dried at 100° C. The precipitate is dissolved in water and filtered, and the solution is evaporated to dryness to give 43.5 mg of product. The yield of guanidine hydrochloride based on carbon dioxide was found to be 61%; the material was about 93.5% pure. (The impurity is probably ammonium chloride.)

Ethyl Carbamate (Urethane)—C^{14}. $H_2NC^*OOC_2H_5$ [11]

$$H_2NC^*ONH_2 + HNO_3 \rightarrow H_2NC^*ONH_2 \cdot HNO_3$$

$$H_2NC^*ONH_2 \cdot HNO_3 + NaNO_2 + C_2H_5OH \rightarrow$$
$$H_2NC^*OOC_2H_5 + N_2 + 2H_2O + NaNO_3$$

Two grams of labeled urea is dissolved in the minimum amount of water and then precipitated as urea nitrate by the dropwise addition of concentrated nitric acid. After most of the liquid is decanted, the residue is dried *in vacuo* over solid potassium hydroxide. The yield of urea nitrate based on urea is 100%. The urea nitrate is converted to urethane by treatment with sodium nitrite.[12] A solution of urea nitrate dissolved in absolute alcohol is refluxed on a water bath, and an equivalent quantity sodium nitrite is added. (Although yields of 70 to 80% have been reported for this step, only 40% yield based on urea was obtained in this work.)

Potassium Cyanide—C^{11},[13] C^{14},[14, 15]. KC^*N

The preparation of this important synthetic intermediate has been studied by several investigators; methods have been developed that make it possible to convert carbon dioxide to cyanide with yields of 96%, and a simplified procedure has been devised which permits the conversion to be performed in a test tube.

Reduction of Carbon Dioxide with Potassium and Ammonia. The equation for the reaction [13, 14] is:

$$4K + NH_3 + C^*O_2 \xrightarrow{\Delta} KC^*N + KH + 2KOH$$

In a study of this preparation [14] all known factors were varied; those found to be important in affecting the yield are time of heating, temperature, initial pressure of carbon dioxide, and the state of dispersion of the metallic potassium. A less important factor is the partial pressure of ammonia, provided that at least as much ammonia as carbon dioxide is used.

Into a Pyrex bomb tube (1 cm in diameter and 40 cm long) flushed with nitrogen is dropped 0.8 gram of clean metallic potassium wiped between folds of a towel. A constriction is made in the bomb tube about 5 cm from the open end so that a reaction bomb of 14-cc volume will be formed when the tube is sealed later. The tube is evacuated through a length of plastic tube attached to a vacuum system, and the whole tube is warmed with a large "soft" flame and shaken horizontally to disperse

[11] H. E. Skipper, C. E. Bryan, and O. S. Hutchinson, *Techniques for the Synthesis and Metabolic Study of Urethane*, Atomic Energy Commission, Isotopes Division Circular C-8, September 1947.

[12] A. Andreocci, *Ber.*, **25**, 639C (1892).

[13] R. D. Cramer and G. B. Kistiakowsky, *J. Biol. Chem.*, **137**, 547 (1941).

[14] R. B. Loftfield, *Nucleonics*, **1**, No. 3, 54 (1947).

[15] A. W. Adamson, *J. Am. Chem. Soc.*, **69**, 2564 (1947).

the potassium along its length. The tube is then clamped horizontally, and a potassium mirror is formed by heating portions of the lower surface with a tiny flame while the upper surface is cooled with a wet towel. After a mirror covering at least 90% of the inner surface is obtained, the tube is immersed in liquid air and 1 mmole of carbon dioxide and 2 mmoles of ammonia are frozen in. The tube is then carefully sealed off at the constriction and placed in a steel bomb tube.

The bomb tube is lowered into an electric furnace and heated at 620° C. The total time of heating is determined by blank runs in the apparatus used; the length of heating is 12 minutes plus the time necessary for the sealed tube to reach the reaction temperature, 620° C. After the proper interval, the steel bomb is removed from the furnace and allowed to cool. The Pyrex tube is then taken out of the bomb and cooled in liquid air. The seal tip is opened by heating with a small hot flame; after the residual pressure has been released, the sealed end of the tube is scratched with a file and cracked off. The hydrides formed and unreacted potassium are decomposed by careful dropwise addition of water or 50% ethanol solution. The yield is found to be 90 to 96%, based on carbon dioxide.

Reduction of Barium Carbonate with Sodium Azide.[15]

$$NaN_3 + BaC*O_3 \xrightarrow{\Delta} NaC*N + N_2 + BaO + O_2$$

One-tenth of a gram of barium carbonate is mixed with 1 gram of sodium azide in a 6-inch Pyrex test tube; a slow stream of nitrogen is directed into the mouth of the tube. With the tube lying almost horizontal, the mixture is carefully heated so as to maintain a steady, but not too rapid, decomposition of the azide. Some fumes are given off, and the reaction should be performed in a hood. The test tube is heated at a dull red heat for 10 minutes after the decomposition is complete. Water is added dropwise cautiously to the cooled mixture until the reaction of sodium and water ceases. After dilution, the solution is acidified with sulfuric acid, and the hydrogen cyanide is distilled into a slight excess of sodium hydroxide solution.

The nature of the barium carbonate crystals and the method of heating the azide mixture are critical in this procedure. Thus it is usually necessary to convert barium carbonate-C^{14} which has been obtained from the Oak Ridge plant of the Atomic Energy Commission to carbon dioxide and back again to barium carbonate before this reduction will work satisfactorily. For best results the azide mixture should be heaped in the bottom of the tube and not spread out. The average yield of cyanide is about 78%.

Purification of Cyanide Reaction Mixtures. The radio cyanide can be separated from the reaction mixture in several ways. In one method the cyanide is precipitated as the insoluble silver salt and filtered off; in another, formic acid is added to the solution and the cyanide distilled out; and in a third dilute sulfuric acid is added and the hydrogen cyanide steam-distilled.

Generation with formic acid: [14] The cyanide reaction mixture is transferred to a vacuum line, and the dissolved gases are removed by a vacuum distillation. The cyanide preparation mixture is placed in a generator (see Fig. 60), and the alcohol and dissolved gases are distilled *in vacuo*. Formic acid is then added and the hydrogen cyanide is distilled into a trap which contains about 1 ml. of water.

Precipitation as silver cyanide: [16] To the cyanide reaction mixture buffered with sodium bicarbonate is added a slight excess of 0.1 N silver nitrate solution; the silver cyanide precipitate is filtered and washed. If hydrogen cyanide is to be prepared from this silver cyanide it may be obtained in several ways.

To manifold

FIG. 60. Pressure-equalized dropping funnel.

The precipitate of silver cyanide is suspended in a few milliliters of water and treated with a small excess of 0.1 M sodium sulfide. The solution is filtered, and the filtrate is transferred to a generator (see Fig. 60) and frozen in liquid air. After the flask is evacuated the solution is allowed to melt and a few milliliters of concentrated sulfuric acid is added. The acid solution is vacuum-distilled into a trap; some water and hydrogen sulfide are carried along with the cyanide.

In another procedure [17] the silver cyanide is introduced into a bulb (see Fig. 61) which is then evacuated and filled to about ½ atmosphere with hydrogen. The silver cyanide is heated until the hydrogen has reduced the silver. When the conversion is completed the gases are pumped off and the hydrogen cyanide is condensed in a liquid-air trap (preferably of the sintered disk type, see Fig. 49).

In yet another procedure [18] the silver cyanide is placed in a small bulb, and a slight excess of hydrogen sulfide is frozen into the bulb. The reaction mixture is warmed and the silver cyanide is converted to sulfide; the mixed gases are passed through a pair of traps in series: the first is cooled in an ice-acetone bath ($-20°$ C) and removes the hydrogen cyanide; the second trap, cooled in liquid air, condenses the hydrogen sulfide.

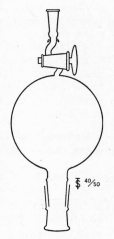

FIG. 61. Gas-solid reaction vessel.

Carbon Monoxide—C^{11},[19] C^{13},[20] C^{14}.[21] [22]   C*O

Labeled carbon monoxide has been prepared by the reduction of carbon dioxide with hot zinc, by the exchange between labeled carbon dioxide and inactive carbon monoxide on a hot tungsten filament, and

[16] C. N. Rice, unpublished experiments.

[17] B. M. Tolbert, unpublished experiments.

[18] C. N. Rice and P. E. Yankwich, unpublished experiments.

[19] J. L. Huston and T. H. Norris, *J. Am. Chem. Soc.*, **70**, 1968 (1948).

[20] R. B. Bernstein and T. I. Taylor, *Science*, **106**, 498 (1947).

[21] S. Weinhouse, private communication.

[22] J. T. Kummer, *J. Am. Chem. Soc.*, **69**, 2239 (1947).

by the reduction of calcium carbonate with zinc powder.   In addition, carbon monoxide, C^{11}, is obtained as about 60% of the yield in the production of C^{11} by bombardment in a cyclotron of a beryllium target with protons.   All the chemical methods (excepting the exchange reaction) will give yields of more than 99%, and the exchange reaction can result in high yields if dilution of the labeled carbon is not undesirable.   The reduction of carbon dioxide with zinc can be carried out in a continuous-flow type system; the other syntheses are batch processes.

Reduction of Calcium Carbonate with Zinc.[21]   Probably the simplest of the several preparations of carbon monoxide is the reduction of calcium carbonate with zinc:

$$CaC^*O_3 + Zn \rightarrow CaO + ZnO + C^*O$$

This reduction proceeds when the calcium salt is used but is unsuccessful with barium carbonate.   The conversion of barium carbonate to calcium carbonate can be accomplished by the homogenization techniques described on page 96 f.   The dried calcium carbonate is then heated at 700 to 750° C in a quartz tube with a onefold excess of zinc dust, and the carbon monoxide is evolved.

It is convenient to perform this reaction in an evacuated system of known volume, so that the rate and extent of the gas evolution can be followed by manometric measurements.   Carbon dioxide ($< 1\%$) and traces of water and hydrogen are found in the carbon monoxide.   If the carbon dioxide and the water are condensed with liquid air, very pure carbon monoxide is obtained.   The yield, based on carbon dioxide, is 99%.

Reduction of Carbon Dioxide with Zinc.   All the procedures used for the reduction of carbon dioxide with zinc are similar:

$$Zn + C^*O_2 \rightarrow ZnO + C^*O$$

In one synthesis 20-mesh zinc washed with dilute acetic acid and water and dried with acetone has been used.[19]   In another preparation the reducing agent is zinc dust supported on asbestos fiber.[20]   This procedure will be described since the equipment is simple and the yield is high.

The zinc reducing agent is prepared as follows: A moistened mixture of 95% (by weight) technical grade zinc dust and 5% asbestos fiber is made into small pellets about 6 mm in diameter; these pellets are dried at 110° C for 24 hours before use. In a continuous-flow apparatus 50 grams of this zinc mixture (in a 15-cm length of Pyrex tubing 25 mm in diameter) heated at 385° to 435° C can reduce carbon dioxide to carbon monoxide at atmospheric pressure at flow rates of 50 to 400 cc/min in yields of 99 to 100%.

If it is desired to carry out this reaction on a small scale, either one of the two batch type units shown in Fig. 62 is suitable; convection currents are utilized to force the gas through the zinc bed.   Unit A, Fig. 62, is designed for use with very small quantities of carbon dioxide; the bulb, of 5 cc volume, is charged with 1 gram of the zinc-asbestos pellets, which are introduced through the sealed-off side tube. The carbon dioxide is vacuum-distilled into the generator, the stopcock closed, and the zinc heated for about 2 hours. The carbon monoxide produced may be transferred with a Toepler pump to the next reaction chamber (see Fig. 59) or stored for future use.

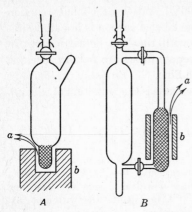

FIG. 62. Apparatus for converting carbon dioxide to carbon monoxide; a, thermocouple leads; b, furnace. (R. B. Bernstein and T. I. Taylor.)

If larger quantities of carbon dioxide are to be converted, the unit B, Fig. 62, is more convenient. This unit has been slightly modified from that described [20] by the addition of a small cold finger to permit vacuum distillation of the carbon dioxide which is to be reduced. The stopcocks which allow circulation of the gas are opened after the furnace has been adjusted to the desired temperature.

Exchange of Carbon Monoxide and Carbon Dioxide.[22]

The exchange reaction between labeled

$$CO + C*O_2 \rightarrow C*O + C*O_2$$

carbon dioxide and carbon monoxide may be used for the production of active monoxide. If high yields are desired, considerable dilution of activity is necessary; thus for a yield of 99% it is necessary to dilute the activity 99 fold.

The equipment for this preparation consists of a combination vacuum and Toepler pump system. Enough carbon monoxide and carbon dioxide to give a total pressure of about 30 cm are transferred into a light globe with a tungsten filament (150 watts, 110 volts) through a tube attached to it for this purpose. The bulb is then closed and the filament heated (60 to 80 volts) for 16 hours. The gas is then passed through a trap cooled in liquid air to separate the carbon monoxide and dioxide; monoxide is transferred with a Toepler pump into a storage vessel.

Formic Acid—C^{14},[23] C^{11},[24] C^{13}.[25]   HC*O_2H

Potassium or alkali formate has been prepared by the high-pressure reduction of labeled potassium bicarbonate with hydrogen in the presence of palladium black catalyst, by the reduction of carbon dioxide with a fresh suspension of *Bacterium coli*,[24] and by the hydrolysis of sodium cyanide.

[23] D. Melville, J. Rachele, and E. Keller, *J. Biol. Chem.*, **169**, 419 (1947).

[24] D. Harman, T. D. Stewart, and S. Ruben, *J. Am. Chem. Soc.*, **64**, 2293 (1942).

[25] S. Gurin, in *Symposium on Use of Isotopes in Biological Research, University of Chicago, March 3-4, 1947.*

Reduction of Potassium Bicarbonate.[23] In the reduction of bicarbonate with hydrogen at high pressures it is necessary to use the potassium salt; the sodium salt will not work.

$$KHC^*O_3 + H_2 \rightarrow HC^*O_2K + H_2O$$

To a tube which contains 0.77 mmole of potassium bicarbonate (page 155) dissolved in 1–2 ml of water is added 2–3 ml of an aqueous suspension containing 50 to 100 mg of freshly prepared palladium black catalyst. The tube containing the solution is placed in a glass liner in a high-pressure bomb [26] and is reduced at 100 atmospheres and 70° C for 24 hours; the solution is shaken during the reduction. The resulting mixture is filtered and dried in a stream of warm air and finally *in vacuo* over phosphorus pentoxide. The yield based on bicarbonate was found to be 98 to 99%.

Hydrolysis of Sodium Cyanide [25]

$$2H_2O + NaC^*N + 2HCl \rightarrow NaCl + NH_4Cl + HC^*O_2H$$

The sodium cyanide with excess 6 N hydrochloric acid is heated in a sealed tube for 8 hours at 75° C. The yield based on cyanide is 50 to 60%.

Conversion to Methyl Formate—C^{11},[24] **C^{14}.**[23] $HC^*O_2CH_3$

$$(CH_3)_2SO_4 + HC^*O_2K \rightarrow HC^*O_2CH_3 + KCH_3SO_4$$

$$H_2SO_4 + CH_3OH + HC^*O_2Na \rightarrow HC^*O_2CH_3 + NaHSO_4 + H_2O$$

The apparatus used for the esterification of potassium formate with methyl sulfate [23] is shown in Fig. 63. To 3.7 mmoles of well-dried powdered potassium formate,

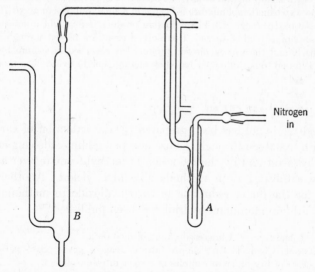

FIG. 63. Apparatus for esterification of potassium formate: A, dimethyl sulfate reaction vessel; B, methyl formate trap. (D. Melville, J. Rachele, and E. Keller.)

[26] American Instrument Co., Silver Springs, Md., Microbomb.

0.6 ml of freshly distilled methly sulfate is added with mixing. (Methyl sulfate serves as the lubricant.) The mixture is then heated slowly with an oil bath over a 2-hour period to a temperature of 185° C. A slow stream of nitrogen is passed through the vessel, and the methyl formate is condensed in a trap cooled in a Dry Ice bath. About 0.2 ml of methyl formate is usually obtained, which represents a yield of more than 90%.

In another procedure [24] sodium formate is placed in a semi-micro distillation apparatus and to it is added 1 ml of a solution prepared from 2.5 grams of sulfuric acid and 5.0 grams of methanol. The first distillate is redistilled to give about 0.1 ml of liquid, which is an approximately 60% yield of methyl formate.

Formaldehyde—C^{14}.[27]   HC*HO

Labeled formaldehyde has been prepared by the partial oxidation of methanol with air over a copper catalyst. The yields are not very satisfactory and are subject to considerable variation.

The catalyst for this oxidation is prepared by covering a copper screen with a heavy layer of freshly precipitated copper hydroxide. The hydroxide is precipitated from a cupric nitrate solution by the addition of dilute ammonium hydroxide; [28] the precipitate is washed with water several times. The copper screen is then rolled, put into a quartz tube (11 mm o.d., 25 cm long), dried, and reduced with hydrogen at 400° to 500° C. The methanol, which contains the water produced by the reduction of carbon dioxide with hydrogen, see page 167, is carried over the catalyst bed (heated at 600° C) with a slow stream of air. To achieve the correct proportions of air and alcohol, the water-methanol mixture is heated in a small bubbler to about 70° C and the air is bubbled through it. The reduction products are caught in another small bubbler containing 1 ml of water. Unabsorbed gases are passed through a copper oxide furnace, and the carbon dioxide produced is absorbed in sodium hydroxide. The yield is found to be 50 to 60% based on methanol or 45 to 55% based on carbon dioxide.

Methanol—C^{14},[29,30] C^{11}.[31]   C*H$_3$OH

Labeled methanol has been prepared by the reduction of carbon dioxide with hydrogen through the use of a potassium oxide-copper oxide-alumina catalyst and by the reduction of methyl formate over a copper chromite catalyst. Both methods give high yields. Another useful method for the direct reduction of carbon dioxide to methanol which employs lithium aluminum hydride has been published.[32]

[27] B. M. Tolbert and F. Christenson, unpublished data.

[28] Mallinkrodt Chemical Co., copper nitrate, reagent grade, gives better yields than any other of five different samples of copper nitrate tested.

[29] B. M. Tolbert, *J. Am. Chem. Soc.*, **69**, 1529 (1947).

[30] D. Melville, J. Rachele, and E. Keller, *J. Biol. Chem.*, **169**, 419 (1947).

[31] D. Harman, T. D. Stewart, and S. Ruben, *J. Am. Chem. Soc.*, **64**, 2293 (1942).

[32] R. F. Nystrom, W. H. Yanko and W. G. Brown, *J. Am. Chem. Soc.*, **70**, 411 (1948).

Direct Reduction of Carbon Dioxide with Hydrogen.[29]   The reaction used is:

$$C^{*}O_2 + 3H_2 \xrightarrow[\substack{\text{K Cu Al}_2\text{O}_3 \\ \text{catalyst}}]{\text{high pressure}} C^{*}H_3OH + H_2O$$

The catalyst used for this reduction contains 10% cupric oxide and 2% potassium hydroxide on 8- to 12-mesh alumina.[33] Alumina is impregnated with copper nitrate, dried at 130° C, saturated with potassium hydroxide solution, redried, ignited at 500° C for 4 hours, and finally reduced at 285° C and 450 atmospheres hydrogen pressure for 3 hours.

The carbon dioxide is generated in an evacuated system, see Fig. 56, from barium carbonate by the action of concentrated sulfuric acid dropped from a pressure-equalizing funnel, see Fig. 60. The dioxide is condensed in a liquid-nitrogen trap, and the air which had been entrapped in the barium carbonate is pumped off. The amount of carbon dioxide used in a reduction may be checked by measurement of its pressure in a system of known volume.

The carbon dioxide is reduced in a small hydrogenation bomb with a free volume of 300 cc.[34] The bomb containing the catalyst is warmed with a flame and evacuated to a pressure of 30 microns. The bomb is then half immersed in liquid nitrogen, and the carbon dioxide is distilled in. The final pressure in the system of such a distillation into an iron bomb cannot usually be reduced below about 40 to 50 microns.

After introduction of the carbon dioxide, the bomb is closed, removed from the line, and warmed to room temperature, and hydrogen is added to 4,000 psi. (*Caution: Do not add hydrogen until the bomb is warm, for steel is brittle when very cold.*) A booster pump is needed to add the hydrogen at sufficient pressure. Care must be taken when the hydrogen is forced into the bomb that the pressure of hydrogen on the supply side is always higher than the pressure in the bomb; this eliminates any possibility of carbon dioxide flowing back into the storage tanks or booster pump. A high-pressure gauge should be placed on the pump side of the system as well as on the reaction vessel.

The reduction of the carbon dioxide may proceed with an initial pressure of 3,500 psi (room temperature), but this is very close to the point where reduction is incomplete. An initial pressure of 4,000 psi (final pressure, 7,000 psi) is preferable. The bomb is heated six hours at 285° C. The products of the reduction and the remaining carbon dioxide are caught in a combination spiral and sintered-glass disk trap cooled in liquid nitrogen (see Fig. 49b); the hydrogen is discharged from the bomb through the spiral system at a rate of 1–2 l/min. The remaining products and the contents of the sintered-glass trap are distilled from the warmed bomb into the larger trap on the line.

The carbon dioxide that is not reduced is separated from the water-methanol mixture by distillation of the product through a spiral trap cooled in a Dry Ice bath. The remaining carbon dioxide is usually 3–4% of the initial gas.

The catalyst has been found to be slowly poisoned; it is unreliable when used for more than two reductions and, preferably, the catalyst should be used only once. The efficiency of any given batch of catalyst should be tested with an inactive run before use with radioactive material. The yield is found to be about 85 to 90% based

[33] High surface alumina with approximately 100 square meters surface area per gram. Aluminum Ore Company of America, Pittsburgh, Pennsylvania.
[34] Microbomb, American Instrument Company, Silver Springs, Maryland.

on carbon dioxide. The product contains appreciable quantities of water, which cannot be separated from the methanol.

Reduction of Carbon Dioxide with Lithium Aluminum Hydride.[32]   By the use of relatively non-volatile solvents, carbon dioxide may be reduced to methanol with lithium aluminum hydride, and a separation of the products may be effected.

$$4CO_2 + 3LiAlH_4 \rightarrow LiAl(OCH_3)_4 + 2LiAlO_2$$

$$LiAl(OCH_3)_4 + 4ROH \rightarrow LiAl(OR)_4 + 4CH_3OH$$

Carbon dioxide (66 mmoles) carried by a stream of nitrogen is passed into a solution of 3.8 grams of lithium aluminum hydride in 500 ml of diethyl carbitol. To this solution is then added 120 grams of *n*-butyl-carbitol, and the reaction mixture is heated. The methanol produced is swept by the continued stream of nitrogen into a small trap cooled with Dry Ice. The yield based on carbon dioxide is 81%, and the product is completely anhydrous.

Methyl Iodide—C^{14},[35, 36] C^{11}.[37] C^*H_3I

Reduction of Methyl Formate to Methanol.   The reduction and conversion of methyl formate to methanol and methyl iodide is carried out

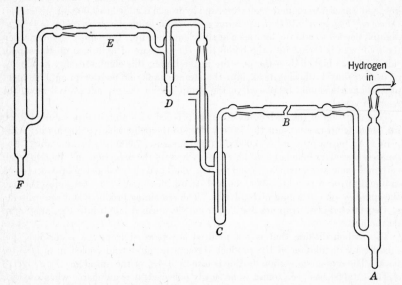

Fɪɢ. 64.   Apparatus for conversion of methyl formate to methyl iodide: *A*, methyl formate trap; *B*, copper chromite catalyst; *C*, hydrogen iodide solution; *D*, aqueous solution of red phosphorus; *E*, calcium chloride; *F*, methyl iodide trap.   (D. Melville, J. Rachele, and E. Keller.)

[35] B. M. Tolbert, *J. Am. Chem. Soc.*, **69**, 1529 (1947).

[36] D. Melville, J. Rachele, and E. Keller, *J. Biol. Chem.*, **169**, 419 (1947).

[37] D. Harman, T. D. Stewart, and S. Ruben, *J. Am. Chem. Soc.*, **64**, 2293 (1942).

according to the following reaction: [36]

$$HC^*O_2CH_3 + 2H_2 \rightarrow 2C^*H_3OH$$

$$C^*H_3OH + HI \rightarrow C^*H_3I + H_2O$$

This reaction is an example of a procedure in which volatile organic compounds are handled by means of a carrying gas and cold traps. This type of procedure is to be contrasted with the preparation of methanol in a vacuum system as just described; it is an illustration of the fact that vacuum systems are not always necessary for such preparations.

The reduction and conversion of methyl formate (3.5 mmoles) to methyl iodide is carried out in one step, and it will therefore be described here as one procedure. The equipment for this reaction is shown in Fig. 64. The methyl formate is carried by a slow stream of hydrogen over a copper chromite catalyst, heated at 160° C, on which the formate is reduced. The methanol thus formed is carried by excess hydrogen into a flask where it is converted to methyl iodide by reaction with 10 ml of hydriodic acid (constant-boiling mixture, density 1.70) heated under a reflux condenser by an oil bath at 135° C. The hydrogen iodide in the methyl iodide thus formed is absorbed in 4 ml of an aqueous suspension of red phosphorus, and the methyl iodide is then dried over calcium chloride. The purified methyl iodide is condensed in a trap cooled with Dry Ice. The yield is 83% based on the methyl formate. (The total time for the conversion of 0.2 ml of methyl formate to methyl iodide is 1½ hours.)

Conversion of Methanol to Methyl Iodide. [35] The following preparation of methyl iodide is designed to be carried out where there is an appreciable amount of water in the methanol.

$$3C^*H_3OH + PI_3 \rightarrow 3C^*H_3I + H_3PO_3$$

Into a Carius tube sealed to an 8-mm stopcock (see Fig. 65), 10 grams of iodine are introduced through a long-stemmed funnel. The tube is chilled in Dry Ice or liquid air (to prevent reaction of iodine and phosphorus), and 2 grams of red phosphorus and 3 ml of water added. The water reduces the pressure in the tube (during the following reaction) since the hydrogen iodide formed dissolves in it; the water does not interfere with the conversion of the methanol to methyl iodide.

The tube is evacuated, and the methanol or methanol-water mixture (see preparation of methanol) is distilled in. The tube is removed from the line, and the stopcock is clamped on. A water jacket is added to the upper half of the tube, and the reaction mixture is warmed carefully (if necessary a cold bath is used to control the initial reaction). The reaction mixture is refluxed for 1 hour on the steam bath; then the tube is transferred to the vacuum line and the methyl iodide, together with part of the water, hydrogen iodide, and phosphine, is distilled, with pumping, into a trap and then distilled into a reaction vessel (about 100-cc volume) (see Fig. 66) containing 10 ml of water. This vessel is removed from the line, warmed to room temperature, and shaken vigorously about 1 minute. It is then reconnected to the line, and the methyl iodide along with some water is distilled into a reaction tube (see Fig. 66) containing 4 to 5 grams of phosphorus pentoxide. This tube is removed from the line, warmed to room temperature, and shaken intermittently for half an hour. The phosphorus pentoxide reacts with most of the phosphine and dries the methyl iodide; enough should be used to leave some dry powder after the methyl iodide is distilled. The methyl iodide is transferred to a storage vessel *in vacuo* (see Fig. 60). The yield is about 95% based on methanol.

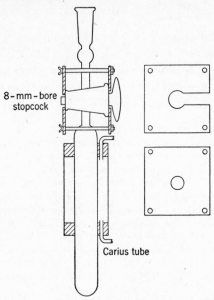

Fig. 65.   Low-pressure water-jacketed bomb tube used in the iodination of alcohols.   The plates used to hold the stopcock plug are made from $\frac{3}{32}$-in. brass sheet.

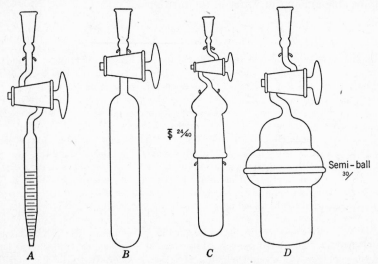

Fig. 66.   Reaction and storage vessels for organic synthesis: *A*, calibrated storage vessel for volatile liquids; *B*, storage or reaction vessel; *C*, jointed reaction vessel; *D*, small high-vacuum desiccator.

Methane—C^{14}.[38] C^*H_4

A preparation by the reduction of carbon dioxide with hydrogen over ruthenium metal offers a high-yield chemical synthesis.

The apparatus used for this conversion is shown in Fig. 67. (This figure includes apparatus for filling counter tubes with methane; see page 75.) The catalyst consists of ruthenium metal which has been boiled with 6 N nitric acid, washed with water, and dried in air at 400° C for ½ hour. In the reduction, approximately 7 to 10 mmoles of carbon dioxide and four to five times as much hydrogen are passed

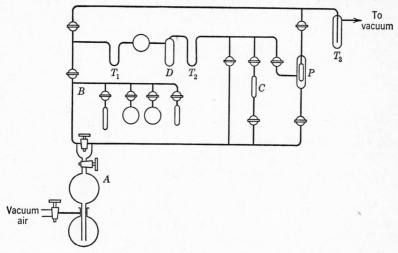

Fig. 67. Vacuum manifold used to prepare methane: A, Toepler pump; B, counter filling manifold; C, copper oxide furnace; D, ruthenium catalyst bed; E, pallidium thimble; T_1, T_2, T_3, traps. (G. R. Hennig.)

repeatedly through the catalyst, which is heated to 200° to 300° C as indicated by an external thermocouple. The gas transfers are performed with a Toepler pump. To ascertain whether the conversion is complete, a trap (T_1, Fig. 67) is cooled with liquid air; if carbon dioxide condenses, the reduction is unfinished. When the reduction has been completed, the excess hydrogen in the system is removed by exposure to a palladium thimble heated to 450° C (see Fig. 67, P). If one of the traps in the system is cooled with liquid nitrogen, most of the methane can be condensed and the removal of the hydrogen is improved. The methane is finally pumped into one of the storage bulbs on line E. The conversion of the carbon dioxide to methane is quantitative.

2. Functionally Labeled Nitriles, Carboxylic Acids, and Their Esters, and Amides

Nitriles, amides, and acids are discussed together in this section as a group related by the synthetic methods used to prepare them.

The preparation of nitriles and hydroxynitriles (cyanhydrins) from

[38] G. R. Hennig, Atomic Energy Commission, AECD 1794.

labeled cyanide has been discussed on pages 150–151. The catalytic ammonolysis of a functionally labeled carboxylic acid has also been used as a preparative method (equation 1).

$$RC^*OOH + NH_3 \xrightarrow[\Delta]{Al_2O_3} RC^*N + 2H_2O \tag{1}$$

Only one labeled amide, phenylacetamide, has been prepared to date. Its synthesis was incidental to a study of the mechanism of the Willgerodt reaction, and the method used is not necessarily that best suited as a synthetic procedure. The functionally labeled amide was prepared by pyrolysis of the ammonium salt of a carboxylic acid (equation 2).

$$2C_6H_5CH_2C^*OOH + (NH_4)_2CO_3 \xrightarrow[\Delta]{CH_3COOH}$$

$$2C_6H_5CH_2C^*ONH_2 + CO_2 + 3H_2O \tag{2}$$

For the preparation of α-labeled phenylacetamide see page 196.

Functionally labeled acids have been prepared by carbonation of an organometallic compound and the hydrolysis of a labeled nitrile (equation 3). Phenylacetic acid has been prepared by the Arndt-Eistert reaction (equation 4) incidentally to a study of the reaction mechanism.[1] No procedural details are available. The methods used for preparing hydroxy and keto acids are described on pages 207–215:

$$RC^*N + 2H_2O \longrightarrow RC^*OOH + NH_3 \tag{3}$$

$$\left.\begin{array}{l} RC^*OCl + CH_2N_2 \longrightarrow RC^*OCHN_2 + HCl \\ RC^*OCHN_2 + H_2O \xrightarrow{Ag} RCH_2C^*OOH + N_2 \end{array}\right\} \tag{4}$$

Acids from Grignard Reagents. Many examples of the preparation of a carboxylic acid by the carbonation of a Grignard reagent are already in the literature, and several techniques have been devised for carrying out the operation. The reaction is conducted by bringing gaseous carbon dioxide into contact with the Grignard reagent; the halomagnesium salt of the acid is formed and is then decomposed by the addition of dilute mineral acid. The major side products are ketones and carbinols, which arise by the action upon the carbonation complex of Grignard compound which has not reacted with carbon dioxide. There are also inactive side products, which arise from coupling during the preparation of the organomagnesium compound and by reaction between unchanged reagent and the mineral acid which is added to break up the carbonation complex.

[1] C. Huggett, R. T. Arnold, and T. I. Taylor, *J. Am. Chem. Soc.*, **64**, 3043 (1942).

The formation of these four classes of substances is described by equations 5–8.

$$RC^*OOMgX + RMgX \rightarrow R_2C^*(OMgX)_2$$
$$R_2C^*(OMgX)_2 + 2H^+ \rightarrow R_2C^*{=}O + 2Mg^{++} + 2X^- + H_2O \Bigg\} \quad (5)$$

$$R_2C^*(OMgX)_2 + RMgX \rightarrow R_3C^*OMgX + MgO + MgX_2$$
$$R_3C^*OMgX + H^+ \rightarrow R_3C^*OH + Mg^{++} + X^- \Bigg\} \quad (6)$$

$$RMgX + RX \rightarrow R-R + MgX_2 \quad (7)$$

$$RMgX + H^+ \rightarrow RH + Mg^{++} + X^- \quad (8)$$

Since all these substances are non-acidic, their separation from the carboxylic acid is easily accomplished by partition between ether and aqueous sodium hydroxide. Although the purity of the product can thus be assured, it is desirable to minimize the formation of ketone and carbinol because they represent a diversion of valuable isotopic carbon dioxide away from the desired product. It is largely this consideration which dictates the conditions under which the carbonation is carried out. An additional consideration is the necessity of protecting the Grignard reagent from moisture and oxygen, since these react with the reagent and, if present in sufficient quantity, will reduce the reagent to an amount below that necessary to react with all the carbon dioxide. The reactions by which oxygen and water exert their effects are given in equations 9 and 10. The effect of oxygen is particularly objectionable

$$RMgX + H_2O \rightarrow RH + Mg(OH)X \quad (9)$$

$$2RMgX + O_2 \rightarrow 2ROMgX$$
$$ROMgX + H^+ \rightarrow ROH + Mg^{++} + X^- \Bigg\} \quad (10)$$

if an arylmagnesium halide is being used, because it forms a phenol, which, because of its acidic character, may not be entirely removed from the carboxylic acid in the isolation procedure. In addition, oxygenation of the reagent introduces an error into the determination of the concentration when this is done by simple titration. It is therefore desirable to prepare the alkylmagnesium halide carefully, so that a reagent of good quality is obtained.

The conditions which work to minimize the formation of ketone and carbinol are a low concentration and a small excess of the Grignard reagent, a short carbonation time, effective agitation of the reaction mixture, and a low reaction temperature. It is difficult to evaluate the relative importance of these factors from the available information. Certain of them do not appear to be critical, at least in some cases.

Acetic acid, for example, has been prepared [2] in 95% yield at room temperature by carbonation of a fivefold excess of $1 M$ methylmagnesium iodide. The carbonation was carried out quickly (10 minutes), however, and this would tend to compensate the effect of the relatively high reaction temperature and the large excess and rather high concentration of the Grignard reagent. Most workers have preferred to carry out the carbonation under conditions better calculated to minimize ketone and carbinol formation.

With the exception of the acetic acid synthesis just mentioned, the carbonation is always carried out at low temperature, usually in the neighborhood of $-20°$ C. Sometimes the Grignard reagent is cooled initially in a Dry Ice bath, then allowed to warm up to room temperature in contact with carbon dioxide. Since the absorption of carbon dioxide is rapid at $-20°$, there is no need to allow the mixture to become warmer than this. When a sodium or lithium alkyl is used, the carbonation is performed at a lower temperature, -50 to $-80°$ C. In addition to its aid in minimizing carbinol and ketone formation, a low reaction temperature has the virtue of reducing the vapor pressure of the ether which is used as solvent. When vacuum line technique is used, this is an advantage because, the lower the vapor pressure of the ether, the faster is the diffusion of carbon dioxide into the reaction mixture.

The carbonation time should be short in order to minimize the period during which the carbonation product is in contact with unchanged Grignard reagent. Unchanged reagent is ordinarily present because an excess is used in order to insure complete absorption of carbon dioxide. To hasten the absorption, the reaction mixture is stirred or shaken.

The amount of excess Grignard reagent used has been varied from 10 to 600% without any striking effect on the yields. A large excess of the reagent serves no useful purpose, however, and should be avoided.

The Grignard reagent is ordinarily employed at a concentration below $0.5 M$. It is desirable to keep the concentration low not only to minimize ketone and carbinol formation but to keep the organomagnesium compound in solution at the reaction temperature used. In general, if the solution does not crystallize at $-20°$ C, the concentration is low enough to give satisfactory results.

The concentration of a Grignard solution is determined by titration. An aliquot of the clear solution is withdrawn and pipetted into a measured excess of $0.1 N$ hydrochloric acid. The excess acid is then titrated with standardized sodium hydroxide. Methyl orange is used as indicator, since the magnesium ion must not be titrated. It has been mentioned earlier that, if oxygen has found its way to the Grignard

2 S. Ruben, M. B. Allen, and P. Nahinsky, *J. Am. Chem. Soc.*, **64**, 3050 (1942).

reagent, the titration does not give an accurate indication of the concentration of the organomagnesium compound. This can be understood by reference to equation 10. The ROMgX compound behaves in the titration like RMgX; the value obtained for the concentration of RMgX is therefore too high.

These remarks on the carbonation of an inactive Grignard reagent apply equally well to the lithium and sodium alkyls, and with especial force to the case where the organometallic compound is prepared from a labeled halide.

Acetic Acid

Acetic Acid-1-C^{11}.[3] Carbon dioxide-C^{11} is obtained from the target chamber of a

$$CH_3MgI + C^*O_2 \rightarrow CH_3C^*OOMgI \xrightarrow{(+H^+)} CH_3C^*OOH + Mg^{++} + I^-$$

cyclotron by pumping the gas through 3 ml of a solution 2 M in sodium hydroxide and 0.67 M in sodium carbonate. The collection tube is chilled in liquid air to insure efficient entrapment of the carbon dioxide. The tube is allowed to warm up, then the solution is transferred to the reaction chamber of a Van Slyke manometric gas apparatus and is acidified with 4 ml of 5 M lactic acid. The carbon dioxide is collected over mercury in a vessel (Fig. 68) which is so designed that the gas can be delivered to a reaction vessel (Fig. 69) containing Grignard reagent. The methylmagnesium iodide is prepared previously from 10 mmoles of methyl iodide and 10 mmoles of magnesium turnings in 10 ml of dry ether. Each of the arms of the 100-ml reaction vessel carries a large stopcock, which when closed protects the Grignard reagent. To carbonate the Grignard solution, the vessel is chilled in liquid air and evacuated through one arm, which is then closed; carbon dioxide is admitted through the other arm from the collecting vessel. The reaction vessel is warmed to 0° with both stopcocks closed and is shaken for 10 minutes. It is then chilled in liquid air, 8 ml

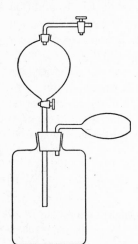

Fig. 68. Carbon dioxide collection vessel. (J. M. Buchanan, A. B. Hastings, and F. B. Nesbett, *J. Biol. Chem.*, **150**, 413 [1943].)

Fig. 69. Carbonation tube. (J. M. Buchanan, A. B. Hastings, and F. B. Nesbett, *J. Biol. Chem.*, **1 5 0**, 4 1 3 [1943].)

of 2.7 N sulfuric acid is added, and the mixture is allowed to warm up. The acetic acid is extracted with three 25-ml portions of ether, and the ether is washed with 1 ml of water, which is discarded. Then 1 ml of water containing phenol red

---

[3] J. M. Buchanan, A. B. Hastings, and F. B. Nesbett, *J. Biol. Chem.*, **150**, 413 (1943).

indicator is added, and the acid is extracted into water by making the solution alkaline with 2 M sodium hydroxide. The acetic acid is obtained as its sodium salt in a volume of 4–5 ml. The total time required is 45 minutes; of the total initial activity in the carbon dioxide, 50% can be obtained as acetic acid.

Propionic acid-1-C^{11} and *n-butyric acid*-1-C^{11} have been prepared by the same procedure from ethyl- and *n*-propylmagnesium iodide respectively. Experimental details are not given, and it may be presumed that no new problems are presented in these syntheses.

Carboxyl-labeled acetic, butyric and *caproic acids* have been prepared by this procedure by other workers, using the same type of carbonation apparatus.[4] No details are given.

Acetic Acid-1-C^{13}.[5] The apparatus shown in Fig. 70 is used to prepare and to carbonate methylmagnesium iodide. Methylmagnesium iodide is prepared by plac-

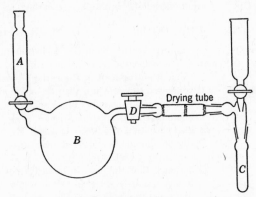

Fig. 70. Apparatus for carbonating Grignard reagent. (W. Sakami, W. E. Evans, and S. Gurin.)

ing magnesium, dry ether, and a little iodine in funnel A, attaching a West condenser to the mouth, and dropping in methyl iodide through the top. The mouth of the funnel is then stoppered.

The apparatus is evacuated, and carbon dioxide is generated in vessel C by dropping 40% perchloric acid on barium carbonate. Stopcock D is closed, and the entire apparatus is cooled in a refrigerator to $-15°$ C. The Grignard reagent is slowly admitted to B while the flask is rotated or shaken until the solution congeals. The acetic acid is worked up by distillation from silver sulfate. From 10 grams of barium carbonate can be obtained 3.67 grams of (fused) sodium acetate, a yield of 89%.

The technique just described has also been used to prepare carboxyl-labeled propionic and butyric acids by carbonation of the corresponding Grignard reagents.[6]

Acetyl phosphate.[6] Acetyl chloride is prepared in 90% yield by refluxing a mixture of labeled sodium acetate, dried by fusion, with a 100% excess of benzoyl chloride.[7]

---

[4] H. A. Barker, M. D. Kamen, and B. T. Bornstein, *Proc. Natl. Acad. Sci. U. S.*, **31**, 373 (1945).

[5] W. Sakami, W. E. Evans, and S. Gurin, *J. Am. Chem. Soc.*, **69**, 1110 (1947).

[6] W. Sakami, private communication.

[7] Procedure of H. J. Strecker.

The acetyl chloride is isolated by distillation. The acetyl chloride is converted to acetyl phosphate by treatment with silver phosphate.[8] Acetyl chloride of correct boiling point prepared from sodium acetate, benzenesulfonyl chloride, and phosphorus trichloride cannot be used.

Acetic Acid-1-C[14].[9] A solution of methylmagnesium iodide is prepared from 9.0 grams (0.37 mole) of magnesium, 25 ml (0.4 mole) of methyl iodide, and 1 liter of dry ether; the solution is poured into flask *B* of the apparatus shown in Fig. 71.

In flask *A* is placed 36.5 grams (0.185 mole) of barium carbonate; *D* receives 150 ml of 8 *N* hydrochloric acid. With *B* immersed in an ice bath, stopcocks 1, 2, and 3 are

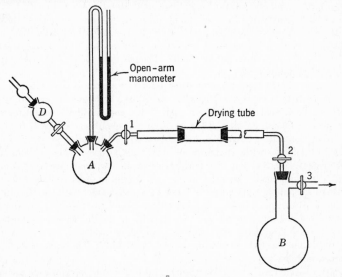

Fig. 71. Apparatus for carbonation of Grignard reagent. (L. B. Spector.)

opened and the system is evacuated to a pressure of 20 cm. At this point stopcock 1 is closed. Evacuation is continued until the ether starts to boil; then stopcocks 2 and 3 are closed and the apparatus is disconnected from the pump. Two persons are needed to complete the operation, one to shake the Grignard solution while the other controls the liberation of carbon dioxide. By cautiously adding hydrochloric acid to the barium carbonate, carbon dioxide is generated as rapidly as possible, but the pressure is kept somewhat below atmospheric. Stopcock 2 is open.

When nearly all the acid has been added, *B* is cooled to reduce the pressure in the system and stopcock 2 is closed. The stopcock of the funnel is opened to admit air, then closed, and 2 is opened. In this way, carbon dioxide remaining in *A* is swept into *B*. The process is repeated until the apparatus is full of air. Then the contents of *B* are poured over 1 kg of cracked ice, and a cooled solution of 25 ml of concentrated sulfuric acid in 200 ml of water is added to dissolve the magnesium salts. The ether is evaporated in a stream of air.

The acetic acid solution is transferred to a 2-liter vacuum-distillation apparatus and treated with 100 grams (a 33% excess) of silver sulfate, followed by a solution of

[8] F. Lipmann and L. C. Tuttle, *J. Biol. Chem.*, **153**, 571–82 (1944).
[9] L. B. Spector, Atomic Energy Commission, MDDC 532.

50 ml of concentrated sulfuric acid in 300 ml of water. The solution is distilled at 100–110 mm through a 12-inch column packed with glass helices until the residue in the flask has a pasty consistency. Water (50–100 ml) is added to the mixture, which is again concentrated; this process is repeated until all the acetic acid has been removed.

To the distillate is added three times as much sodium hydroxide (pellets) as necessary to neutralize the acetic acid, and the solution is evaporated to a thick paste at reduced pressure in a distillation apparatus. Then 15 ml (1 ml excess) of sulfuric acid dissolved in an equal volume of water is added, and a relatively concentrated solution of acetic acid is obtained by distillation at 100–130 mm.

The distillate is saturated with sodium chloride, and the acetic acid is removed by continuous extraction with alcohol-free ether for 24 hours. By distilling this solution and collecting the material boiling above 60°, concentrated acetic can be obtained in a 70–77% yield, based on barium carbonate. The purity is about 83% by weight; the remainder presumably is water.

Acetic Acid-1-C^{14}.[10]   The apparatus used for the synthesis is shown in Fig. 72. The essential features are: a manifold H, attached to a high-vacuum system and carrying outlets for attaching the reaction flask K, the carbon dioxide generator F and G, a manometer C, and an inlet B for nitrogen. The carbonation flask K is fitted with an induction stirrer (page 336) and is pear-shaped in order to permit freezing the Grignard solution without danger of cracking the flask. The carbon dioxide generator consists of an Erlenmeyer flask G for barium carbonate and a compensated funnel F for sulfuric acid. An Erlenmeyer flask is used in order to have the barium carbonate in as shallow a pile as possible, to facilitate contact with the sulfuric acid. If the charge of barium carbonate is large enough to fill the flask to more than one-fifth of its total volume, a larger flask is substituted. In this case, a round-bottom flask is used since large Erlenmeyer flasks may collapse when evacuated. A drying tube E is placed between the generator and the manifold.[11] The manometer C is the simple open mercury type.

The flask G is charged with 3.535 grams (17.9 mmoles) of barium radiocarbonate, the funnel F with 25 ml of concentrated sulfuric acid (5–8 ml of acid per gram of barium carbonate), and the carbon dioxide generator is assembled and attached to the manifold. The system is evacuated to a pressure of about 0.1 micron, stopcock A is closed, and the system is tested for leaks. Then pure nitrogen is admitted through B until atmospheric pressure is reached; excess nitrogen passes out through the manometer. The plug M is removed, and 40 ml (25.6 mmoles) of a 0.64 M solution of methylmagnesium iodide is placed in flask K by means of a pipet previously flushed with nitrogen and operated by a hypodermic syringe. The Grignard solution is diluted with 25 ml of dry ether, and plug M is quickly replaced. Stopcock B is closed, and a bath of liquid nitrogen is placed about K. Stopcock A is slightly opened for a moment to remove nitrogen and prevent an appreciable amount of it from being trapped in the solidifying solution; the stopcock is closed when the ether commences to boil. When the contents of the flask have been frozen solid, A is opened again, and the system is evacuated to a pressure of 0.1 micron. Then A is closed, and the liquid nitrogen is replaced by a bath at −20°. When the contents of the flask have come to thermal equilibrium with the bath, the stirrer is started and

---

[10] R. M. Lemmon, unpublished work.

[11] This is probably superfluous when concentrated sulfuric acid is used to generate the carbon dioxide, since yields are not detectably lowered by omitting the drying tube.

carbonation is effected by dropping sulfuric acid onto the barium carbonate. The acid is added cautiously at first, so that the initial surge of gas does not carry out particles of barium carbonate, then as rapidly as possible without allowing the pressure to exceed 50 cm. When the initial evolution has subsided, flask *G* is warmed with a small flame to dissolve most of the barium sulfate and thereby facilitate reaction of remaining carbonate; in addition, the heating serves to expel the last traces of gas from the acid. The manometer reading becomes constant in 5 to 15 minutes.

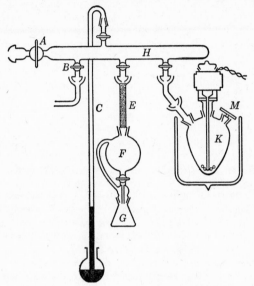

FIG. 72.   Grignard carbonation apparatus.

Since the presence of ether vapor interferes with the diffusion of carbon dioxide when the pressure of the carbon dioxide has fallen to a value near that of the ether, the flask *K* is again immersed in liquid nitrogen to draw any remaining carbon dioxide into *K*, the stopcock at *H* is closed, the flask is again warmed to −20°, and stirring is continued for 10 minutes. Nitrogen is then admitted to the system, and 10 ml of sulfuric acid is added to hydrolyze the reaction product. A 30% excess of silver sulfate is added to *K*, which is still immersed in the cooling bath, and the mixture is stirred 5 minutes. The flask *K* is then removed from the manifold and fitted with a fractionating head, and the ether is removed by distillation.

The acetic acid is obtained by steam distillation, and the distillate is neutralized with standardized sodium hydroxide. The yield, determined from the amount of alkali required, is 89–94%. After filtration to remove a small amount of sediment which may be present, evaporation of the solution gives pure sodium acetate, whose weight agrees closely with that calculated from the titration value.

For the preparation of anhydrous acetic acid from sodium acetate see page 195.

By the procedure just described for acetic acid, benzoic, *p*-anisic, phenylacetic, 1-naphthoic, 2-naphthoic, hendecanoic, and palmitic acids have been prepared. Procedural notes are given below.

Benzoic Acid-Carboxyl-C^{14} [12]

$$C_6H_5MgBr + C^*O_2 \rightarrow C_6H_5C^*OOMgBr \xrightarrow{(+H^+)}$$
$$C_6H_5C^*OOH + Mg^{++} + Br^-$$
$$85\%$$

Thirty-one millimoles of an approximately 0.8 M solution of phenylmagnesium bromide in ether is carbonated at $-20°$ C with carbon dioxide generated from 5.885 grams (29 mmoles) of barium radiocarbonate. The reaction mixture is acidified, and the organic material is extracted with ether. Benzoic acid is extracted from the ether with sodium hydroxide, then precipitated with a slight excess of 6 M hydrochloric acid. Yield: 3.105 grams, 85.4% based on barium carbonate; m.p., 122–123° cor.

p-Anisic Acid-Carboxyl-C^{14} [13]

$$CH_3O\langle\rangle MgBr + C^*O_2 \rightarrow CH_3O\langle\rangle C^*OOMgBr \xrightarrow{(+H^+)}$$
$$CH_3O\langle\rangle C^*OOH + Mg^{++} + Br^-$$
$$84\%$$

A solution of p-methoxyphenylmagnesium bromide is prepared under nitrogen from 9.3 grams (50 mmoles) of p-bromoanisole and 1.32 grams (55 mmoles) of magnesium turnings. The reaction is started under ether, then the bulk of the bromide is run into the refluxed solution over a period of 2 hours as a solution in 40 ml of a 50% mixture of dry ether and dry benzene. The reaction mixture is refluxed 6 hours longer to complete the reaction, which is sluggish. Then 100 ml more of a 50% ether-benzene mixture is added. This is necessary to dissolve the sparingly soluble Grignard reagent. The concentration of the solution is found to be 0.276 M.

p-Anisic acid is prepared by carbonating 7.2 mmoles of the Grignard solution at $-25°$ with carbon dioxide generated from 1.02 grams (5.18 mmoles) of barium radiocarbonate. The product is isolated by extraction with sodium hydroxide and acidification of the alkaline solution. The reported yield of purified acid is 0.64 gram; 84% based on barium carbonate.

Phenylacetic Acid-Carboxyl-C^{14} [14]

$$C_6H_5CH_2MgCl + C^*O_2 \rightarrow C_6H_5CH_2C^*OOMgCl \xrightarrow{(+H^+)}$$
$$C_6H_5CH_2C^*OOH + Mg^{++} + Cl^-$$
$$89\%$$

A solution of benzylmagnesium chloride is prepared by standard technique from 2.6 grams (0.11 mole) of magnesium and 12.7 grams (0.10 mole) of benzyl chloride in 100 ml of dry ether. The concentration of the final solution is found to be 0.80 M.

Carbonation of 43.2 mmoles of the Grignard solution is effected at $-20°$ with carbon dioxide generated from 8.00 grams (40.6 mmoles) of barium radiocarbonate. The phenylacetic acid is isolated by extraction with alkali, followed by acidification of the alkaline solution. The crude acid is purified by crystallization from 170 ml of petroleum ether (boiling range, 30–60°). The reported yield of pure acid is 4.9 grams, 88% based on barium carbonate; m.p., 75–76.5° C.

[12] W. G. Dauben, J. C. Reid, and P. E. Yankwich, *Anal. Chem.*, **19**, 828 (1947)
[13] J. C. Reid and H. B. Jones, *J. Biol. Chem.*, **174**, 427 (1948).
[14] W. G. Dauben, J. C. Reid, and P. E. Yankwich, unpublished work.

Phenylacetamide-1-C^{14}.[15] In a 5-ml modified Claisen flask are placed 0.52 gram

$$2C_6H_5CH_2C^*OOH + (NH_4)_2CO_3 \xrightarrow[\substack{\Delta \\ 48\%}]{CH_3COOH}$$

$$2C_6H_5CH_2C^*ONH_2 + CO_2 + 3H_2O$$

of carboxyl-labeled phenylacetic acid, 0.78 ml of glacial acetic acid, and 0.47 gram of ammonium carbonate. The flask has a 5-cm indented section in the side neck to serve as a rectifying column. The upper part of the apparatus is wrapped in asbestos. The mixture is heated in an oil bath, which is brought to 175° over a period of ¾ hour, then gradually raised to 265° during 2 hours. At this point the head temperature begins to rise rapidly. The flask is allowed to cool somewhat, and 1 ml of boiling water is added to dissolve the contents. The solution is poured into 2 ml of 1 M sodium hydroxide; the flask is boiled out with an additional 0.5 ml of water. The aqueous mixture is cooled and filtered. The amide on the filter is washed with two 2-ml portions of water, followed by two of ether, which removes a brown coloration usually present. Yield, 0.25 gram; 48% based on phenylacetic acid; m.p., 155–58°.

1-Naphthoic Acid-Carboxyl-C^{14} [16]

A solution of 1-naphthylmagnesium bromide is prepared under nitrogen from 0.75 gram (31 mmoles) of magnesium and 6.2 grams (30 mmoles) of 1-bromonaphthalene dissolved in a mixture of 50 ml of anhydrous ether and 10 ml of dry benzene. The concentration of the resulting solution is about 0.5 M.

Carbonation of 21 mmoles of the Grignard solution is carried out with carbon dioxide generated from 3.64 grams (18.4 mmoles) of radioactive barium carbonate, at a temperature of 0° C. The crude acid is isolated in the usual way and purified by crystallization from 25 ml of dry toluene to which has been added a little Norite. The reported yield is 2.60 grams (82.4% based on barium carbonate); m.p., 162.5–163.5°.

2-Naphthoic Acid-Carboxyl-C^{14} [17]

15 W. G. Dauben, J. C. Reid, and P. E. Yankwich, unpublished experiments.

16 W. G. Dauben, *J. Org. Chem.*, **13**, 313 (1948).

17 C. Heidelberger, P. Brewer, and W. G. Dauben, *J. Am. Chem. Soc.*, **69**, 1389–1391 (1947).

A solution of 2-naphthylmagnesium bromide is prepared under nitrogen from 0.48 gram (20 mmoles) of magnesium turnings and 4.14 grams (20 mmoles) of 2-bromonaphthalene dissolved in a mixture of 16 ml of dry ether and 4 ml of dry benzene. After the reaction starts, the mixture is refluxed for 1 hour. The concentration of the dark solution which is obtained is about 1.2 M.

A volume of solution containing 9.66 mmoles of naphthylmagnesium bromide is taken for carbonation. In order to prevent the Grignard compound from crystallizing at low temperature, the solution is diluted with 10 ml of a 2:1 mixture of anhydrous ether and benzene. The solution is carbonated at $-20°$ with carbon dioxide generated from 1.586 grams (8.05 mmoles) of radioactive barium carbonate. By alkali extraction followed by acidification, there is obtained 1.00 gram (73% based on barium carbonate) of 2-naphthoic acid melting at 181–183.5° cor.

n-Hendecanoic Acid-1-C^{14} [18]

$$n\text{-}C_{10}H_{21}MgBr + C^*O_2 \rightarrow n\text{-}C_{10}H_{21}C^*OOMgBr \xrightarrow{(+H^+)}$$
$$n\text{-}C_{10}H_{21}C^*OOH + Mg^{++} + Br^-$$

A solution of n-decylmagnesium bromide is prepared from 1.8 grams (74 mmoles) of magnesium and 15 grams (68 mmoles) of n-decyl bromide, dissolved in 80 ml of dry ether. The concentration of the solution is about 0.75 M.

A volume of Grignard solution containing 11.7 mmoles of decylmagnesium bromide is carbonated with carbon dioxide generated from 1.86 grams (9.42 mmoles) of barium radiocarbonate. The acid is isolated by extraction with sodium hydroxide, followed by acidification of the alkaline solution.

n-Hendecanoic Acid-1-C^{14} Methyl Ester.[18] An ether solution of diazomethane is

$$n\text{-}C_{10}H_{21}C^*OOH + CH_2N_2 \rightarrow n\text{-}C_{10}H_{21}C^*OOCH_3 + N_2$$
$$83\%$$

used to esterify the n-hendecanoic acid whose synthesis is described in the foregoing section. The ether is evaporated, and the ester is distilled in a small sublimation apparatus. The pressure at which the distillation is carried out is 0.3 mm; the block temperature is 54–58° C. The yield is 1.56 grams; 82.9% based on the barium carbonate used in the preparation of the hendecanoic acid.

Palmitic Acid (Hexadecanoic Acid-1-C^{14}) and Methyl Ester [18]

$$n\text{-}C_{15}H_{31}MgBr + C^*O_2 \rightarrow n\text{-}C_{15}H_{31}C^*OOMgBr \xrightarrow{(+H^+)}$$
$$n\text{-}C_{15}H_{31}C^*OOH + Mg^{++} + Br^-$$
$$n\text{-}C_{15}H_{31}C^*OOH + CH_3OH \xrightarrow{H^+} n\text{-}C_{15}H_{31}C^*OOCH_3$$
$$80\%$$

A solution of n-pentadecylmagnesium bromide is prepared under nitrogen from 1.6 grams (66 mmoles) of magnesium and 15.9 grams (54.7 mmoles) of n-pentadecyl bromide in 110 ml of anhydrous ether. The concentration of the solution is found to be 0.44 M.

A volume of 110 ml (48.4 mmoles) of Grignard solution is carbonated with carbon dioxide generated from 9.1 grams (46 mmoles) of radioactive barium carbonate. The acid is isolated in the usual way by extraction with sodium hydroxide.

The purification procedure found to be most suitable is distillation of the methyl ester. The ester is prepared by refluxing the crude acid for 1 hour with 48.6 ml of

18 W. G. Dauben, *J. Am. Chem. Soc.*, **70**, 1376 (1948).

methanol and 5 ml of sulfuric acid. The reaction mixture is diluted with 200 ml of water, and the ester is extracted with n-hexane. The hexane solution is washed with water, dried over magnesium sulfate, and concentrated under vacuum. Fractional distillation of the residue yields 10.0 grams (80.4% based on barium carbonate) of methyl hexadecanoate.

Free hexadecanoic acid is prepared from its methyl ester by overnight hydrolysis on a steam bath of a solution of 10.0 grams (37 mmoles) of methyl hexadecanoate, 2.3 grams of potassium hydroxide, 35 ml of methanol, and 2 ml of water. The major portion of the alcohol is removed by distillation, then the residue is acidified with hydrochloric acid and heated on a steam bath for 1 hour. The mixture is diluted with ether, then washed with water, and dried over magnesium sulfate. The crude acid, obtained by evaporating the ether, is recrystallized from 40 ml of 10% aqueous acetone. The reported yield of pure acid is 8.55 grams (90.1%). Based on barium carbonate this is a 72.4% overall yield of purified hexadecanoic acid.

Glyceryltripalmitate-1-C^{14} (Tripalmitin).[18] Hexadecanoyl chloride is prepared by

$$C_{15}H_{31}C^*OOH \xrightarrow{\text{SOCl}_2} C_{15}H_{31}C^*OCl$$

$$3C_{15}H_{31}C^*OCl + HOCH_2CH(OH)CH_2OH \longrightarrow \underset{76\%}{Tripalmitin \,*}$$

refluxing 8.3 grams (32.4 mmoles) of carboxyl-labeled hexadecanoic acid with 10 ml of purified thionyl chloride. The thionyl chloride is then removed at reduced pressure.

To the residue is added 25 ml of anhydrous benzene, which is distilled to carry off residual thionyl chloride. This operation is carried out three times. The acid chloride is then dissolved in 25 ml of dry chloroform. This solution is added slowly to a stirred, cooled solution of 0.975 gram (0.106 mole) of redistilled glycerin, 8 ml of dry pyridine, and 25 ml of dry chloroform. The solution is allowed to stand 3 days at room temperature; then it is refluxed for 2 hours. The chloroform is evaporated and the residue treated with 100 ml of 0.5 N sulfuric acid. The resulting syrup is dissolved in 500 ml of ether, and the solution is washed successively with 100 ml of 0.5 N sulfuric acid and 200 ml of 5% sodium carbonate. Emulsions which form during the washing are broken by adding sodium chloride. The ether solution is dried over magnesium sulfate, then evaporated under reduced pressure. After purification by two crystallizations from acetone, using Norite, a residue weighing 6.15 grams is obtained; this is a yield of 75.5% based on palmitic acid and 54.7% based on barium carbonate.

Veratric Acid (3,4-Dimethoxybenzoic Acid-Carboxyl-C^{14}) [19]

[19] J. C. Reid, unpublished work.

Veratric acid is prepared by carbonating 4-veratryllithium by a procedure essentially the same as that described for the last eight acids, with the exception of a few changes made necessary by the use of a lithium alkyl instead of the magnesium. The lithium derivative is used because of the difficulty of preparing veratrylmagnesium bromide.

A solution of n-butyllithium is prepared by refluxing overnight, in an atmosphere of purified nitrogen, a mixture of 2.5 grams of lithium, cut into small pieces, and 10 grams of n-butyl chloride, dissolved in 20 ml of pentane. Then 80 ml of pentane is added, and the solution is filtered anaerobically. The clear, colorless filtrate is found to be 0.632 M in butyllithium by adding excess standardized acid to an aliquot and titrating the excess acid with standardized base.

The vacuum system is evacuated and filled with nitrogen as usual. Then 20.0 ml (12.6 mmoles) of butyllithium solution is pipetted into the carbonation flask, and the pentane is distilled in vacuum until about 1 ml remains. The carbonation flask is chilled, and about 20 ml of dry ether is distilled in from a flask attached to the manifold. The stirrer is run for a moment to mix the butyllithium and ether, then stopped. The solution is frozen with liquid nitrogen, and 30 ml more ether is distilled in. This too is frozen. Purified nitrogen is admitted to the system, and 4.08 grams [20] (18.8 mmoles) of 4-bromoveratrole, dissolved in a little ether, is added. When this has frozen, the system is evacuated and the manifold closed off from the pump.

The liquid nitrogen is replaced by isopropanol chilled to −60°, and as soon as the contents of the carbonation flask have become sufficiently fluid the stirrer is started. A precipitation of pure white veratryllithium commences in a few minutes, and stirring is continued for 15 minutes to permit the reaction to become complete. Carbonation is effected at −60° as rapidly as possible (7 minutes) with carbon dioxide from 1.25 grams (6.35 mmoles) of radioactive barium carbonate. Nitrogen is admitted to the system, and 10 ml of concentrated hydrochloric acid is added to the reaction mixture. The appearance of a deep red color is reported.[21] The cooling bath is removed, and the contents of the flask are stirred as they warm up. The acid is extracted from the reaction mixture with ether, then taken into sodium hydroxide. The water solution is warmed to remove ether, treated with charcoal, filtered, and acidified. The reported yield of veratric acid is 1.03 grams (89.6% of theory based on barium carbonate); m.p., 176–178 uncor.; neutralization equivalent 184(calculated, 182). No halide can be detected in the product by sodium fusion.

p-Aminobenzoic Acid-Carboxyl-C[14] [22]

$$\text{Br-}C_6H_4\text{-}NH_2 + n\text{-}C_4H_9Li \rightarrow \text{Li-}C_6H_4\text{-}NLi_2 + n\text{-}C_4H_9Br + 2C_4H_{10}$$

[20] By using excess bromoveratrole, all the butyllithium is converted to veratryllithium and no butyric acid is formed in the carbonation.

[21] The nature of the substance responsible was not investigated. The color disappears during the ether extraction.

[22] A. Murray, III, W. W. Foreman, and W. Langham, *J. Am. Chem. Soc.*, **70**, 1037 (1948).

$$\text{Li} \quad + C^*O_2 \rightarrow \quad \text{C*OOLi} \quad \xrightarrow{\text{(+H}^+)} \quad \text{C*OOH} \quad + Li^+$$

with benzene rings:

Li / NLi$_2$ + C*O$_2$ → C*OOLi / N? $\xrightarrow{\text{(+H}^+\text{)}}$ C*OOH / NH$_2$ (48%) + Li$^+$

The apparatus used to carry out the synthesis is shown in Fig. 73. A solution of
n-butyllithium is prepared under nitrogen in L, and its concentration is determined
by differential titration.[23]   Meanwhile, carbon dioxide is generated in A, purified by

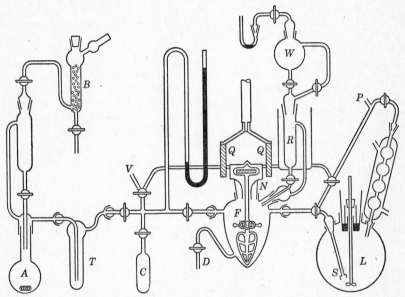

Fig. 73.   Carbonation apparatus for lithium alkyls.   (A. Murray, W. W. Foreman,
and W. Langham.)

passage through trap T, which is cooled to $-80°$, and stored in C.   The required
volume of butyllithium is forced under nitrogen pressure into the calibrated reaction
vessel F through the glass wool filter S.   The addition tube R, which is jacketed so
that its contents may be cooled with Dry Ice, contains an ether solution of the halide
to be used.   After the halide has been added to F, the lithium alkyl which forms is
washed with anhydrous ether stored over sodium wire in the reservoir W; the washings are removed under nitrogen through the siphon D to an evacuated [24] flask
immersed in a freezing mixture.   Agitation is provided by the sealed magnetic stirrer N, which is actuated by the two motor-driven bar magnets Q.   Carbon dioxide
which may remain unabsorbed, or which may be liberated when the reaction mixture
is acidified, is recovered by freezing the gas into C.   It is later swept in a current of

23 H. Gilman and A. H. Haubein, *J. Am. Chem. Soc.*, 66, 1515 (1944).
24 The dry lithium alkyl is inflammable in contact with air.

nitrogen into the bead tower B, which contains alkali. The reaction system is connected to a vacuum pump at V; provision is made for introducing purified nitrogen at P.

To a stirred solution of 23.8 mmoles of n-butyllithium in 29 ml of ether is added, over a 5-minute period, 4.74 mmoles of vacuum-dried p-bromoaniline dissolved in 8 ml of ether. The solution is cooled during the addition, and stirring is continued at room temperature for 1.5 hours after the beginning of the formation of a bright yellow precipitate of the organolithium compound. It is remarked that this precipitate appears in 20 to 90 minutes, depending on the age of the n-butyllithium preparation. Varying the reaction time between 1 and 3 hours does not change the yield. The fine precipitate, which settles rapidly, is washed with anhydrous ether until the amount of unreacted butyllithium remaining is reduced to a calculated value of 0.1%.

The lithium alkyl is then suspended in ether, the system is evacuated, and carbonation is effected at $-80°$ with 1.029 mmoles of radioactive carbon dioxide, of which 32.5% is recovered. The reaction mixture is acidified with 8 ml of 6 M hydrochloric acid and transferred to a modified Soxhlet extractor. Continuous ether extraction is carried out for 4 to 8 hours, and the ether is discarded. The water solution is made alkaline with potassium hydroxide, and the ether extraction is repeated. The water solution is then adjusted to pH 3, and p-aminobenzoic acid is extracted with ether (8 to 16 hours).[25] By evaporating the ether, crude p-aminobenzoic acid equivalent to 32.8% of the barium carbonate used is obtained; the yield is 48.2% based on carbon dioxide unrecovered. Melting point: 84–85° C.

Nicotinic Acid-Carboxyl-C^{14} [22]

$$\text{(Br-pyridine)} + n\text{-C}_4\text{H}_9\text{Li} \rightarrow \text{(Li-pyridine)} + \text{C}_4\text{H}_9\text{Br}$$

$$\text{(Li-pyridine)} + \text{C*O}_2 \rightarrow \text{(C*OOLi-pyridine)} \xrightarrow{(+\text{H}^+)} \text{(C*OOH-pyridine)} + \text{Li}^+$$

27%

The synthesis is carried out with the apparatus used for p-aminobenzoic acid. To 1.63 mmoles of n-butyllithium in 2.76 ml of ether cooled to $-35°$ is added, over a 4-minute period, 2.44 mmoles of redistilled 3-bromopyridine in 5 ml of ether, also cooled to $-35°$. One minute later the solution is carbonated at $-80°$ with 0.81 mmole of carbon dioxide, of which 11.4% can be recovered. The reaction mixture is quickly acidified with 3 ml of 2.5 N nitric acid. The ether layer is separated and discarded; the water solution is placed in a modified Soxhlet extractor, and non-basic impurities are extracted with ether for 3 to 4 hours. The aqueous solution is made alkaline, and non-acid impurities are removed by further extraction for 4 to 6 hours. The aqueous solution is then adjusted to pH 3, and nicotinic acid is extracted with fresh ether; the extraction requires 24 to 48 hours. By evaporating the ether, crude acid is obtained equivalent to 62.4% of the barium carbonate used, or 70.3% based

---

[25] Ether extraction is found to be superior to the formation of the copper or silver salt for isolating small amounts of the acid.

on the carbon dioxide unrecovered. Vacuum sublimation followed by crystallization from methanol gives 30 mg of colorless powder, a yield of 27.4% based on carbon dioxide unrecovered; m.p., 225–28°.

Nicotinic acid-carboxyl-C^{13} has also been prepared, by a procedure which differs from that described in that the acid is purified through the silver salt. The reported yield of pure material is 55% based on barium carbonate; m.p., 227–229°.

9-Fluorenecarboxylic Acid-Carboxyl-C^{14} [26]

The fluorene to be used is given a preliminary purification by dissolving 20 grams of the Eastman practical grade material in 100 ml of benzene and passing the solution through a 1.35 by 12 cm column of 80–200 mesh alumina. The column is washed with benzene until a drop of the effluent liquid taken to dryness gives no residue. The solvent is evaporated in an air stream until the point of incipient crystallization is reached; then the solution is warmed and diluted with 150 ml of methanol. Upon cooling and standing 24 hours, the solution deposits 6.4 grams of purified fluorene; m.p., 114–114.5°.

Triphenylmethylsodium is prepared by a method already in the literature,[27] but variation in the results of experiments leads the authors to describe their preparation in detail. It is particularly stressed that, to obtain satisfactory results, a triphenylmethylsodium solution freshly prepared and rigidly protected from oxygen and moisture must be used for the carbonation reaction.

The reaction vessel used is a 270 by 40 mm glass tube with a side arm, terminating in a 19/38 inner ground joint, sealed into it at the middle. The apparatus is filled with dry nitrogen, and 2.0 grams of sodium sand [28] is washed in through the side arm with 40 ml of dry benzene. Two 1.7 by 15 cm Pyrex test tubes are broken into coarse pieces, and these are added, followed by 5 grams of triphenylchloromethane dissolved in 40 ml of dry ether. The air introduced during these operations is swept out of the vessel with nitrogen, and a cap, consisting of a 19/38 outer joint sealed to a stopcock, is attached to the mouth of the side arm.

The mixture is shaken vigorously until the color of the solution becomes red (7–12 minutes). At this point, the solution becomes warm and is cooled under a tap to prevent the internal pressure from rising. The vessel is shaken for 2 hours to complete the reaction.

26 C. J. Collins, *J. Am. Chem. Soc.*, **70**, 2418 (1948).

27 W. E. Bachman and F. Y. Wiselogle, *J. Am. Chem. Soc.*, **58**, 1943 (1936).

28 Prepared by melting sodium under xylene in an atmosphere of nitrogen and stirring violently while the solution is cooled.

The carbonation is carried out in the apparatus shown in Fig. 74. In vessel II is placed 100 mg (0.508 mmole) of radioactive barium carbonate. Air is swept out of the apparatus with dry nitrogen, which is led out through stopcocks 3 and 4 and the barium hydroxide bubbler. Decomposition of the barium carbonate is effected by adding 5–8 ml of 5 M perchloric acid through stopcock 1. Next, nitrogen is passed through the system (stopcock 1) at a rate of 60–100 bubbles per minute for 15 minutes. Trap A is cooled in a bath at $-50°$ to remove water; cooling to a lower temperature causes entrainment of carbon dioxide. Carbon dioxide is collected in trap B, which is cooled in liquid nitrogen. After 15 minutes, the decomposition mixture is heated gently to remove the last of the carbon dioxide.

In flask I is placed 3.5 ml. (0.79 mmole based on a theoretical yield in the preparation) of triphenylmethyl sodium and 150 mg (0.905 mmole) of purified fluorene, and

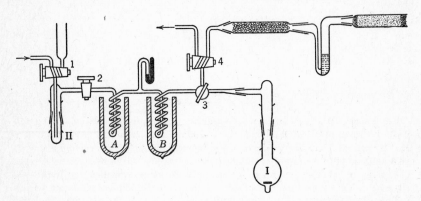

Fig. 74.   Apparatus for carbonation of sodium alkyls.   (C. J. Collins and W. G. Brown.)

the flask is connected to the line. The entire operation is carried out under dry nitrogen. After stirring for 3 minutes, the color of the mixture is observed to change from red to light yellow, and at this point the mixture is frozen in liquid nitrogen. Stopcock 2 is closed, and traps A and B and flask I are evacuated through stopcocks 3 and 4, until the manometer shows a pressure less than 1 mm. The system A, B, and I is isolated from the rest of the line (stopcocks 2 and 3), and the carbon dioxide is distilled from B into I. The vessel I is isolated (stopcock 3) and the liquid nitrogen removed. Upon warming until the magnetic bar will just turn in the yellow slush, reaction is complete, as indicated by the manometer reading when the mixture is frozen at $-50°$.

The vacuum is broken, and 10 ml of water is added to the flask. The two layers are separated, the organic layer is washed twice with 5-ml portions of water, and the combined water layers are washed twice with 3-ml portions of ether. To the water solution is added 10 ml of 1 M hydrochloric acid, and the fluorenecarboxylic acid is extracted with four 4-ml portions of ether. The ether solution is washed once with 4 ml of water and then treated with three 4-ml portions of saturated sodium bicarbonate solution. The combined bicarbonate solutions are washed once with 3 ml of ether, then 10 ml of 6 M hydrochloric acid is added, and the product is again extracted with ether. By evaporation of the solvent there is obtained 72–75 mg

(68–71% based on barium carbonate) of 9-fluorenecarboxylic acid; m.p. 222–26° uncor.

9-Fluorenecarboxylic Acid-Carboxyl-C^{14} Methyl Ester.[26] To 115.5 mg of 9-fluorenecarboxylic acid-carboxyl-C^{14}, prepared as described above, is added a chilled mixture of 5.0 ml of methanol and 0.1 ml of acetyl chloride. After standing 1 hour at room temperature, the solvent is removed at reduced pressure, leaving 120 mg (98%) of methyl 9-fluorenecarboxylate; m.p. 63.0–63.5° uncor.

Isovaleric Acid-1-C^{14} [29]

$$i\text{-C}_4\text{H}_9\text{MgBr} + \text{C*O}_2 \rightarrow i\text{-C}_4\text{H}_9\text{C*OOMgBr} \xrightarrow{(+\text{H}^+)}$$
$$i\text{-C}_4\text{H}_9\text{C*OOH} + \text{Mg}^{++} + \text{Br}^-$$
$$84\%$$

The apparatus used is shown in Fig. 75.

In the Erlenmeyer flask is placed 6 ml (6 mmoles) of a 1 M solution of i-butylmagnesium bromide in ether, followed by 10 ml of dry ether to dilute the solution. The air is pumped out of the flask through stopcock B, which is then closed. In the gen-

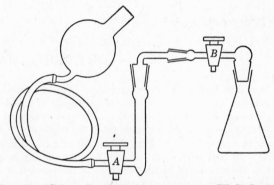

FIG. 75. Grignard carbonation apparatus. (W. B. Leslie.)

erator tube are placed 97.7 mg (0.922 mmole) of sodium carbonate and 15.5 mg (0.078 mmole) of radioactive barium carbonate. The generator is attached to the flask with stopcock A closed, and stopcock B is opened. The flask is chilled in a Dry Ice-acetone bath, and carbon dioxide is generated by cautiously opening A to admit 6 N hydrochloric acid from the reservoir. The flask is shaken well and allowed to stand 15 minutes at room temperature. At the end of the period, the flask is opened, water and very dilute sulfuric acid are added, and the mixture is slowly distilled. The reported yield, determined by titration with sodium hydroxide, is 83.6% based on carbonate used.

Octanoic Acid-1-C^{13} [30]

$$n\text{-C}_7\text{H}_{15}\text{MgBr} + \text{C*O}_2 \rightarrow n\text{-C}_7\text{H}_{15}\text{C*OOMgBr} \xrightarrow{(+\text{H}^+)}$$
$$n\text{-C}_7\text{H}_{15}\text{C*OOH} + \text{Mg}^{++} + \text{Br}^-$$
$$80\%$$

[29] W. B. Leslie, Atomic Energy Commission, MDDC 674.
[30] S. Weinhouse, G. Medes, and N. F. Floyd, *J. Biol. Chem.*, **155**, 143 (1944).

Carbon dioxide is prepared by the oxidation of 0.49 gram (10 mmoles) of sodium cyanide-C^{13} with aqueous potassium permanganate. The carbon dioxide is released by sulfuric acid into a high-vacuum system where it is condensed in a trap cooled in liquid nitrogen. It is then purified by warming the trap to $-80°$ and subliming the carbon dioxide into another trap cooled in liquid nitrogen; this operation is repeated. The carbon dioxide is condensed into a highly evacuated flask, containing an excess of n-heptylmagnesium bromide in ethereal solution, by cooling the flask with liquid nitrogen.

The flask is closed off from the vacuum system, the liquid nitrogen bath is removed, and the apparatus is allowed to stand several hours, to allow the carbonation to occur.

The mixture is then acidified with dilute sulfuric acid, and the octanoic acid is distilled with steam. The acid is extracted from the distillate with ether, then from the ether with dilute sodium hydroxide. Acidification of the sodium octanoate solution gives the free acid, which is once more extracted with ether. By evaporation of the ether a colorless oil weighing 1.175 grams is obtained; this is a yield of 81% based on cyanide. The Duclaux constants are found to reveal no detectable volatile acid other than n-octanoic. The neutralization equivalent is found to be 143.0; calculated, 144.2.

Lauric Acid (Dodecanoic Acid-1-C^{14}) [31]

$$n\text{-}C_{11}H_{23}MgBr + C^*O_2 \rightarrow n\text{-}C_{11}H_{23}C^*OOMgBr \xrightarrow{(+H^+)}$$
$$n\text{-}C_{11}H_{23}C^*OOH + Mg^{++} + Br^-$$
$$95\%$$

An undecylmagnesium bromide solution is prepared from 14.1 grams (60 mmoles) of undecyl bromide and 1.5 grams (62.5 mmoles) of magnesium in 125 ml of anhydrous ether. Radioactive carbon dioxide is prepared by adding concentrated sulfuric acid to 0.5 gram of barium carbonate containing 0.315 millicurie of C^{14}. The gas is carried by means of a stream of nitrogen (25 cc/min) into the Grignard solution, which is cooled to $-40°$ and well stirred. After 40 minutes, the flow rate of the nitrogen is increased to 100 cc/min for 10 minutes, and the carbonation of the Grignard reagent is completed by passing ordinary carbon dioxide through the solution at a rate of 50–100 cc/min while the solution is allowed to warm up to 25°.

The reaction product is hydrolyzed with dilute hydrochloric acid, and the ether solution is washed free of hydrochloric acid with water. Evaporation of the ether leaves a mixture of lauric acid and impurities, which include undecane and docosane. The hydrocarbons are extracted from a dilute alcohol solution of potassium laurate with petroleum ether (b.p., 60–70°). Concentration of the potassium laurate solution to remove petroleum ether and alcohol, followed by acidification and filtration, yields free lauric acid. To purify the acid further, it is washed with water and crystallized from acetonitrile at $-20°$. The crystallized acid weighs 6.80 grams; f.p., 43.52°. Evaporation of the filtrate yields 0.7 gram of residual acid. The active acid in this residue can be recovered in a pure condition by adding 3.0 grams of inert lauric acid and crystallizing the mixture from acetonitrile at $-20°$; the yield is 3.30 grams.

The workers choose to dilute a portion of the acid further by the addition of 3.37 grams of the combined crop to 1.63 grams of inert lauric acid, followed by crystallization from acetonitrile. The crystallized acid weighs 4.7 grams. A total activity of 0.10 millicurie is found in this material; on the basis of this figure, the yield of lauric acid can be calculated to be 95% based on barium carbonate.

[31] H. J. Harwood and A. W. Ralston, *J. Org. Chem.*, **12**, 740 (1947).

Lauronitrile-1-C^{14} [31]

$$C_{11}H_{23}C^*OOH + NH_3 \xrightarrow[97\%]{Al_2O_3} C_{11}H_{23}C^*N + 2H_2O$$

Lauric acid is vaporized by dropping it into an empty flask heated to 320–340° C, and the vapor is swept in a current of ammonia, flowing at a rate of 20 cc/min, through a chamber containing alumina heated to 390°. The nitrile formed is collected in petroleum ether. The catalyst chamber is a tube 22 by 1.6 cm; a 7.25-mm thermocouple well is provided. The chamber holds about 10 grams of alumina. Over a period of 130 minutes, a 6.73-gram portion of radioactive lauric acid is passed through the apparatus and followed by a 3.23-gram portion of inactive acid. The current of ammonia is then maintained 60 minutes longer. The petroleum ether solution is washed with water, dried with potassium carbonate, and evaporated. The residue of crude lauronitrile weighs 8.82 grams; yield, 97.4% based on lauric acid.

Oxalic Acid-C^{11} [32]

$$C^*O_2 + K \xrightarrow[50\%]{\Delta} KOOC^*C^*OOK\ (+\ K_2C^*O_3)$$

Carbon dioxide is converted to potassium oxalate by passing it into an evacuated flask containing molten potassium mixed with sand. The total time from the beginning of filling the flask is less than 25 minutes. Potassium carbonate is obtained as a side product. A solution of potassium oxalate is prepared from the solid reaction product by cautiously adding water. The purity of the preparation is improved by acidification to remove carbonate, followed by treatment with charcoal. The mixture is filtered, and the filtrate is neutralized.

For a synthesis of oxalic acid from pyruvic acid, see page 228.

Oxalic acid has also been prepared by the action of alkaline permanganate on carboxyl-labeled propionic acid (page 249). This was done as a degradative procedure.

Succinic Acid-1,4-C^{11} [33]

$$KC^*N + ClCH_2CH_2Cl \xrightarrow[50\%]{} NC^*CH_2CH_2C^*N$$

$$NC^*CH_2CH_2C^*N + H_2O \xrightarrow[100\%]{H^+} HOOC^*CH_2CH_2C^*OOH + NH_4^+$$

A solution of potassium cyanide is prepared by the method described on page 160. A volume of this solution containing approximately 0.02 mmole of potassium cyanide is heated in a sealed tube for 15 minutes at 150° with an unspecified excess of ethylene dichloride. The nitrile is then hydrolyzed in essentially quantitative yield by refluxing it for 10 minutes at 100° with 12 N hydrochloric acid.

Malonic Acid-1-C^{14} [34]

Malonic acid labeled in one carboxyl group with carbon 14 has been prepared by the following scheme:

[32] F. A. Long, *J. Am. Chem. Soc.*, **61**, 570 (1939).

[33] M. B. Allen and S. Ruben, *J. Am. Chem. Soc.*, **64**, 949 (1942).

[34] P. E. Yankwich, unpublished experiments.

$$ClCH_2CO_2H \xrightarrow{Na_2CO_3} ClCH_2CO_2Na \xrightarrow{NaC*N} C*NCH_2CO_2Na \xrightarrow[H_2O]{NaOH}$$

$$NaC*O_2CH_2CO_2Na \xrightarrow{CaCl_2} \overset{C*O_2}{\underset{CO_2}{\diagup CH_2 \diagdown Ca}} \xrightarrow{HCl} HOOC*CH_2COOH$$

The procedure is essentially that which has been described elsewhere.[35]

Ten grams of chloroacetic acid is dissolved in 15 ml of water in a 100-ml round-bottomed flask. The solution is warmed to 50°, neutralized with sodium carbonate (6 grams), and cooled to room temperature. To the slightly alkaline distillate from a cyanide preparation (see page 161) is added enough inactive sodium cyanide to make a total of 6 grams of this salt; the final volume of cyanide solution should be about 15 ml. The cyanide and chloroacetate solutions are mixed rapidly and heated on the steam bath for 40 minutes.

The solution is cooled, and to it is added slowly 5 grams of solid sodium hydroxide; when all the solid is dissolved the flask is warmed slowly on the steam bath and so heated for 1½ hours. The last traces of ammonia are removed by bubbling steam through the hot solution for 10 minutes. A solution of 8 grams of anhydrous calcium chloride in 30 ml of water is warmed to 50° and added slowly to the hot sodium malonate solution. The precipitate of calcium malonate becomes crystalline on standing 15–20 hours. The calcium malonate is filtered and washed with several 10-ml portions of ice-cold water, and sucked dry.

The dried calcium malonate is placed in a 200-ml beaker, surrounded by an ice bath, with 15–20 ml of reagent-grade ether. The two are mixed to a paste which is treated with 1 ml of 12 N hydrochloric acid for each gram of dry salt; the acid is added dropwise at first. The solution is transferred to a continuous extractor, and ether extraction is carried out until no more malonic acid is obtained; 12 hours should be allowed for this step.

The product obtained by concentration of the ether solution is recrystallized from ether-petroleum ether mixture, if a very pure product is desired. Yield (crude product) 8.4 grams, 76% based on chloroacetic acid, m.p. 132° or higher.

Analysis (recrystallized product). Calculated for $C_3H_4O_4$: C, 34.62; H, 3.87. Found: C, 34.68; H, 3.82.

Because of an isotope effect, decarboxylation of malonic acid results in acetic acid which contains more than one-half the total label.[36]

3. Non-Functionally Labeled Acids and Derivatives

In this section is described the preparation of organic carboxylic acids and amides which do not have other functional groups and which are not labeled in the carboxyl position. Acetic acid-α-C^{14},[1] propionic

[35] N. Weiner, in Org. Syntheses, Coll. Vol. II, John Wiley & Sons, New York, 1943, p. 376.

[36] P. E. Yankwich and M. Calvin, unpublished experiments.

[1] B. M. Tolbert, J. Biol. Chem., 173, 205 (1948).

acid-α-C^{13},[2] propionic acid-β-C^{13},[2] and butyric acid-α-C^{13} [2] have been prepared in yields of 65 to 80% by the carbonation of the respective labeled alkyl magnesium iodides. Acetic acid-α-C^{13} [3] has also been prepared by oxidation of methyl-labeled p-cresol. From this acid, acetyl chloride-α-C^{13} [2] has been prepared in about 90% yield by treatment of the powdered sodium salt with excess benzoyl chloride.

Sodium Acetate-α-C^{14}.[1]   C*H$_3$CO$_2$Na

From Methyl Iodide. The following reactions are used in the preparation of the acetate from labeled methyl iodide (page 169):

$$C^*H_3I + Mg \rightarrow C^*H_3MgI \quad \text{Yield } 100\%$$

$$\left.\begin{array}{l} C^*H_3MgI + CO_2 \rightarrow C^*H_3CO_2MgI \\ H^+ + C^*H_3CO_2MgI \rightarrow CH_3CO_2H + Mg^{++} + I^- \end{array}\right\} \text{Yield } 70\text{--}80\%$$

$$NaOH + C^*H_3CO_2H \rightarrow C^*H_3CO_2Na + H_2O \quad \text{Yield } 100\%$$

The first two steps of this preparation are carried out in an evacuated closed system (Fig. 76). The 150-cc conical reaction flask D, containing 50 ml of dry ether and 0.5 gram of magnesium turnings, is chilled with liquid nitrogen, evacuated, and 1 ml

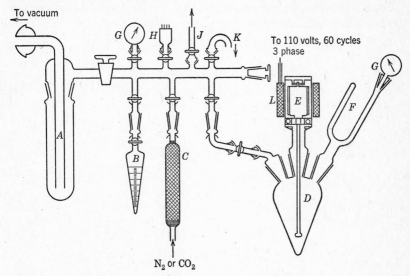

FIG. 76. Manifold used in preparation of methyl-labeled acetic acid (see also Fig. 56): A, large trap; B, methyl iodide container; C, drying tube, anhydrous calcium sulfate; D, reaction vessel; E, induction stirrer, see Appendix IX; F, reflux condenser; G, brass vacuum gauge; H, vacuum thermocouple gauges; J, to carbon dioxide storage bulb; K, to mercury manometer; L, selsyn generator stator.

[2] W. Sakami, private communication.
[3] H. S. Anker, *J. Biol. Chem.*, **166**, 219 (1946).

(2.28 grams) of methyl iodide-C^{14} is distilled in from the storage vessel B. The reaction vessel is then closed and the ether refluxed for 1 hour (an ice-water mixture is used in the low-temperature condenser). The solution is vigorously stirred by means of an induction stirrer (see Appendix IX). The reaction flask is then cooled to $-20°$ C, and purified carbon dioxide is added from bulb J; a pressure of about 30 cm is maintained in the system for 20 minutes. (For purification, tank carbon dioxide is condensed with liquid nitrogen in a large trap where traces of air are pumped off. The gas is then distilled through a Dry Ice-cooled spiral (to remove water) into a storage bulb.)

After the carbonation is complete, the reactor flask is removed from the line and opened in the hood, and the cold (-20 to $-50°$ C) Grignard complex is decomposed with 15 ml of 6 N sulfuric acid. An additional 35 ml of water is then added. In order to precipitate iodide formed in the reaction and to prevent distillation of any free iodine in the next step, 5 grams of silver sulfate is added and the solution is stirred several minutes. The ether is distilled, and then the acetic acid is steam-distilled from the mixture. The distillate is neutralized to pH 8 with 1 N sodium hydroxide solution, evaporated to a small volume, filtered, evaporated to dryness, and dried *in vacuo* (at about 10 microns pressure). The yield of white anhydrous sodium acetate is 70 to 80%; the titration and weighing agree closely.

Sodium Acetate-α-C^{13}.[3] $C^*H_3CO_2Na$

From Cyanide. In the preparation of acetate from labeled cyanide the following steps are used:

$$2NaC^*N + Zn^{++} \rightarrow Zn(C^*N)_2 \downarrow + 2Na^+$$

$$3HCl + Zn(C^*N)_2 + 2 \; \bigcirc\!\!\!\!\!-OH \rightarrow 2HO\!\!-\!\!\bigcirc\!\!-\!\!C^*\!\!\overset{H}{=}\!\!NH\cdot HCl + ZnCl_2$$

$$4H^+ + HO\!\!-\!\!\bigcirc\!\!-\!\!C^*\!\!\overset{H}{=}\!\!NH\cdot HCl + 2Zn \rightarrow$$

$$HO\!\!-\!\!\bigcirc\!\!-\!\!C^*H_3 + 2Zn^{++} + NH_4Cl$$

$$104H^+ + 3HO\!\!-\!\!\bigcirc\!\!-\!\!C^*H_3 + 13Cr_2O_7^= \rightarrow$$

$$26Cr^{+++} + 15CO_2 + 3C^*H_3CO_2H + 58H_2O$$

$$C^*H_3CO_2H + NaOH \rightarrow C^*H_3CO_2Na + H_2O$$

In order to prepare the p-hydroxybenzaldimine hydrochloride, 5.9 grams of zinc cyanide-C^{13} is condensed with 13 grams of phenol; the cyanide and phenol are mixed with 0.1 gram of potassium chloride and 130 ml of dry ether in a 500-ml three-necked flask equipped with gas inlet tube, stirrer, and reflux condenser with drying tube. While the solution is stirred, dry hydrogen chloride is introduced rapidly; saturation takes about an hour. The reaction is continued for 3 more hours. (Direct sunlight should be avoided during the reaction.) The precipitated crystals of the hydrochloride are filtered and washed with dry ether.

The imine is reduced as follows: The hydroxybenzaldimine hydrochloride is dissolved in 60 ml of concentrated hydrochloric acid. This solution is added dropwise over an hour to a hot, rapidly refluxing mixture of 60 grams of amalgamated zinc (mossy or turnings) and 120 ml of 6 N hydrochloric acid. Refluxing is continued for 3 hours, and the solution is then filtered through glass wool and diluted with 3 to 5 volumes of water. The solution is extracted with ether several times. The ether is evaporated to give a mixture of p-cresol with small amounts of o-cresol.

The cresols are oxidized with chromic acid; 2 grams of the cresol is dissolved in 25 ml of concentrated sulfuric acid, and this solution is added to a mixture of 30 grams of chromium trioxide dissolved in 25 ml of water and 150 grams of ice. After the mixture has stood for 12 hours at room temperature, 75 ml of sulfuric acid is added and the solution is refluxed for 3 hours. The acetic acid is then steam-distilled to give an aqueous solution of acid that can be neutralized with sodium hydroxide to give sodium acetate.

The fate of the oxidized o-cresol is not known. Degradations of the acetic acid showed no carboxyl label within the limits of error of the experimental determination of isotope concentrations.

Conversion of Sodium Acetate to Acetic Acid. Although sodium acetate may be used for most biological tracer experiments, acetic acid is sometimes needed for chemical experiments and preparations. Several methods have been used for this conversion.

Reaction with Dry Hydrogen Chloride. Anhydrous sodium acetate can be converted to acetic acid with dry hydrogen chloride.[4] In this procedure hydrogen chloride dried with aluminum chloride is passed over hot sodium acetate and the resulting acetic acid is collected in a series of Dry Ice-cooled traps. At the completion of the conversion, the acetic acid is distilled *in vacuo* into one trap or into the reaction vessel. Water (about 10%) has been found in the acetic acid; hydrogen chloride is also present.

This reaction may be also carried out on the vacuum line.[5] The sodium acetate is placed in the reaction vessel (see Fig. 62), which is warmed and evacuated. Enough dry hydrogen chloride is then let into the bulb to give about a half mole excess over that necessary to react with the acetic acid. The reaction begins almost immediately; the sodium acetate-sodium chloride mixture is shaken and finally heated to insure complete reaction of the acetate. The reaction vessel is then reconnected to the vacuum system (see Fig. 56) and the product is distilled into a storage vessel. Most of the hydrogen chloride can be removed by distillation with evacuation of the acetic acid into a Dry Ice-cooled trap (the hydrogen chloride is not condensed). The yield of acetic acid based on sodium acetate is approximately 100%.

Reduction of Silver Acetate. Silver acetate can be reduced with hydrogen at elevated temperatures to yield metallic silver and acetic acid. The procedure is the same as that described above for the conversion of sodium acetate with hydrogen chloride. The yield of acetic acid is about 80% based on silver acetate; considerable amounts of water are formed by pyrolysis of the acetate.

Preparation by Ether Extraction.[6] Sodium acetate is treated with an excess of dilute sulfuric acid solution. The acetic acid is steam-distilled, and the distillate is saturated with sodium chloride; the acetic acid is then extracted overnight in a con-

[4] R. Ostwald, *J. Biol. Chem.*, **173**, 207 (1948).

[5] B. M. Tolbert, unpublished experiments.

[6] L. B. Spector, *Experimental Use of C¹⁴; Synthesis of Acetic Acid from Radioactive Carbon Dioxide*, Atomic Energy Commission, MDDC 532.

tinuous liquid-liquid extractor. After the ether is dried, the acetic acid and ether are separated by distillation.

n-Butyric Acid-β-C^{13}.[2] $CH_3C^*H_2CH_2CO_2H$

$$CH_3C^*H_2I + [CH(CO_2C_2H_5)_2]^-Na^+ \rightarrow$$

$$CH_3C^*H_2CH(CO_2C_2H_5)_2 + NaI$$

$$CH_3C^*H_2CH(CO_2C_2H_5)_2 + 2H_2O \xrightarrow[\text{or OH}^-]{H^+}$$

$$CH_3C^*H_2CH(CO_2H)_2 + 2C_2H_5OH$$

$$CH_3C^*H_2CH(CO_2H)_2 \xrightarrow{\Delta} CH_3C^*H_2CH_2CO_2H + CO_2$$

In the malonic ester synthesis of β-labeled butyric acid, ethyl iodide-1-C^{13} (page 202) and malonic ester are condensed together. The butyric acid and contaminating non-isotopic acetic acid are separated by fractionation of the methyl esters.

n-Hexadecanoic Acid-6-C^{14} (Palmitic Acid.)[7] $C_{10}H_{21}C^*H_2(CH_2)_4CO_2H$

Labeled 5-keto-n-hexadecanoic acid, page 213, has been reduced using hydrazine as the reducing agent to give the hexadecanoic acid.

$$C_{10}H_{21}C^*H_2CO(CH_2)_3CO_2H + NaOH + NH_2NH_2 \rightarrow$$

$$C_{10}H_{21}C^*H_2(CH_2)_4CO_2Na + N_2 + 2H_2O$$

$$C_{10}H_{21}C^*H_2(CH_2)_4CO_2Na + HCl \rightarrow$$

$$C_{10}H_{21}C^*H_2(CH_2)_4CO_2H + NaCl$$

The keto acid is reduced as follows: A mixture of 6.4 ml of diethylene glycol, 0.8 gram of sodium hydroxide, 0.77 ml of 100% hydrazine hydrate, and 0.89 gram crude keto acid is heated for 1 hour at 150° C and then for 4 hours at 220°. The warm mixture is acidified with 25 ml of dilute hydrochloric acid, diluted with 75 ml of water, and extracted with ether; the ethereal solution is washed with water, then with saturated sodium chloride solution, and dried over magnesium sulfate. After the solvent is evaporated, the residual liquid is distilled onto a cold finger at the bath temperature of 110° and a pressure of 1 mm. The distillate is dissolved in 15 ml of 10% aqueous acetone, treated with Norite, and recrystallized to give 700 mg of the acid, m.p. 61–62°. The yield based on the keto acid was found to be 82% in inactive runs.

Phenylacetamide-α-C^{14}.[8] $C_6H_5C^*H_2CONH_2$

[7] W. G. Dauben, *J. Am. Chem. Soc.*, **70**, 1376 (1948).

[8] W. G. Dauben, J. C. Reid, and P. E. Yankwich, unpublished experiments.

In a Carius tube are placed 1.20 grams (10 mmoles) of acetophenone-α-C^{14} (see page 200), 1.51 grams (47.2 mmoles) of sulfur, 1.25 ml of pyridine, and 2 ml of concentrated ammonia solution. The tube is sealed and heated 5 hours in a tube furnace; the temperature of the furnace is stabilized at 165° C before insertion of the tube. After the tube is cooled, it is opened and the contents are washed into a beaker with concentrated ammonia solution. The mixture is evaporated to dryness and the residue is leached with 35 ml of hot water, used in portions. The hot solution is cooled and filtered. The phenylacetamide collected on the filter weighs about 0.90 gram; 66.7% yield based on acetophenone.

If the filtrate is concentrated a second crop of crystals is obtained. These weigh 0.19 gram and bring the total yield to 80%.

4. Functionally Labeled Aldehydes

The reactions which have found application in the synthesis of functionally labeled aldehydes are the Rosenmund reduction of a carboxylic acid chloride and the hydration of a terminal acetylenic bond.

Acetaldehyde-1,2-C^{11} [1]

$$C^*H{\equiv}C^*H + H_2O \xrightarrow[75\%]{\text{HgSO}_4} C^*H_3C^*HO$$

Acetylene is generated from about 0.6 mmole of radioactive barium carbide by the procedure on page 204, and collected in a trap. The trap containing acetylene is connected to a tube containing 10 ml of a hydration catalyst prepared by diluting a mixture of 2 grams of mercuric sulfate and 6 grams of concentrated sulfuric acid to a volume of 100 ml with water. After the acetylene has been distilled into the catalyst solution, the tube is sealed and the mixture is heated for 5 minutes at 100° to effect hydration. The yield is 75%, based on acetylene. The acetaldehyde can be separated from water by distillation.

p-Anisaldehyde (*p*-methoxybenzaldehyde-carbonyl-C^{14}) [2]

$$p\text{-}CH_3OC_6H_4C^*OOH + SOCl_2 \rightarrow p\text{-}CH_3OC_6H_4C^*OCl + HCl + SO_2$$

$$p\text{-}CH_3OC_6H_4C^*OCl + H_2 \xrightarrow[73\%]{\text{Pd-BaSO}_4} p\text{-}CH_3OC_6H_4C^*HO + HCl$$

The apparatus used for the reduction is shown in Fig. 77. It consists of a 30-ml pear-shaped flask bearing three 14/20 ground necks. Provision is made for introducing a current of purified hydrogen through one of the side necks. The hydrogen leaves the flask through a 20-cm length of 11-mm tubing, which serves as an air condenser. A 3-cm section of "Drierite" at the exit of the condenser serves to keep out moisture. The effluent gas passes finally through a coarse sintered-glass disperser into a sodium hydroxide solution. The hydrogen is purified by passage

[1] R. D. Cramer and G. B. Kistiakowsky, *J. Biol. Chem.*, **137**, 554 (1941).
[2] J. C. Reid and H. B. Jones, *J. Biol. Chem.*, **174**, 427 (1948).

through Fieser's solution.[3]   A sealed induction stirrer is attached at the center neck. As a precaution against poisoning of the catalyst, no lubricant is used on the ground joints.

Before the reduction apparatus is assembled, anisoyl chloride is prepared in the 30-ml flask.   Its two side necks are plugged, and 0.64 gram (4.2 mmoles) of radioactive anisic acid (page 180) is added through the center neck, which is then fitted with a small reflux condenser.   Through this is added 5 ml of thionyl chloride, purified by distillation from quinoline and then boiled linseed oil, and the mixture is refluxed 5 hours.   The thionyl chloride is removed at reduced pressure, and the residue of acid

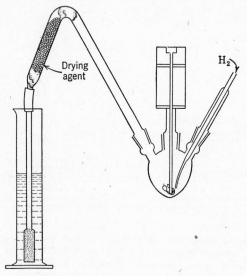

FIG. 77.   Rosenmund reduction apparatus.

chloride is dissolved in 7 ml of c.p. xylene.   To the solution is added 0.05 gram of 5% palladium-barium sulfate catalyst and 3 microliters of quinoline-sulfur poison.[4] The apparatus is assembled, and the Rosenmund reduction [5] is carried out at reflux temperature with violent stirring.   The evolution of hydrogen chloride is followed by passing the effluent gas through 40 ml of water containing phenolphthalein indicator and adding small measured increments of 0.1 N sodium hydroxide as necessary to keep the solution alkaline.   A fairly abrupt cessation of hydrogen chloride evolution, which occurs after about 4 hours, indicates completion of the reduction.   The

[3] Fieser's solution is prepared by adding 2 grams of sodium anthraquinone-β-sulfonate and 15 grams of sodium hydrosulfite to a warm solution of 20 grams of potassium hydroxide in 100 ml of water.   The reagent removes oxygen from the hydrogen gas.   If oxygen is present, catalytic formation of water occurs in the reduction mixture, and the yield is lowered.

[4] Prepared by refluxing a mixture of 1 gram of sulfur with 6 grams of quinoline for 5 hours and diluting the product with 70 ml of xylene.

[5] For an annotated description of a typical Rosenmund reduction, see E. Hershberg and J. Cason, *Org. Syntheses*, **21**, 84–88, John Wiley & Sons, New York, 1941.

amount of alkali consumed is equivalent to 88% of the theoretical amount, based on anisic acid, of acid chloride present. In a pilot run the yield of anisaldehyde was found to be 73%, based on anisic acid, by converting the aldehyde to the 2,4-dinitrophenylhydrazone and weighing it. In the radioactive preparation, the aldehyde was used for another synthesis (page 224) without purification, and no yield was determined.

Veratraldehyde (3,4-Dimethoxybenzaldehyde-Carbonyl-C^{14}) [6]

Veratraldehyde is prepared by a technique identical with that employed for anisaldehyde.

Veratroyl chloride is prepared by refluxing a mixture of 1.03 grams of labeled veratric acid (page 183) with 10 ml of purified thionyl chloride for 5 hours. After removal of thionyl chloride, the acid chloride is dissolved in a mixture of 15 ml of dry C.P. xylene and 2 microliters of quinoline-sulfur poison. To the solution is added 0.05 gram of 5% palladium-barium sulfate catalyst, and the aldehyde is formed by Rosenmund reduction. The evolution of hydrogen chloride is equivalent to 73% of the veratric acid used. The aldehyde was used directly in further synthetic operations and its yield was not directly determined.

5. Functionally Labeled Ketones

Functionally labeled ketones have been prepared by pyrolysis of the barium salt of a functionally labeled carboxylic acid, by the Friedel-Crafts reaction between a carboxylic acid or its chloride or anhydride and an aromatic ring, and by the hydrolysis of an acylmalonic ester. For the preparation of an α-ketoaldehyde by selenium dioxide oxidation of a methyl ketone see page 214.

Carbonyl-labeled 4-(1-naphthoyl)-7-methylhydrindene (page 233) and 1-(2-naphthoyl)-2-methylnaphthalene (page 232) have been prepared as intermediates in the synthesis of labeled methylcholanthrene and dibenzanthracene respectively.

[6] J. C. Reid, unpublished work.

Acetone (Propanone-2-C^{14})

Carbonyl-labeled acetone has been prepared by several workers by pyrolysis of barium acetate. Most of the preparations have been incidental to degradation studies (page 248), but the method has also been used synthetically.[1]

$$Ba(OOC*CH_3)_2 \xrightarrow[95\%]{\Delta} CH_3C*OCH_3 + BaC*O_3$$

Barium acetate is prepared by neutralizing acetic acid-1-C^{14} with barium hydroxide. The barium acetate is dried and then pyrolyzed at 500° C in vacuum.

Carbonyl-labeled diethyl ketone has been prepared by pyrolysis of barium propionate-1-C^{13} in 30% yield. This was done in the course of a degradation study (page 249).

Acetophenone-Carbonyl-C^{13} [2]

$$2CH_3C \; OONa + p\text{-}CH_3C_6H_4SO_2Cl \rightarrow$$
$$(CH_3C*O)_2O + p\text{-}CH_3C_6H_4SO_3Na + NaCl$$
$$91\%$$

$$(CH_3C*O)_2O + 2C_6H_6 \xrightarrow{AlCl_3} 2C_6H_5C*OCH_3 + 2HCl + AlOCl$$
$$95\%$$

Acetic anhydride is prepared from 1.8 grams (21.9 mmoles) of dry sodium acetate-1-C^{14} by heating it with 4.25 grams (22.3 mmoles) of p-toluenesulfonyl chloride. The yield is 1.0 gram (91%) based on sodium acetate. The acetic anhydride is refluxed for half an hour with 15 ml of dry benzene and 6 grams of anhydrous aluminum chloride; 1.14 grams (95%) of crude acetophenone is isolated.

Acetophenone-Carbonyl-C^{14}

Malonic Ester Synthesis.[3]   Diethyl sodiomalonate is prepared in a three-neck

$$C_6H_5C*OOH + SOCl_2 \longrightarrow C_6H_5C*OCl + SO_2 + HCl$$

$$C_6H_5C*OCl + CH(Na)(COOC_2H_5)_2 \longrightarrow C_6H_5C*OCH(COOC_2H_5)_2 + NaCl$$

$$C_6H_5C*OCH(COOC_2H_5)_2 + H_2O \xrightarrow{H^+} C_6H_5C*OCH_3 + CO_2 + 2C_2H_5OH$$
$$54\%$$

flask fitted with a dropping funnel, a mercury-sealed stirrer, and a reflux condenser. The flask is charged with 2 grams (87 mmoles) of sodium wire and 16 grams (100 mmoles) of diethyl malonate dissolved in 200 ml of absolute ether. The reaction is complete after stirring for 6 hours at reflux temperature.

While the diethyl sodiomalonate is forming, benzoyl chloride is prepared by refluxing for 1 hour a mixture of 2.00 grams (16.4 mmoles) of benzoic acid-carboxyl-C^{14} (page 180) with 16.5 grams of purified thionyl chloride. The thionyl chloride is

[1] A. V. Grosse and S. Weinhouse, *Science*, **104**, 402–3 (1946).

[2] E. M. Shantz and D. Rittenberg, *J. Am. Chem. Soc.*, **68**, 2109–2110 (1946).

[3] W. G. Dauben, J. C. Reid, and P. E. Yankwich, unpublished work.

removed under vacuum, and the benzoyl chloride is freed of residual volatile impurities by solution in 10 ml of benzene followed by evaporation in vacuum. This purification operation is performed three times to insure complete removal of thionyl chloride.

Ethyl benzoylmalonate is then prepared by adding the benzoyl chloride, dissolved in a little benzene, to the diethyl sodiomalonate preparation. The mixture is refluxed and stirred for 8 to 11 hours; then the ether is removed by distillation at reduced pressure and replaced by a mixture of 30 ml of concentrated hydrochloric acid, 30 ml of glacial acetic acid, and 20 ml of water. The diethyl benzoylmalonate is then hydrolyzed and decarboxylated by refluxing the mixture for 11 hours. The mixture is diluted with 500 ml of water, and the acetophenone is extracted with ether. Acidic impurities are extracted from the ether with sodium bicarbonate solution, and the ether is evaporated. By distilling the residue of crude acetophenone through a short-path still, 1.05 grams (53.6% based on benzoic acid) of purified acetophenone is obtained. The distillation is carried out at a pressure of 25 mm with a block temperature of 100°.

Friedel-Crafts Synthesis.[4]   The acetic acid used in the synthesis must be dry,

$$C_6H_6 + CH_3C^*OOH \xrightarrow[79\%]{AlCl_3} C_6H_5C^*OCH_3$$

since aluminum chloride, which is used as a catalyst for the Friedel-Crafts condensation, reacts with water. In the synthesis of labeled acetic acid, a product may be obtained which contains some water; if this happens the water is removed by azeotropic distillation with benzene: In a 200-ml two-neck flask are placed 9 grams [5] of dry benzene and crude acetic acid equivalent to 3.0 grams (50 mmoles) of anhydrous acetic acid. A short column packed with glass helices is inserted in the center neck of the flask, and the mixture is distilled until the head temperature reaches 74° C. The flask is allowed to cool, and 30 grams of dry benzene is poured in through the top of the column. The column is removed, and replaced by a small reflux condenser fitted with a drying tube filled with Drierite; 20 grams (0.15 mole) of anhydrous aluminum chloride is then added in one portion to the flask. The reaction is allowed to proceed until the evolution of hydrogen chloride slackens, then the flask is gradually heated by an electrical heating mantle until the benzene is refluxing vigorously.[6] The mixture is refluxed 8 hours; then the orange-colored product is cooled in ice, and 100 ml of 6 M hydrochloric acid is cautiously added through the condenser. After standing overnight, the mixture consists of a colorless water layer and a nearly colorless benzene layer; these are separated, and the water is washed twice with 10 ml of benzene. The combined benzene solutions are washed with two 10-ml portions of 10% sodium hydroxide and three 10-ml portions of water.

A 50-ml flask is fitted with the helix column used in the Friedel-Crafts condensation and an addition funnel. A small amount of the benzene solution is run in, and the flask is heated with a mantle until distillation commences. As the benzene-water azeotrope is removed through the column, more solution is added from the funnel. When all the solution has been added, an additional 10 ml of benzene is run in; the distillation is stopped when the head temperature reaches the boiling point of pure

[4] W. G. Brown and O. K. Neville, Atomic Energy Commission, MDDC 1168.

[5] For a preparation of acetic acid containing 10% water.

[6] It is necessary to maintain vigorous reflux to provide a blanket of benzene vapor over the solution. If this is not done, a certain amount of oxidation occurs, which forms a dark red impurity that is difficult to remove from the product.

benzene. The flask is allowed to cool, and 5 grams of benzene is run through the packing of the column into the flask. The column is replaced by a simple distillation head, and the remaining benzene is distilled. The receiver is changed and distillation is continued at atmospheric pressure until the head temperature reaches 190°. A clean condenser is substituted for the one in the apparatus, and the receiver is replaced by a 5-ml graduated cylinder cooled in an ice-salt bath. Acetophenone is collected from 190–199° (uncor.). The distillation is interrupted before the pot goes dry as a precaution against contaminating the product with a certain amount of colored tar which remains in the flask. Yield, 4.73 grams; 78.8% based on acetic acid.

6. Alcohols, Amines, and Halides

A labeled alcohol is usually prepared by the reduction of the ester of the labeled acid; this general method can be applied to many saturated aliphatic and aromatic alcohols. In the synthesis of the first members of the aliphatic series, it is usually desirable to make the ester with the same alcohol that is to be prepared since this simplifies the problem of purifying the product.

The alcohols described in this section have been prepared by the high-pressure hydrogenolysis of the corresponding esters. The reduction of esters and acid chlorides with lithium aluminum hydride [1,2] offers an alternative method of reduction which has been employed in the synthesis of labeled 9-fluorenylcarbinol (see page 234).

The synthesis of methanol is described in the section on the one carbon compounds; the synthesis of n-hendecanol-1-C^{14} is described in the preparation of n-hendecyl-1-C^{14} bromide; see page 213.

By reduction of the corresponding labeled esters (i.e., ethyl acetate and propyl propionate), the following alcohols have been prepared: [3] ethanol-1-C^{13}, ethanol-2-C^{13}, propanol-1-C^{13}. The reduction with hydrogen at 250° C and 220 atmospheres pressure, catalyzed by copper chromite catalyst (2.5 g/50 mmole ester), is generally slow but complete in 12 hours.

By treatment of the corresponding labeled alcohol with constant boiling hydriodic acid, the following alkyl halides have been prepared: [3] ethyl iodide-1-C^{13}, ethyl iodide-2-C^{13}, and, propyl iodide-1-C^{13}. In addition propyl bromide-1-C^{14} has been prepared by treatment of labeled propanol with phosphorus and bromine. [4] The yield of propyl bromide was 76% based on propanol.

[1] A. E. Finholt, A. C. Bond, and H. I. Schlesinger, *J. Am. Chem. Soc.*, **69**, 1199 (1947).

[2] R. F. Nystrom and W. G. Brown, *J. Am. Chem. Soc.*, **69**, 1197 (1947).

[3] W. Sakami, private communication.

[4] B. A. Fries and M. Calvin, *J. Am. Chem. Soc.*, **70**, 2235 (1948).

n-Propanol-1-C^{14}. CH$_3$CH$_2$C*H$_2$OH [4]

The carboxyl-labeled sodium propionate used in this synthesis is prepared by carbonation of ethyl magnesium bromide with labeled carbon dioxide (page 176). This salt is then converted to propyl propionate. which is reduced; the alcohol is distilled from the reduction mixture.

$$CH_3CH_2C*O_2Na + H_2SO_4 + CH_3CH_2CH_2OH \rightarrow$$
$$CH_3CH_2C*O_2C_3H_7 + NaHSO_4 + H_2O$$
$$CH_3CH_2C*O_2C_3H_7 + H_2 \rightarrow 2CH_3CH_2C*H_2OH$$

The esterification of the labeled sodium propionate is carried out on a 40-mmole scale. A mixture of 9 ml of n-propyl alcohol, 10 ml of benzene, and 1.1 ml of concentrated sulfuric acid together with the anhydrous sodium propionate is refluxed for several hours in a 30-ml flask. In order to drive the reaction to completion, water is removed as a ternary azeotrope (b.p., 68.5° C) with n-propyl alcohol and benzene; a vacuum-jacketed unpacked column (6 mm i.d., 25 cm long) is used for the distillation. When the temperature of the distillate reaches 74° C, the flask is cooled and 1.0 gram of calcium carbonate is added to destroy the excess sulfuric acid. The distillation is then continued, and the remaining benzene is removed as a binary azeotrope (b.p., 77.1° C) with propyl alcohol. The distillation is stopped when the temperature reaches 92° C. The ester-alcohol solution is completely removed from the calcium sulfate-calcium carbonate mixture by vacuum transfer. This solution, about 8 ml in volume, is pipetted into a high-pressure hydrogenation bomb (43-cc volume) containing 2.0 grams of copper chromite catalyst (Adkins).

The bomb is charged to 2,500 psi with hydrogen, heated to 250° C, and shaken at that temperature for 9 hours. The contents of the bomb are transferred on the vacuum line (see procedure for transfer of methanol, page 167) into a flask containing calcium oxide where the alcohol is dried. The alcohol is again transferred on the vacuum line into a small distillation flask and is fractionally distilled at atmospheric pressure using the column described above. The fraction boiling from 96° to 97° C is recovered. The fraction which boiled below 96° C (about 2 ml) is returned to the distilling flask with 2.5 ml of n-propyl alcohol, and the mixture is redistilled. This operation is repeated with 2.0 ml of n-propyl alcohol. All the fractions boiling at 96° to 97° C are combined to give 10.3 ml of labeled propanol. In an inactive run the yield of alcohol was 95% based on the amount of sodium propionate taken.

Ethylamine-1-C^{13}.[5] CH$_3$C*H$_2$NH$_2$

$$NaC*N + CH_3I \rightarrow CH_3C*N + NaI$$
$$CH_3C*N + 2H_2 \rightarrow CH_3C*H_2NH_2$$

A solution of 11.3 grams of sodium cyanide-C^{13} in 17 ml of water is shaken 24 hours with 36.3 grams (0.249 mole) of methyl iodide. After storage of the solution overnight in a refrigerator, enough water is added to dissolve a slight precipitate which forms, and the solution is very slowly distilled. A fraction boiling at 76–100° and weighing 13.8 grams is collected as crude acetonitrile.

The nitrile solution is rinsed into a hydrogenation bottle containing 10 grams of Raney's nickel paste, and diluted to 75 ml with water. Hydrogenation is carried

⁵ G. W. Kilmer and V. duVigneaud, *J. Biol. Chem.*, **154**, 247 (1944).

out at room temperature and atmospheric pressure; the reduction is complete after the solution has been shaken 4 hours. The reaction mixture is chilled in ice and filtered. The catalyst is washed 10 times with water and 5 N sodium hydroxide solution. To determine the yield of ethylamine, N-ethyl-p-bromobenzenesulfonamide was prepared from an aliquot of the combined filtrates. The yield was 70% based on sodium cyanide.

Dodecylamine-1-C^{14}.[6] $C_{11}H_{23}C^*H_2NH_2$

$$C_{11}H_{23}C^*N + 4Na + 4H_2O \rightarrow C_{11}H_{23}C^*H_2NH_2 + 4Na^+ + 4OH^-$$

To 6 grams of finely divided sodium vigorously stirred in 75 ml of boiling toluene is added 8.82 grams of radioactive lauronitrile (see page 191) in 19 grams of anhydrous butanol-1. The addition requires 10 minutes. An additional 25 ml of toluene and 10 ml of butanol are added, and the mixture is heated and stirred until all the sodium has reacted. Then water is cautiously added and the toluene solution is separated and dried with anhydrous potassium carbonate.

The solvent is removed, and the crude amine is dissolved in 100 ml of 50% ethanol containing 4 ml of concentrated hydrochloric acid. Remaining nitrile is extracted with four portions of petroleum ether, most of the alcohol is boiled out, the solution is made alkaline, and the amine is extracted with petroleum ether. After the solution is dried with anhydrous potassium carbonate, the solvent is evaporated to give 8.25 grams (91.5%) of dodecylamine. The acetate is prepared by solution of the amine in 50 ml of benzene and the addition of 2.5 ml of glacial acetic acid; crystallization occurs at 15°. Recrystallization at 15° from 50 ml of benzene yields 9.5 grams of radioactive dodecylammonium acetate; m.p. 68.5–69.0 corr. The yield based on the amount of lauronitrile used is 85%.

7. Aliphatic Hydrocarbons

The synthesis of methane is described in the section on the one-carbon compounds. The formation of n-docosane-11,12-C^{14} is mentioned as a major side product in a preparation of palmitic acid (page 214). The synthesis of ethylene-1-C^{14} is described in the preparation of methionine (page 219), but the ethylene was not isolated.

Acetylene

Acetylene has been prepared by numerous investigators from barium carbide obtained by the reaction between barium carbonate and magnesium; a micro-scale conversion of carbon dioxide to acetylene has also been developed.

Acetylene-C^{11}.[1] $HC^* \equiv C^*H$

Barium carbonate and an excess of magnesium are heated together in an iron boat in an iron tube which is heated in a furnace at about 700° C in an atmosphere of hydrogen. (This reaction has also been carried out in an atmosphere of helium and in a thick-walled glass bomb tube. Although an exothermic flash reaction occurs, high pressures do not develop in the bomb.) After 5 minutes, the iron pipe is removed from the furnace and cooled in a spray of water. The boat is removed and placed

[6] H. J. Harwood and A. W. Ralston, *J. Org. Chem.*, **12**, 740 (1947).

[1] R. D. Cramer and G. B. Kistiakowsky, *J. Biol. Chem.*, **137**, 549 (1941).

in a test tube; water is added, and the solution is gently warmed. The acetylene generated is swept into a liquid nitrogen trap; the tube is heated about 10 minutes

$$BaC^*O_3 + 2Mg \rightarrow BaC^*_2 + BaO$$

$$BaC^*_2 + 2H_2O \rightarrow HC^* \equiv C^*H + Ba(OH)_2$$

to drive off all the acetylene. The generator is closed and the trap evacuated to remove non-condensible gases. The acetylene is then distilled into a storage or reaction vessel. The yield based on barium carbonate is at least 60%.

Acetylene-C¹³.[2] $HC^* \equiv C^*H$. The chemistry of this preparation of acetylene is the same as for the synthesis just described; the reaction is carried out on a larger scale and the equipment is improved.

Ten grams (51 mmoles) of barium carbonate is ground with 24 grams of magnesium powder (60 mesh). The mixture is placed in an iron bomb (Fig. 78); air is

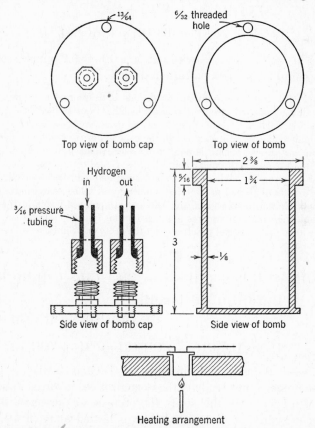

FIG. 78. Iron bomb used in preparation of barium carbide. All dimensions are given in inches; the gasket is not shown. (W. Sakami.)

² W. Sakami, private communication.

swept out of the bomb with a slow stream of hydrogen, and, with the hydrogen still passing through the vessel, the bomb is heated to and maintained at red heat for 10 minutes. Hydrogen is passed through the bomb until it has cooled. The barium carbide is removed from the bomb and immediately placed in an acetylene generator (a Pyrex test tube, $11\frac{1}{16}$ inches i.d. by $6\frac{3}{8}$ inches long, fitted with a dropping funnel and gas inlet and outlet tubes). In order to convert the barium carbide to acetylene, water is introduced into the generator drop by drop while the vessel is cooled in an ice bath. When vigorous evolution of gas has subsided, the generator is heated to boiling (gas may be evolved vigorously at this point but it does not contain an appreciable amount of acetylene). Boiling is continued for 10 to 15 minutes, and nitrogen is passed through the solution 30 to 40 minutes longer to insure complete evolution of the gas. The yield of acetylene based on barium carbonate is 75%.

Acetylene, Micro Preparation. Carbon dioxide has been converted to acetylene on a micro scale; an interesting method of purification was

$$2C^*O_2 + 5Ba \rightarrow 4BaO + BaC^*_2$$

$$BaC^*_2 + 2H_2O \rightarrow Ba(OH)_2 + HC^* \equiv C^*H$$

used.[3] The synthesis was carried out on a 0.1- to 0.2-mmole scale with a yield of 90 to 98% based on carbon dioxide.

By means of a vacuum system carbon dioxide is transferred to a stainless-steel bomb containing a onefold excess of barium which has been scraped as clean as possible before it is weighed. The bomb is closed and transferred to a furnace and heated for 5 to 10 minutes. When it has cooled, the contents of the bomb are dissolved in water. The acetylene produced is purified by selective adsorption on charcoal; the mixture of gases is passed through a spiral Dry Ice-cooled trap to remove most of the water, and then the ammonia, water vapor, acetylene, and traces of ethylene are adsorbed on active charcoal at Dry Ice temperatures. The charcoal trap is then warmed to 0° C, and the acetylene and ethylene are pumped into a liquid-nitrogen trap. If not more than 10 minutes is taken for this last step, almost no water or ammonia will be desorbed and practically all the acetylene will be recovered.

Propene-1-C^{14}.[4] CH_3—CH=$C^{14}H_2$

$$CH_3\text{—}CH_2\text{—}C^*H_2Br + (CH_3)_3N \rightarrow CH_3\text{—}CH_2\text{—}C^*H_2N(CH_3)_3Br$$

$$CH_3CH_2\text{—}C^*H_2N(CH_3)_3Br + [AgOH] \rightarrow$$

$$CH_3CH_2C^*H_2N(CH_3)_3OH + AgBr$$

$$CH_3CH_2\text{—}C^*H_2N(CH_3)_3OH \xrightarrow{\text{heat}} CH_3CH=C^*H_2 + (CH_3)_3N + H_2O$$

One-labeled propene and mixtures of 1- and 3-labeled propene have been prepared in a study of the isomerizations involved in the preparation of propene. In this study the propene was prepared by three methods: dehydration of 1-propanol over heated alumina at 400° C, dehydration of propanol with metaphosphoric acid, and pyrolysis of

³ W. J. Arrol and R. Glascock, *Nature*, **159**, 810 (1947).

⁴ B. A. Fries and M. Calvin, *J. Am. Chem. Soc.*, **70**, 2235 (1948).

n-propyl trimethyl ammonium hydroxide. The position of the label introduced in these preparations was determined by a degradation method described on page 259.

Both the preparations in which dehydration was carried out showed that extensive shift of the double bond occurred in the synthesis. When metaphosphoric acid was used as the dehydrating agent an equilibrium mixture of the two isomers, the 1- and the 3-labeled propene, was obtained. Under the conditions of the experiment in which alumina was used extensive rearrangement occurred although the equilibrium mixture with respect to isomerization of the hydrogen was not obtained. However, pyrolysis of the quarternary ammonium hydroxide gave practically pure one-labeled propene, and this preparation will be described here.

The quarternary ammonium bromide is prepared by the addition of 5 ml of *n*-propyl bromide (labeled in the 1 position, see page 202) to excess trimethyl amine in alcohol. The mixture is refluxed for several hours, and the solvent is evaporated. The bromide is dissolved in water, and excess freshly prepared silver oxide is added to convert the bromide to the hydroxide. After the silver bromide and the excess silver oxide are filtered off, the aqueous solution is evaporated to dryness in a closed sytem swept with a slow stream of nitrogen. The system contains, in the following order: a condenser to remove most of the water, a gas wash bottle containing 1 N hydrochloric acid solution to remove the methylamine, a tube of Drierite to remove water from the scrubbed gases, and a liquid-nitrogen-cooled trap to condense the propene. After the solution is evaporated nearly to dryness the contents of the flask are carefully heated and the generated propene is condensed. The yield of propene based on propyl bromide was approximately 90%; analysis of the gas by mass spectrometer showed 99% propene, 0.5% butene, and 0.5% ethylene.

8. Hydroxy and Keto Acids

Lactic Acid

Lactic acid has been prepared containing isotopic carbon (C^{11}) [1] by the addition of isotopic potassium cyanide to acetaldehyde to obtain the cyanohydrin, which on hydrolysis gave a 40% yield of carboxyl-labeled lactate. By a similar sequence of reactions, inactive cyanide was added to labeled acetaldehyde to give α,β-labeled lactate in 50% yield. In the preparation of these compounds with the short-lived isotope, speed and simplicity of operations are essential. The total time consumed in the entire synthesis is only 2 hours. Improved yields of these compounds are reported. [2] The use of C^{13} furnishes the time required for the extensive manipulations which were made necessary by improvements in the preparation of barium carbide and potassium cyanide with the use of vacuum techniques.

[1] R. D. Cramer and G. B. Kistiakowsky, *J. Biol. Chem.*, **137**, 549 (1941).

[2] W. Sakami, W. E. Evans, and S. Gurin, *J. Am. Chem. Soc.*, **69**, 1110 (1947).

Lactic Acid-1-C^{11}.[1]   About 1 ml of acetaldehyde is added to a solution of 0.6 mmole of potassium cyanide (see page 160) in 7 ml of water contained in a Carius

$$HC^*N + CH_3CHO \rightarrow CH_3CHOHC^*N$$

$$CH_3CHOHC^*N + 2H_2O + HCl \rightarrow CH_3CHOHC^*OOH + NH_4Cl$$
40% overall yield

tube. The reaction of cyanide with acetaldehyde is almost quantitative under these conditions and is very rapid because of the free alkali in solution. An excess of acetaldehyde is needed because of the reversibility of the reaction. The alkaline solution is neutralized and adjusted to an acid concentration of 8 N in concentrated hydrochloric acid. The tube is sealed and heated to 100° for 5 minutes. The acid solution is then neutralized with sodium hydroxide and evaporated to dryness in vacuum. The residue is made acid to phenol red by the addition of a solution of hydrogen chloride in ether, and the lactic acid thus liberated is extracted with five 75-ml portions of ether. The combined extracts are evaporated to 10 ml, and the lactic acid is extracted from the ether solution with several 5-ml portions of water. The water extract contained about 50 mg of lactic acid, 40% yield based on carbon dioxide.

Lactic Acid-1-C^{13}.[2]   One gram of labeled sodium cyanide is dissolved in 4 ml of

$$HC^*N + CH_3CHO \rightarrow CH_3CHOHC^*N$$

$$CH_3CHOHC^*N + 2H_2O + HCl \rightarrow CH_3CHOHC^*OOH + NH_4Cl$$

water. The solution is cooled to 0°, 11 ml of ice-cold 2 N sulfuric acid is added, followed by 1.4 ml of acetaldehyde and 2.0 ml of 1 N sodium hydroxide solution. After thorough shaking, the mixture is allowed to stand at room temperature for 20 minutes. Forty milliliters of concentrated hydrochloric acid is added, and the mixture is rapidly shaken and boiled for 6 minutes. The product is diluted with 100 ml of water, cooled, and neutralized with saturated sodium hydroxide. An excess of sodium hydroxide is then added, the solution is distilled until the ammonia is completely removed, and the remaining solution is exactly neutralized with sulfuric acid. The solution is evaporated until it starts to bump, 50 ml of toluene is added, and the remaining water is removed as the azeotrope by continuous distillation, using a water trap. The residue after evaporation of the remaining toluene is extracted with three 50-ml portions of absolute ethanol. The ethanol is distilled, and the residue is extracted with 15 ml of absolute alcohol. The solid material is removed by centrifugation and is washed with three 1-ml portions of absolute alcohol. The solutions are combined, and the solvent is removed by distillation; the last traces are removed in a vacuum desiccator. Based on the sodium cyanide employed, the yield of sodium lactate was 94–96%.

Lactic Acid-2,3-C^{11}.[1]   Labeled acetylene is prepared by the method described on

$$HC^* \equiv C^*H + H_2O \xrightarrow[HgSO_4]{H_2SO_4} C^*H_3C^*HO$$

$$C^*H_3C^*HO + HCN \longrightarrow C^*H_3C^*HOHCN$$

$$C^*H_3C^*HOHCN + 2H_2O + HCl \longrightarrow C^*H_3C^*HOHCOOH + NH_4Cl$$
50% overall yield

page 204. The catalyst solution is prepared by dissolving 2 grams of mercuric sulfate and 6 grams of sulfuric acid in water and diluting to 100 ml. A glass tube containing the acetylene and the mercuric sulfate solution is sealed and heated to 100° for 5 minutes. The tube is opened, and the contents are rinsed into a flask. The acetaldehyde is distilled in a current of air into 5 ml of 2 N potassium cyanide. The solution of hydroxypropionitrile and potassium cyanide is transferred to a glass tube, and sufficient concentrated hydrochloric acid is added to make the resulting solution 8 M in acid. The tube is sealed and heated to 100° for 5 minutes, and the product is isolated as previously described. This synthesis required about 100 minutes The yield is 50% based on carbon dioxide.

Lactic Acid-2,3-C^{13}.[2] The acetylene is prepared in a steel bomb as described on

$$HC^* \equiv C^*H + H_2O \xrightarrow[\text{HgSO}_4]{\text{H}_2\text{SO}_4} C^*H_3C^*HO$$

$$C^*H_3C^*HO + HCN \longrightarrow C^*H_3C^*HOHCN$$

$$C^*H_3C^*HOHCN + 2H_2O + HCl \longrightarrow C^*H_3C^*HCHCOOH + NH_4Cl$$

page 205. The hydration is carried out in an evacuated system and the product is isolated by the method described for the carboxyl labeled isomer, page 208. The yield is 40% based on barium carbonate.

3-Hydroxypropionic Acid-1-C^{11}

This compound was prepared [3] by the following reactions:

$$CH_2OHCH_2Cl + KC^*N \rightarrow CH_2OHCH_2C^*N + KCl$$

$$CH_2OHCH_2C^*N + 2H_2O + HCl \rightarrow CH_2OHCH_2C^*OOH + NH_4Cl$$

The alkaline solution of potassium cyanide prepared by the method described on page 160, is evaporated almost to dryness, and the residue is taken up with a small volume of absolute ethanol containing 2-chloroethanol. The solution is refluxed for 40 minutes, the solution is cooled to 0°, and carrier β-hydroxypropionitrile is added. The solid that separates is filtered, and a carbonate-bicarbonate buffer solution is added to prevent distillation of the formate which results from hydrolysis of the cyanide. The solvents are removed by vacuum distillation, and the product is purified by redistillation. The pure nitrile is hydrolyzed for 10 minutes at 100°, and the acid is isolated. No quantities or yields are furnished.

Pyruvic Acid

α,β- and carboxyl-labeled pyruvic acids have been prepared [2] by the oxidation of the corresponding labeled butyl lactates with acid permanganate.

Carbonyl-labeled pyruvic acid has been prepared [4] by the reaction of acetyl bromide with cuprous cyanide and subsequent hydrolysis.

Pyruvic Acid-1-C^{13} or Pyruvic Acid-2,3-C^{13}.[2] The appropriately labeled anhydrous sodium lactate is treated with 2.5 N sulfuric acid in n-butanol, followed by the addition of benzene. The mixture is boiled for 12 hours, using a trap to collect the water formed during the reaction. After removal of the benzene by distillation, the excess sulfuric acid is neutralized with sodium n-butoxide in butanol. The blue end point

[3] P. Nahinsky, C. S. Rice, S. Ruben, and M. D. Kamen, *J. Am. Chem. Soc.*, **64**, 2299 (1942).

[4] M. Calvin and R. Lemmon, *J. Am. Chem. Soc.*, **69**, 1232 (1947).

of benzeneazonaphthylamine (0.1% in butanol) is satisfactory for this titration. The sodium sulfate is removed by centrifugation and washed with butanol, and the

$$CH_3CHOHCOOH + C_4H_9OH \xrightarrow{H_2SO_4} CH_3CHOHCOOC_4H_9 + H_2O$$

$$CH_3CHOHCOOC_4H_9 \xrightarrow{KMnO_4} CH_3COCOOC_4H_9$$

$$CH_3COCOOC_4H_9 + NaOH \longrightarrow CH_3COCOONa + C_4H_9OH$$

combined solution is distilled in vacuum from a small quantity of non-volatile gum. The distillate is redistilled at atmospheric pressure through a small fractionating column with an outer jacket maintained at 120°. The yield is about 80%.

Butyl lactate (1.94 grams) is oxidized by addition to an ice-cold solution consisting of 26.14 ml of 0.167 M potassium permanganate and 4.44 ml of 1.96 N sulfuric acid. Thirty milliliters of cold water is added with shaking, and the solution is allowed to stand for 3 hours at 18–20°. The solution is then chilled, made alkaline with 5 ml of cold sodium carbonate solution, and repeatedly extracted with ether. The ethereal solution is dried over calcium chloride and evaporated, and the residual oil is distilled at a bath temperature of 190–205°. The yield of butyl pyruvate is 1.41 grams (74%), shown to be 95% pure.[5] Sodium pyruvate is obtained by titration of butyl pyruvate with 1 N sodium hydroxide at room temperature. Under these conditions rapid hydrolysis occurs. The butyl alcohol is extracted with ether, and the aqueous solution is freed from ether by aeration.

Pyruvic Acid-2-C^{14}.[4]   The conversion of carboxyl-labeled acetic acid, prepared as described on page 178, to acetyl bromide is carried out in a three-neck round-bottom

$$3CH_3C*OOH + PBr_3 \rightarrow 3CH_3C*OBr + P(OH)_3$$

$$2CH_3C*OBr + Cu_2(CN)_2 \rightarrow 2CH_3C*OCN + CuBr_2$$

$$CH_3C*OCN + HCl + 2H_2O \rightarrow CH_3C*OCOOH + NH_4Cl$$

flask equipped with a dropping funnel, mechanical stirrer, and reflux condenser. The apparatus is protected from moisture with a calcium chloride tube. A slight excess of phosphorus tribromide (about 0.35 mole per mole of acetic acid) is placed in the flask, and the acetic acid is slowly added, with stirring, from the dropping funnel. After addition of the acetic acid, the reaction mixture separates into two liquid phases, of which the lower is phosphorous acid, and the upper, acetyl bromide. The reaction flask is then heated in an oil bath for 1 hour at 40–50°, with continued stirring. The flask is cooled, boiling chips are added, and the flask is fitted with a small fractionating column. The acetyl bromide is then distilled at 71–76° directly into a second three-neck flask fitted with a stirrer and a condenser, protected from moisture, in which has been placed cuprous cyanide powder (1 molar equivalent to the acetic acid started with). The acetyl bromide is distilled during the course of ½ hour, with constant stirring of the reaction flask, which is then maintained at 70–80° (bath temperature) for 1 hour. The reaction flask is cooled and fitted with a small fractionating column, and the pyruvonitrile (acetyl cyanide) is distilled at 90–95°.

The pyruvonitrile is hydrolyzed by the slow addition, with stirring and cooling, of an equal volume of 12 N hydrochloric acid. The mixture is allowed to come to room temperature, and, as the hydrolysis occurs, the contents of the flask solidify to a crystalline mass. To the flask is added enough water to dissolve the crystalline material, and the mixture is heated at 70° under a reflux condenser for 1 hour. The

⁵ C. Fromageot and P. Desneuille, *Biochem. Z.*, **279**, 174 (1935).

flask is cooled, and the contents are extracted ten times with small portions of ether. The combined ether extracts are dried over anhydrous sodium sulfate, and the ether is distilled through a fractionating column. The residual liquid is transferred to a small Claisen flask, with a small amount of ether. The low-boiling material is removed, and the pyruvic acid is distilled at 60–75° at 25 mm. The yield of pyruvic acid from acetic acid is 45–55%, and the yield from barium carbonate is 40–52%.

Conversion to the potassium salt is accomplished by addition of 10 volumes of methanol to the pyruvic acid, titration with methanolic potassium hydroxide, and precipitation of the potassium pyruvate by addition of ether. The yield in the conversion depends on the purity of the pyruvic acid.

Acetoacetic Acid

Three differently labeled acetoacetates have been synthesized.[2] Acetoacetate labeled in the carbonyl and carboxyl groups is prepared by modifications of the usual synthesis,[6] and the product is obtained in 26% yield.

Carboxyl-labeled acetoacetate is prepared by a modification of the reaction [7] in which the Grignard reagent from isotopic ethyl bromoacetate is allowed to react with non-isotopic methyl acetate. If the Grignard reagent from non-isotopic ethyl bromoacetate is treated with isotopic methyl acetate, acetoacetate labeled only in the carbonyl position is obtained. All these reactions employ carboxyl-labeled acetate as the starting material, but with the current availability of methyl-labeled acetate (page 193) it is possible to prepare acetoacetates labeled in the methyl and/or methylene groups.

Acetoacetic Acid-1,3-C¹³.[2] Fused sodium acetate (2.4 grams), see page 178, is refluxed with 8 ml of diethyl sulfate in flask A, Fig. 79, for 20 minutes, and the ethyl acetate is distilled into B (oil bath, 100–150°). The yields are usually quantitative.

$$2CH_3COOC_2H_5 \xrightarrow[29\%]{(C_6H_5)_3CNa} CH_3COCH_2COOC_2H_5 + C_2H_5OH$$

$$CH_3COCH_2COOC_2H_5 \xrightarrow{91\%} CH_3COCH_2COONa + C_2H_5OH$$

Triphenylmethyl sodium is prepared,[6] when a mixture of 9.1 grams of triphenylchloromethane and 336 grams of 1% sodium amalgam are shaken together in 240 ml of dry ether. At the first appearance of a red color, the separatory funnel is cooled in a wet towel, and the mixture is shaken for 30 minutes thereafter. The yield is usually quantitative. The ethyl acetate is redistilled from B directly into the separatory funnel. The color changes from deep red to light orange in less than a minute; the mixture is allowed to stand for 3 additional minutes, and 3.2 ml of glacial acetic acid is added. The ethereal layer is washed with dilute sodium bicarbonate and dried with Drierite, and most of the ether is distilled through a short column. The triphenylmethane precipitates on cooling and is filtered. The residue is distilled, and a yield of 0.55 gram (29% based on acetate) of ethyl acetoacetate is obtained, b.p. 73–76°/14 mm. The product is hydrolyzed by allowing it to stand for

⁶ B. E. Hudson, R. H. Dick, and C. R. Hauser, *J. Am. Chem. Soc.*, **60**, 1960 (1938).
⁷ F. Rottinger and R. Wenzel, *Monatsh.*, **34**, 1867 (1913).

6 hours in a slight excess of 1 N sodium hydroxide.[8]   The excess alkali is neutralized, and the preparation is freed of ethanol by lyophilization.   The yield is 91%.

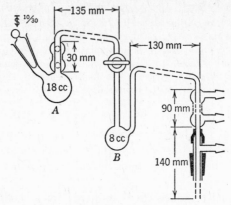

FIG. 79.   Apparatus for the preparation of ethyl acetoacetate.   (Sakami, Evans, and Gurin.)

Acetoacetic Acid-3-C^{13}.[2]   Isotopic carboxyl-labeled potassium acetate (6.5 grams), see page 178, is converted to methyl acetate by heating with dimethyl sulfate.   The

$$CH_3COOCH_3 + BrMgCH_2COOC_2H_5 \rightarrow \xrightarrow{H^+}$$

$$CH_3C^*OCH_2COOC_2H_5 + MgOHBr$$

$$CH_3C^*OCH_2COOC_2H_5 + NaOH \rightarrow CH_3C^*OCH_2COONa + C_2H_5OH$$

yield of redistilled methyl acetate is quantitative.   The methyl acetate, diluted with 15 ml of anhydrous ether, and 3 grams of magnesium turnings are placed in a 50-ml round-bottom flask equipped with a side-arm dropping funnel and reflux condenser. The stirrer extends through the center of the condenser.   Ethyl bromoacetate (7.4 ml) is added dropwise with gentle stirring to start the reaction.   The mixture is maintained at boiling by controlling the rate of addition of the ethyl bromoacetate.   The product is obtained by hydrolysis of the Grignard reaction mixture, ether extraction, and distillation.   The ethyl acetoacetate weighed 0.80 gram and upon analysis [9] was found to be 88% pure.

Acetoacetic Acid-1-C^{13}.[2]   Labeled ethyl acetate is converted into ethyl bromoacetate by treatment with phosphorus and excess bromine [10] followed by distillation at 159°.   From 6 grams of sodium acetate, 10.5 grams of ethyl bromoacetate was

$$CH_3COOCH_3 + BrMgCH_2C^*OOC_2H_5 \rightarrow \xrightarrow{H^+} CH_3COCH_2C^*OOC_2H_5 + MgOHBr$$

$$CH_3COCH_2C^*OOC_2H_5 + NaOH \longrightarrow CH_3COCH_2C^*OONa + C_2H_5OH$$

obtained (86%).   The Grignard reagent was prepared from this substance in the presence of non-isotopic methyl acetate as described above.

[8] G. Ljunggren, *Biochem. Z.*, **145**, 425 (1924).
[9] V. Lorber, *Biochem. Z.*, **181**, 366 (1929).
[10] K. Auwers and R. Bernhardi, *Ber.*, **24**, 2219 (1891).

5-Keto-*n*-hexadecanoic Acid-6-C^{14}

This compound was prepared [11] as an intermediate in the synthesis of palmitic acid labeled in the 6 position, and makes use of the reaction between a dialkyl cadmium derivative and an ester chloride of a dibasic acid. This method can be extended to become a convenient way to prepare 3- or 4-keto acids. [12] By means of the following set of reactions, palmitic acid has been prepared in 30% yield from carbon dioxide:

$$n\text{-}C_{10}H_{21}MgBr \xrightarrow{C^*O_2} C_{10}H_{21}C^*OOH \xrightarrow{CH_2N_2} C_{10}H_{21}C^*OOCH_3 \xrightarrow[H_2]{CuCr_2O_4}$$

$$\underset{I}{\qquad} \qquad \underset{II}{\qquad} \qquad \underset{III}{\qquad}$$

$$C_{10}H_{21}C^*H_2OH \xrightarrow{HBr} C_{10}H_{21}C^*H_2Br \xrightarrow[2.\ CdCl_2]{1.\ Mg}$$

$$\underset{IV}{\qquad} \qquad \underset{V}{\qquad}$$

$$(C_{10}H_{21}C^*H_2)_2Cd \xrightarrow[2.\ KOH]{1.\ CH_3OOCCH_2CH_2CH_2COCl}$$

$$\underset{VI}{\qquad}$$

$$C_{10}H_{21}C^*H_2COCH_2CH_2CH_2COOH \xrightarrow[NH_2NH_2]{NaOH}$$

$$\underset{VII}{\qquad}$$

$$C_{10}H_{21}C^*H_2CH_2CH_2CH_2CH_2COOH$$

Yields: I → III 83%
III → V 79%
V → VIII 45%

Carboxyl-labeled methyl hendecanoate (1.548 grams, 0.767 mmoles), see page 182, is hydrogenated over 1.0 gram copper chromite catalyst [13] at an initial pressure of hydrogen of 3,000 psi at room temperature. The hydrogenolysis takes place at 250° and is complete in 6 hours. The catalyst is filtered, and the filtrate is heated under reflux for 1 hour with a mixture of 10 ml of 6 N sodium hydroxide and 5 ml of methanol. The saponified mixture is extracted with ether, the ethereal solution is washed with water and dried over magnesium sulfate, and the ether is evaporated. The residual liquid is converted directly to the bromide by passage of anhydrous hydrogen bromide through the alcohol on the steam bath. After 15 minutes the absorption appears to be complete. The reaction mixture is cooled and diluted with 15 ml of hexane, and the solution is extracted with 2 ml of cold concentrated sulfuric acid. The acid layer is removed, and the hexane layer is neutralized with dilute aqueous ammonia. The hexane layer is removed, washed with saturated sodium chloride solution, and dried over magnesium sulfate. The solvent is evaporated, and the hendecyl bromide is distilled in a small sublimation-type still, block temperature 70–75°, pressure 0.5 mm, yield 1.432 grams (79.3%), n_D^{25} 1.4548.

Analysis. Calculated for $C_{11}H_{23}Br$: C, 56.17; H, 9.86. *Found:* C, 56.61, H, 10.28.

The Grignard reagent is prepared from 0.15 gram of magnesium turnings and 1.412 grams of *n*-hendecyl bromide, labeled at carbon 6, in 50 ml of anhydrous ether.

[11] W. G. Dauben, *J. Am. Chem. Soc.*, **70**, 1376 (1948).
[12] See J. Cason, *Chem. Revs.*, **40**, 15 (1947), for a review of this reaction.
[13] *Org. Syntheses, Coll. Vol.* II, p. 142, John Wiley & Sons, New York, 1943.

The bromide is added slowly over the course of 90 minutes to the magnesium to minimize losses due to the coupling reaction. The resulting Grignard reagent is converted to the corresponding dialkyl-cadmium compound with 0.71 gram of anhydrous cadmium chloride. After addition of the cadmium chloride, the mixture is heated under reflux until a negative test [14] for a Grignard reagent is obtained. This requires about 2 hours. The ether is distilled and replaced with benzene, and the resulting suspension is treated with 1.00 gram of γ-carbomethoxybutyryl chloride.[15] The reaction mixture after being heated under reflux for 1 hour sets to a solid mass and is then decomposed with acid. The crude reaction mixture is directly saponified with a solution of 0.4 gram of potassium hydroxide in 10 ml of methanol. After dilution to 50 ml with water, the mixture is extracted with ether to remove the neutral by-products. n-Docosane (100 mg) labeled at carbons eleven and twelve, is thus isolated. The alkaline phase is acidified and extracted with ether. The ethereal solution is washed first with water, then with saturated sodium chloride solution; it is dried with Drierite, and the solvent is distilled. The crude keto acid is then reduced to palmitic acid as described on page 196. In a practice experiment using non-isotopic materials, the keto acid was isolated and recrystallized from methanol, m.p. 84.5–85.0°, yield 64% based on bromide. Robinson [16] reports a melting point of 88°.

Mandelic Acid-α-C^{14}

Mandelic acid has been prepared [17] by the following sequence of reactions:

$$\text{C6H5-C*OCH}_3 + SeO_2 \rightarrow \text{C6H5-C*OCHO} + Se + H_2O$$

$$\text{C6H5-C*OCHO} + NaOH + H_2O \rightarrow \text{C6H5-C*HCOONa}\;(\text{OH})$$

Degradation of the mandelic acid showed that there is no rearrangement of the carbon skeleton during the dismutation of the phenylglyoxal. [18]

The preparation of acetophenone is given on page 201. Acetophenone, 1.00 gram, is weighed into a 10-ml flask, and to this is added 1.66 grams of selenium dioxide, 6 ml of purified dioxane, and 0.2 ml of water. The mixture is boiled under reflux for 8 hours and allowed to stand at room temperature for 8 hours. The solution is removed from the precipitated selenium by means of a capillary pipet and is transferred to a 100-cc flask. Most of the dioxane is distilled through a short column, 30 ml of ether is added, and the mixture is refluxed to dissolve the solid phenyl-

[14] H. Gilman and F. Schulze, J. Am. Chem. Soc., 47, 2002 (1925).

[15] S. A. Harris, D. E. Wolf, et al., J. Am. Chem. Soc., 67, 2096 (1945); Org. Syntheses, 25, 12 (1945).

[16] R. Robinson, J. Chem. Soc., 745 (1930).

[17] W. G. Brown and O. K. Neville, Atomic Energy Commission, MDDC 1168.

[18] Mandelic acid acid-α-C^{13} has also been prepared by a different method by W. v E. Doering, T. I. Taylor, and E. F. Schoenewaldt, J. Am. Chem. Soc., 70, 455 (1948).

glyoxal hydrate. The reaction is cooled, and 30 ml of 10% sodium hydroxide is added very slowly through the condenser. After the vigorous reaction has subsided, the mixture is allowed to stand with occasional shaking for 1 hour. The contents of the flask are transferred to a separatory funnel, the layers are separated, and the aqueous phase is carefully neutralized with dilute hydrochloric acid to pH 6. Charcoal, 0.1 gram, is added to remove the red coloration, and the solution is filtered. To the filtrate is added excess cadmium chloride; the cadmium mandelate is precipitated and is filtered and dried. The crystals are dissolved in the minimum amount of concentrated hydrochloric acid; the solution is saturated with sodium chloride and is extracted with five 10-ml portions of ether. The ether is evaporated, and the resulting mandelic acid is recrystallized from benzene, collected, and dried in a vacuum. The yield is 0.95 gram (75%).

9. α Amino Acids

Glycine

This substance, labeled with isotopic carbon, has been synthesized by several different methods in yields of 34–81%. The choice of synthetic method might well be governed by the choice of isotope, availability of starting materials, and general convenience. Carboxyl-labeled acetate has been converted into glycine in 34% yield with bromoacetic acid as an intermediate,[1] and in 53% yield with chloroacetic acid as an intermediate.[2] Isotopic cyanide has been used to make glycine through N-chloromethylphthalimide in 81% yield [3] and through methylene-amino acetonitrile in 45% yield.[4] Doubly labeled glycine has also been prepared with acetylene as the intermediate.[5]

Glycine-1-C^{13}.[3] N-Hydroxymethylphthalimide [6] (22.5 grams) is allowed to stand for 2 hours with excess sulfurous oxychloride. The mixture is heated for 30

$$\text{H}_2\text{NCH}_2\text{C*OOH} + \quad \text{(81\% overall yield)} \quad + \text{NH}_4\text{Cl}$$

[1] N. Olsen, A. Hemingway, and A. O. Nier, *J. Biol. Chem.*, **148**, 611 (1943).
[2] R. Ostwald, *J. Biol. Chem.*, **173**, 207 (1948).
[3] W. Sakami, W. E. Evans, and S. Gurin, *J. Am. Chem. Soc.*, **69**, 1110 (1947).
[4] R. B. Loftfield, *Nucleonics*, **1**, No. 3, 54 (1947).
[5] S. Gurin and A. M. Delluva, *J. Biol. Chem.*, **170**, 545 (1947).
[6] F. Sachs, *Ber.*, **31**, 1225, 3230 (1898).

minutes on a boiling water bath, the excess sulfurous oxychloride is removed by evaporation, and the residue is recrystallized from toluene. N-chloromethylphthalimide (19 grams) melting at 133–134° is obtained (yield 77%).

To a solution of isotopic sodium cyanide in 25 ml of acetone-free methanol is added 2.0 grams of N-chloromethylphthalimide dissolved in 8 ml of warm dioxane. After it has stood for 2 hours at room temperature, the mixture is evaporated to dryness, and the residue is successively extracted with 15-, 10-, and 5-ml portions of warm dioxane. These extracts are combined and evaporated to dryness. The resulting material is hydrolyzed by heating it under reflux for 15 hours with a mixture of 11 ml of acetic acid, 12 ml of concentrated hydrochloric acid, and 13 ml of water. After the reaction mixture is chilled to 0°, phthalic acid is removed by filtration, and the residue is evaporated to dryness in vacuum. The residue is dissolved in water, and chloride ion is removed with excess silver carbonate. The filtrate and washings are combined, evaporated to approximately 25 ml, and saturated with hydrogen sulfide. After removal of the silver sulfide by filtration, the filtrate and washings are evaporated to dryness, the residue is taken up in a few milliliters of water, and the glycine is precipitated by means of 95% ethanol. The product after being washed with 95% ethanol is dried (m.p. 238–239°). The yield of glycine is 0.62 gram (81% based on the sodium cyanide used).

Glycine-1-C^{14} and Glycine-2-C^{14}.[2] Acetic acid obtained from 1.408 grams of carboxyl-labeled acetate is distilled into the small reaction vessel (see Fig. 80) which is cooled in liquid nitrogen. The product consisted of 80–85% acetic acid, 10–15%

$$CH_3C^*OOH + Cl_2 \xrightarrow[\substack{PCl_5 \\ 67\%}]{P, I_2} \underset{\underset{Cl}{|}}{CH_2C^*OOH} + HCl$$

$$\underset{\underset{Cl}{|}}{CH_2C^*OOH} + NH_3 \xrightarrow[79\%]{(NH_4)_2CO_3} \underset{\underset{NH_2}{|}}{CH_2C^*OOH} + NH_4Cl$$

This sequence of reactions has also been carried out on methyl-labeled acetate.

water, and considerable hydrogen chloride. The low-temperature condenser, cooled with a Dry Ice-isopropyl alcohol mixture, is attached to the reaction vessel, which is allowed to come to room temperature; 0.65 gram of non-radioactive acetic anhydride is added, and the mixture is boiled under reflux for 1 hour to remove the water that is present. A mixture of 0.02 gram of iodine, 0.04 gram of red phosphorus, and 0.08 gram of phosphorus pentachloride is added, and dry chlorine gas is passed through the system at reflux temperature for $2\frac{1}{2}$ hours. The whole apparatus is then evacuated to 3×10^{-2} mm, and all the material from the condenser and gas inlet tube is distilled back into the reaction vessel, which is cooled in liquid nitrogen. The chloroacetic acid is isolated by fractional sublimation onto a cold-finger condenser filled with powdered Dry Ice. The yield of pure product was 1.52 gram (67% based on sodium acetate), m.p. 60°. Other runs gave yields of 85–90%.

A mixture of 3.2 grams of powdered ammonium carbonate, 10 ml of concentrated ammonium hydroxide, and 4 ml of water is heated in a small three-neck flask fitted with a pressure-equalizing dropping funnel, a condenser, and a thermometer. After the salt has dissolved, 1.014 grams of carboxyl-labeled chloroacetic acid in 3 ml of water is added dropwise through the dropping funnel at such a rate that the temperature of the solution does not exceed 60°. The mixture is held at 60° for 6 hours and is then allowed to stand for 12 hours at room temperature. The solution is then concentrated until the temperature reaches 112°. The distillate shows only slight radioactivity. The yellowish solution is cooled to 70°, and 15 ml of methanol is added slowly with agitation. The mixture is cooled in the refrigerator for 1 hour. The precipitate is filtered and washed with methanol and ether. The yield of pure

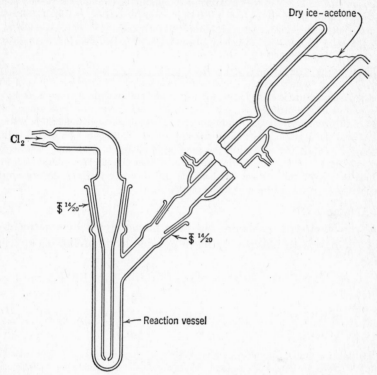

FIG. 80. Apparatus for the chlorination of acetic acid. (Ostwald.)

white crystals gives no test for chloride ion and weighs 0.54 gram. Upon concentration, the mother liquor gives an additional 0.08 gram, increasing the yield to 0.62 gram or 79% based on chloroacetic acid.

Glycine-1-C^{14}.[4] Glycine is prepared from methyleneamino acetonitrile [7] by a known procedure.[8]

$$2HCHO + KC^*N + NH_4Cl \rightarrow CH_2{=}NCH_2C^*N + KCl + 2H_2O$$
$$CH_2{=}NCH_2C^*N + 2C_2H_5OH + H_2SO_4 \rightarrow H_2NCH_2C^*N \cdot H_2SO_4 + CH_2(OC_2H_5)_2$$
$$2H_2NCH_2C^*N \cdot H_2SO_4 + 3Ba(OH)_2 \rightarrow$$
$$(H_2NCH_2C^*OO)_2Ba + 2BaSO_4 + 2H_2O + 2NH_3$$
$$(H_2NCH_2C^*OO)_2Ba + H_2SO_4 \rightarrow 2H_2NCH_2C^*OOH + BaSO_4$$

Hydrogen cyanide, prepared from 195 μmoles of radioactive barium carbonate as described on page 160, is distilled into a centrifuge tube (cooled in liquid nitrogen)

[7] R. Adams and W. P. Langley, *Org. Syntheses, Coll. Vol.* I, 2nd Ed., p. 355, John Wiley & Sons, New York, 1941.

[8] W. V. Anslow and H. King, *Org. Syntheses, Coll. Vol.* I, 2nd Ed., p. 298, 1941.

containing 1.0 ml of 40% aqueous formaldehyde (formalin), 0.30 gram of ammonium chloride, and 0.06 gram of potassium hydroxide. The vessel is warmed to 0° for 20 minutes and is chilled in liquid nitrogen while 0.13 gram of non-isotopic potassium cyanide in 0.7 ml of water is added. After 20 minutes more at 0°, the vessel is again frozen and 0.19 ml of acetic acid and 0.13 gram of potassium cyanide dissolved in 0.7 ml of water are added. After standing at 0° for 1 hour, the mixture is centrifuged and the solid material is washed by decantation. Methyleneamino acetonitrile is obtained in 60–65% yield.

The dried crystals are dissolved in 3 ml of hot ethanol, the tube is cooled to 10°, and 0.18 ml of sulfuric acid in 1 ml of ethanol is added. After the addition of 5 ml of ether, the mixture is chilled at 0° for 1 hour and the crystals of amino acetonitrile are separated by centrifugation and decantation, and are washed with ether. The yield in this step is 90–91%. A mixture of 1 ml of sulfuric acid and 2 ml of water is added, and the solution is heated on the steam bath for 6 hours. Saturated barium hydroxide solution is added until the solution is almost neutral, and then barium carbonate is added. Centrifugation and decantation give a clear solution which is evaporated to 0.7 ml. Ethanol (1.5 ml) is added, and crystals of glycine appear which after recrystallization weigh 200 mg (85%).

DL-Alanine-1-C^{14}

Carboxyl-labeled DL-alanine has been prepared [9,10] by treatment of acetaldehyde with isotopic hydrogen cyanide by the following reaction scheme:

$$CH_3CHO + HC^*N + NH_3 \rightarrow CH_3CHC^*N + H_2O$$
$$\underset{NH_2}{|}$$

$$CH_3CH-C^*N + HCl + 2H_2O \rightarrow CH_3CHC^*OOH + NH_4Cl$$
$$\underset{NH_2}{|} \qquad\qquad \underset{NH_2}{|}$$

Hydrogen cyanide, 2 mmoles (see page 160), is transferred to a reaction flask to which is added 4 mmoles of ammonia and 2 mmoles of acetaldehyde. The mixture is allowed to stand overnight. Then 4 ml of 40% hydrobromic acid is added, and the solution is boiled to a paste during 4 hours. The paste is stirred at −40° with 3 ml of methanol, and the mixture is filtered and washed once with 2 ml of methanol. The solution is neutralized with ammonium hydroxide, and 0.30 gram of carrier alanine is added. The solution is cooled and 0.27 gram of alanine is obtained by filtration. The compound is recrystallized and melts at 250° (dec.). More alanine is available from the mother liquors.

DL-Serine-N^{15}-1-C^{13} [11]

$$H_2N^*CH_2C^*OOH \xrightarrow{C_2H_5OH-HCl} ClH_3N^*CH_2C^*OOC_2H_5 \xrightarrow[NaOH]{C_6H_5COCl}$$

$$C_6H_5CON^*HCH_2C^*OOC_2H_5 \xrightarrow{HCOOC_2H_5}$$

$$HOCH{=}C(N^*HCOC_6H_5)C^*OOC_2H_5 \xrightarrow{Al-Hg}$$

$$HOCH_2CH(N^*HCOC_6H_5)C^*OOC_2H_5 \xrightarrow{HCl}$$

$$HOCH_2CH(N^*H_2)C^*OOH$$

[9] S. Gurin and D. W. Wilson, *Federation Proc.*, **1**, 114 (1942).
[10] R. B. Loftfield, *Nucleonics*, **1**, No. 3, 54 (1947).
[11] D. Shemin, *J. Biol. Chem.*, **162**, 297–307 (1946).

Doubly labeled glycine is converted to its ethyl ester. The ester is benzoylated,[12] the ethyl hippurate obtained is condensed with ethyl formate, and the α-hydroxy-methylene-N-benzoylglycine is reduced with aluminum amalgam.[13] The N-ben-zoylserine obtained is hydrolyzed with 20% hydrochloric acid. The solution is filtered, and chloride ion is removed with silver carbonate. The silver salts are removed by filtration, then the solution is concentrated and serine precipitated by adding alcohol.[14] Since no yield data are given, it may be presumed that the experience in this synthesis ran parallel to that reported in the literature cited.

Methionine

DL-Methionine-S^{34}-β,γ-C^{13}.[15]   Although the authors labeled the

$$CH_3C^*H_2NH_2 + CH_3I + NaOH \rightarrow CH_3C^*H_2N(CH_3)_3I$$
$$\searrow$$
$$NaI + H_2O$$

$$\xrightarrow{(+Ag_2O\ +H_2O)} CH_3C^*H_2N(CH_3)_3OH$$

$$CH_3C^*H_2N(CH_3)_3OH \xrightarrow{\Delta} CH_2{=}C^*H_2 \xrightarrow{(+Cl_2)} ClC^*H_2C^*H_2Cl$$
$$\searrow \qquad\qquad\qquad\qquad\qquad 80\%$$
$$+ (CH_3)_3N + H_2O$$

$$C^*H_2ClC^*H_2Cl + C_6H_5CH_2SNa \rightarrow C_6H_5CH_2SC^*H_2C^*H_2Cl + NaCl$$
$$\underset{58\%}{(I)}$$

$$II + NaOH \xrightarrow{(+HCl)}$$
$$C_6H_5CH_2SC^*H_2C^*H_2CH(NH_2)COOH + CO_2 + C_2H_5OH$$
$$\underset{\substack{(III)\\70\%}}{}$$

$$III + Na \xrightarrow{liq.\ NH_3} \xrightarrow{(+CH_3I)} CH_3SC^*H_2C^*H_2CH(NH)_2COOH$$
$$78\%$$

methionine with both sulfur and carbon, the synthesis of thio-labeled benzyl mercaptan [16] will not be described here.

[12] H. Franzen, *Ber.*, **42**, 2465 (1909).
[13] E. Erlenmeyer and F. Stoop, *Ann. Chem.*, **337**, 236 (1904).
[14] A. R. Moss and R. Schoenheimer, *J. Biol. Chem.*, **135**, 415 (1940).
[15] G. W. Kilmer and V. du Vigneaud, *J. Biol. Chem.*, **154**, 247–53 (1944).
[16] H. Tarver and C. L. A. Schmidt, *J. Biol. Chem.*, **130**, 67 (1939).

In a 1-liter three-neck flask fitted with a sealed stirrer, an efficient condenser, and a dropping funnel is placed 11 grams of ethylamine-1-C^{13} (0.24 mole) as a 10% solution in water (page 203). The solution is cooled in ice, and 23.6 grams (0.590 mole) of sodium hydroxide is added in portions. The ice bath is removed, and 65 ml (1.5 mole) of methyl iodide is added slowly enough to prevent boiling at a rate greater than gentle reflux.

More sodium hydroxide is added if necessary to keep the solution alkaline. The solution is stirred for 1 hour at room temperature and 2 hours at reflux temperature. The excess methyl iodide is then removed by distillation. Silver oxide, prepared from 220 grams (1.3 moles) of silver nitrate, is added slowly, while the solution is shaken and cooled. The silver iodide is filtered and washed, and the combined filtrates are concentrated to 200 ml at a pressure of 15 mm.

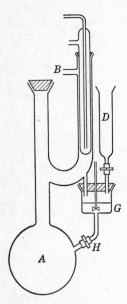

This solution is filtered into a 250-ml distilling flask sealed to a condenser arranged for downward distillation. The condenser is sealed to two receivers in series which are cooled in ice and so arranged that the gas bubbles through an excess of 6 N sulfuric acid. To the exit of the second receiver are sealed four traps in series, cooled by a Dry Ice-trichloroethylene mixture. The first serves to condense moisture, and each of the other three contains 15 ml of a 50 volume per cent solution of chlorine in methylene dichloride; this solution absorbs the ethylene. The vent on the last trap is connected through a calcium chloride tube to a bubble counter. Ground joint connections are used throughout. Provision is made for passing a stream of nitrogen through the apparatus; an open-arm manometer is provided to indicate the pressure drop. The bulk of the water in the distillation flask is distilled into the first trap at a bath temperature of 130–140°; then the temperature is raised to 140–150° and held there for 4 hours. Most of the ethylene is evolved at the end of this period. Finally, the temperature is raised gradually to 210° where it is held for a few minutes.

Fig. 81. Condensation apparatus. (Kilmer and duVigneaud.)

The chlorine traps are unsealed and the chlorine is allowed to evaporate. The residues in the traps are combined, and remaining chlorine is removed by shaking the mixture with sodium bisulfite solution. The organic layer is dried over magnesium sulfate and fractionally distilled. By redistilling the intermediate fraction, a total of 19.3 grams of crude ethylene dichloride, boiling at 77–86°, is obtained. This is an 80% yield based on ethylamine. By titration of the acid in the first two traps it can be shown that the evolution of trimethylamine is essentially quantitative.

In order to minimize the formation of dibenzylethyldisulfide in the condensation of benzyl mercaptan with ethylene dichloride, it is necessary to have the latter present at a concentration 5–10 times that of the mercaptan. Since it would be wasteful of labeled ethylene dichloride to use such an excess and laborious to recover it, the apparatus shown in Fig. 81 is used. Its purpose is to manage the reaction in such a way that a local excess of ethylene dichloride is maintained without the necessity of using a stoichiometric excess.

In the 125-ml bulb A is placed 8.9 grams (90 mmoles) of labeled ethylene dichloride. The dropping funnel D is charged with a solution of 2.2 grams (96 mmoles) of sodium and 11.8 grams (95 mmoles) of benzylmercaptan in 50 ml of dry n-propanol. Calcium chloride tubes at B and the mouth of D keep out moisture. A bath at 100–150° is placed around A, and distillation commences. Ethylene dichloride distils into the 15-ml cup G, where its level is controlled by pinchcock H. Sodium mercaptide solution is run slowly in from D, where it reacts with ethylene dichloride to form the condensation product, which then flows into A. As the circulation proceeds, benzyl-β-chloroethyl sulfide, being relatively non-volatile, accumulates (in A), but the ethylene chloride concentration at the site of reaction remains fairly constant. Ten hours is required for adding the mercaptide.

The reaction mixture is poured into 400 ml of water, the water phase is washed four times with benzene, and the organic solutions are combined. Distillation at reduced pressure yields 9.8 grams of benzyl-β-chloroethyl sulfide, b.p. (1.5 mm) 105–8°. This is a yield of 58% based on ethylene chloride.

Equally good results are obtained with 1-chloro-2-bromoethane, but this is less convenient to prepare.

In a 100-ml centrifuge tube fitted with a rubber stopper carrying a calcium chloride tube are placed 8.3 grams (44.5 mmoles) of the labeled benzyl-β-chloroethyl sulfide, 15.7 grams (48 mmoles) of ethyl sodiophthalimidomalonate, and 1–2 ml of dry toluene. The mixture is heated 5 hours at 170°, then centrifuged. The liquid is decanted, the precipitated sodium chloride is washed well with toluene, and the organic solutions are combined. The toluene is removed at reduced pressure; then the residue is heated for 2 hours in a bath of boiling water with 19.5 ml of ethanol and 50.5 ml of 5 N sodium hydroxide. The lumps of solid that form are broken up as completely as possible during the heating. The mixture is cooled in ice; the solid is collected on a filter and washed twice with alcohol-water (15:1 ml). The filtrate is concentrated to a thick paste in vacuum, and a second crop of solid is obtained which is collected in the same way. The crude sodium salt thus obtained weighs 21.4 grams. This is heated on a steam bath with 222 ml of water and 36.3 ml of concentrated hydrochloric acid for 2 hours; then 135 ml more of hydrochloric acid is added, and the mixture is heated for 45 minutes. The cooled mixture is treated with 1 gram of infusorial earth and 1 gram of charcoal to remove oil, and then filtered; the filtrate is then concentrated to 125 ml and cooled in ice. Ammonia is added until the solution is alkaline to Congo red but acid to litmus, and the solution is placed in a refrigerator. After a few hours, crystals of S-benzylhomocysteine appear which are collected and washed with ice water, alcohol, and ether. The yield is 7.0 grams, 70% based on benzyl-β-chloroethyl sulfide.

A solution of 8.5 grams (37.8 mmoles) of labeled S-benzylhomocysteine in about 75 ml of dry liquid ammonia is prepared in a three-neck flask fitted with a sealed stirrer and a calcium chloride tube. Through the free neck is added sodium metal in small pieces until the persistence of a blue color shows that a slight excess is present. The flask is cooled in a Dry Ice-ether mixture during the reaction. Enough methyl iodide to discharge the color is cautiously added, then 2.4 ml more. The ammonia is allowed to evaporate, the residue is dissolved in 15 ml of water, and 45% hydriodic acid is added until the solution is just alkaline to litmus. A precipitate of 4–5 grams of methionine appears which is collected on a filter. The filtrate is concentrated almost to dryness, 200 ml of absolute ethanol is added, and the mixture is stored overnight in a refrigerator. This brings out 0.9 gram more solid which is combined with the main crop. Combined and recrystallized from water, the crystals weigh 4.4 grams and contain no halogen. The yield is 78%, based on S-benzylhomocysteine.

L-Methionine-methyl-C^{14}.[17]   The synthesis employs the methylation of S-benzylhomocysteine by methyl iodide in liquid ammonia.   Ordi-

$$C*H_3I + C_6H_5CH_2SCH_2CH_2CH(NH_2)COOH \xrightarrow[\text{liq. NH}_3]{Na}$$
$$C*H_3SCH_2CH_2CH(NH_2)COOH$$

narily in this procedure a slight excess of methyl iodide is used.   To minimize loss of valuable radioactive methyl iodide, it would be desirable to use excess benzylhomocysteine, but the authors find that a pure product cannot be obtained by this procedure.   The difficulty is ob-

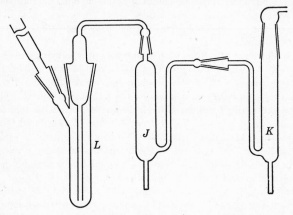

Fig. 82. Apparatus for the synthesis of methionine.   (D. B. Melville, J. R. Rachele, and E. B. Keller.)

viated by using a slight deficiency of radioactive methyl iodide, then finishing the reaction by adding a slight excess of inert methyl iodide; in this way the amount of radioactivity incorporated into the methionine is maximized.

The apparatus used for the preparation is shown in Fig. 82.   In flask L is placed 1.55 grams of dry, powdered S-benzyl-L-homocysteine.[18]   The flask is cooled in a Dry Ice-cellosolve mixture, and 30 ml of anhydrous ammonia is introduced by distillation.   Dry nitrogen is bubbled through the mixture to hasten solution of the solid. Sodium wire is then added through the side arm until a blue color persisting for several minutes indicates that the stoichiometric amount has been added.   Then the temperature of the reaction flask is raised to −50° and the vessel J, containing 0.37 ml of radioactive methyl iodide (page 168), is attached along with the trap K; the methyl iodide is vaporized in a slow current of nitrogen and swept into L.   Trap K is immersed in a Dry Ice-cellosolve mixture to remove water from the nitrogen. The vessel J is warmed to 50°, at which temperature all the methyl iodide evaporates in 30 minutes.   A nitroprusside test is performed on a small sample of the reaction

- [17] D. B. Melville, J. R. Rachele, and E. B. Keller, *J. Biol. Chem.*, **169**, 419–426 (1947).
- [18] V. du Vigneaud and W. I. Patterson, *J. Biol. Chem.*, **109**, 97 (1935).

mixture; if positive, inert methyl iodide is added in 0.025-ml portions through the side arm until a negative response is obtained. The ammonia is then evaporated slowly in the current of nitrogen.

The white, solid residue is dissolved in 15–20 ml of water, and hydriodic acid is added until the solution is acid to litmus but alkaline to Congo red. The solution is filtered, then concentrated at reduced pressure to 5–10 ml. The mixture is heated to dissolve material which has crystallized, then to the hot solution is added 100 ml of boiling absolute ethanol. After standing overnight at 5°, the mixture is filtered; the silvery crystals of methionine are washed with alcohol, then ether, and dried. The yield is 860 mg; 84% based on total methyl iodide used. The product melts at 283° with decomposition; $[\alpha]_D^{22} - 7.75°$ (2-dm tube, C = 0.95 in water).

Analysis. Calculated for $C_5H_{11}O_2NS$: N, 9.38; S, 21.48. *Found:* N, 9.32; S, 21.70.

DL-Phenylalanine-α, Carboxyl-C¹⁴.[19]

$$H_2NC^*H_2C^*OOH + C_6H_5COCl + 2NaOH \rightarrow$$
$$C_6H_5CONHC^*H_2C^*OONa + NaCl + 2H_2O$$

$$C_6H_5CONHC^*H_2C^*OONa + HCl \rightarrow$$
$$C_6H_5CONHC^*H_2C^*OOH + NaCl$$

$$C_6H_5CONHC^*H_2C^*OOH + C_6H_5CHO \xrightarrow[(AcO)_2O]{AcONa}$$

$$3C_6H_5CH_2C^*H(NH_3I)C^*OOH + 3C_6H_5COOH + 2H_3PO_3$$

$$C_6H_5CH_2C^*H(NH_3I)C^*OOH + NH_4OH \rightarrow$$
$$C_6H_5CH_2C^*H(NH_2)C^*OOH + NH_4I$$
$$69\%$$

As the first step in the preparation of phenylalanine, doubly labeled glycine (page 215) is benzoylated to form hippuric acid.[20] The azlactone is then prepared by

[19] S. Gurin and A. M. Delluva, *J. Biol. Chem.*, **170**, 545–550 (1947). Experimental details through the courtesy of the authors.

[20] A. W. Ingersoll and S. H. Babcock, *Org. Syntheses, Coll. Vol.* II, p. 328, John Wiley & Sons, New York, 1943.

condensing 2.35 grams (13.1 mmoles) of the hippuric acid with 1.33 grams (13.2 mmoles) of benzaldehyde; to catalyze the reaction, 3.71 ml of acetic anhydride and 1.08 grams of fused sodium acetate are added. The mixture is constantly stirred for 1 hour at 110° C, then heated to the point of complete liquefaction; the reaction is completed by placing the mixture in a bath of boiling water for 2 hours. The mixture is removed from the bath and kept cool while 5 ml of ethanol is gradually added to decompose the acetic anhydride; then the azlactone is allowed to crystallize overnight in a refrigerator. The cold mixture is filtered and the product is washed with a few milliliters of cold ethanol, followed by a similar amount of boiling water. The yield of crude product, melting at 162–167°, is 2.36 grams; 72% based on glycine.

To a stirred mixture of the crude azlactone (9.9 mmoles) with 1.9 grams (59 mmoles) of red phosphorus and 12 ml of acetic anhydride is added, over a period of $\frac{1}{2}$ hour, 12 ml of hydriodic acid (d, 1.7). The mixture is refluxed 5 hours, then filtered. The filtrate is evaporated to dryness in vacuum, the residue is dissolved in 10 ml of water, and the evaporation is repeated to remove as much hydriodic acid as possible. The residue is dissolved in a mixture of 15 ml of water and 15 ml of ether, and benzoic acid is extracted with three 10-ml portions of ether. The water solution is warmed to expel ether, and a small amount of free iodine which is present is reduced with sodium sulfite. The solution is concentrated somewhat, Norite is added, and the solution is heated to boiling; it is then cooled in ice and filtered. The filtrate is concentrated to about 10 ml and adjusted at the boiling point to pH 6 with concentrated ammonia. Several fractions of phenylalanine can be obtained from this solution. The total yield of recrystallized product is 1.08 grams, 69% based on the azlactone. The overall yield, based on glycine, is 50%.

DL-Tyrosine-β-C^{14} [21]

$$3(I) + 2P + 9HI + 12H_2O \rightarrow$$

$$+ 3NH_4I + 3CO_2 + 2H_3PO_3 + 3CH_3I$$

[21] J. C. Reid and H. B. Jones, *J. Biol. Chem.*, 174, 427 (1948).

Carbonyl-labeled *p*-anisaldehyde is prepared in the manner described on page 197 from 0.64 gram of labeled *p*-anisic acid. On the basis of the known yield in this synthesis, the quantity of aldehyde can be calculated to be 0.42 gram (3.08 mmoles). To the aldehyde, contained in a 14 by 100 mm heavy-wall Pyrex ignition tube, is added 0.55 gram (5.5 mmoles) of hydantoin, 0.7 ml of dry diethylamine, and 1.2 ml of dry pyridine. The tube is sealed and heated 72 hours in steam. It is opened, and the solvent is removed in vacuum at room temperature; then pumping is continued 1.5 hours at 100°. The residue is stirred with three 2-ml portions of hot water, each portion being removed by a filter stick before the addition of the next. The yellow residue of anisalhydantoin weighed 0.60 gram after drying at 90°. This is a yield of 93% based on anisaldehyde and is in agreement with values around 90% found in pilot experiments with pure anisaldehyde.

To the anisalhydantoin, still contained in the ignition tube, is added 0.19 gram of red phosphorus and 2.4 ml of freshly distilled hydriodic acid (*d*, 1.7). A cold finger, made from a 5-ml conical centrifuge tube, is hung in the mouth of the test tube, and the mixture is refluxed 5 hours; 0.63 gram of iodine is then added, and the mixture is refluxed 5.5 hours longer.

The solution is filtered into a 30-ml flask and evaporated to dryness under vacuum at room temperature. To remove as much hydriodic acid as possible, the residue is dissolved in 5 ml of water and the evaporation is repeated; the residue is then dissolved in 5 ml of water. A yellow turbidity is present, which increases with dilution. Water is added until no further increase in turbidity occurs (25 ml), and the solution is clarified by centrifugation. The solution is then adjusted to *p*H 5 with concentrated ammonia, and a slight precipitate which appears is removed by filtration.[22] The filtrate is evaporated in vacuum, and the residue is heated 15 minutes at 100°. The residue is washed with water onto a filter, where it is well washed with water, followed by alcohol. The yield is 177 mg (36% based on anisalhydantoin). Reported analysis of a specimen prepared in this way (starting with inactive barium carbonate):

Analysis. *Calculated for* $C_9H_{11}NO_3$: C, 59.66; H, 6.12; N, 7.74.
Found: C, 58.15; H, 6.01; N, 7.76
58.24; 6.15; 7.66.

DL-3,4-Dihydroxyphenylalanine-β-C^{14} (Dopa) [23]

(I)
83%

<hr />

[22] This precipitate appears to be impure tyrosine. Since it is scanty in amount and turns brown on drying, it is discarded.

[23] J. C. Reid, unpublished work.

$$
\text{I} + \text{Na—Hg} + \text{H}_2\text{O} \xrightarrow[\text{NaOH}]{\text{(+HCl)}}
$$

C*H₂—CH——C=O (ring structure with HN, NH, C=O; CH₃O and OCH₃ on aromatic ring)

+ NaCl

(II)
60%

$$
\text{II} + \text{Ba(OH)}_2 \xrightarrow[\text{NH}_3 + \text{BaCO}_3]{\text{(H}_2\text{SO}_4)}
$$

C*H₂CH(NH₂)COOH (aromatic ring with CH₃O and OCH₃)

+ BaSO₄

(III)
73%

$$
\text{III} + \text{HI} \rightarrow
$$

C*H₂CH(NH₂)COOH (aromatic ring with HO and OH)

+ CH₃I

79%

Hydantoin Condensation. Carbonyl-labeled veratraldehyde is prepared in the manner described on page 199 from 1.03 grams of labeled veratric acid. From yield data for this operation, the amount of aldehyde can be calculated to be 0.69 gram (4.1 mmoles). To the aldehyde, contained in a 14 by 100 mm heavy-wall Pyrex ignition tube, are added 0.60 gram (6.0 mmoles) of hydantoin, 0.60 gram of fused sodium acetate, and 2.5 ml of acetic anhydride. The tube is evacuated and sealed, then completely submerged for 80 minutes in an oil bath at 130° C. The tube is opened, and the contents are stirred 5 minutes with 10 ml of hot water to hydrolyze the acetic anhydride, then hot water (30 ml) is added until no more precipitate forms. The mixture is promptly filtered, and the yellow veratralhydantoin is washed with hot water. The dried crude compound melts at 176–186° and weighs 0.85 gram; 83% based on veratraldehyde.

Reduction of Veratralhydantoin. The veratralhydantoin is dissolved in 25 ml of water containing 1 ml of 6 N sodium hydroxide, and reduction is effected by adding 3% sodium amalgam to the solution, which is stirred mechanically. Twelve grams of amalgam is added over a period of 4 hours, then stirring is continued 7 hours more. The solution is adjusted to pH 8 with concentrated hydrochloric acid, 2 grams more of amalgam is added, and stirring is continued 1.5 hours. The solution is decanted, exactly neutralized with hydrochloric acid, charcoaled, and filtered. The filtrate is concentrated to 5 ml under vacuum and filtered. The pure white veratrylhydantoin on the filter is washed with three 2-ml portions of cold water and dried. It weighs 0.50 gram (60% based on veratralhydantoin); m.p. 148–153 uncor.

Hydrolysis of Veratrylhydantoin. To a mixture of 20 ml of water and 10 grams of barium hydroxide monohydrate is added the veratrylhydantoin, and the solution is refluxed 9 hours. The mixture is diluted with 10 ml of water and kept hot while exactly enough 6 N sulfuric acid to precipitate the barium is added. The mixture is filtered and the barium sulfate washed with four 20-ml portions of hot water.[24] The filtrate is concentrated to 2 ml in a stream of air and diluted with 5 ml of ethanol. After standing in a refrigerator overnight, the pure white dimethoxyphenylalanine which has crystallized is collected by filtration, washed twice with 3-ml portions of ethanol, and dried. The weight is 0.33 gram (73% based on veratrylhydantoin); decomposition temperature, about 215°.

Demethylation of Dimethoxyphenylalanine. The dimethoxyphenylalanine is placed in a 14 by 100 mm heavy-wall Pyrex ignition tube with 0.02 gram of red phosphorus and 4.5 ml of freshly distilled hydriodic acid (sp. gr., 1.7). The tube is evacuated, sealed, and submerged for 1 hour in an oil bath at 120°. The contents are then filtered into a small flask and evaporated in vacuum. The residue is dissolved in 3 ml of water and evaporated again, to remove as much hydriodic acid as possible. The residue is dissolved in 4 ml of water and adjusted to pH 6 with concentrated ammonia. The solvent is evaporated in vacuum; the residue is triturated under 2 ml of water and washed onto a filter. There it is washed twice with 1 ml of water and twice with 1 ml of ethanol. After drying in a vacuum desiccator, the nearly colorless (slightly gray) dihydroxyphenylalanine weighs 0.23 gram (79% based on dimethoxyphenylalanine); m.p., 270–273 uncor. (dec.).

Analysis. Calculated for $C_9H_{11}O_4N$: C, 54.82; H, 5.62; N, 7.10.
     Found: 52.98; 5.76; 6.50.
         53.02; 5.60; 6.32.

DL-Tryptophan-β-C^{14} [25]

DL-Tryptophan-β-C^{14} has been prepared by suitable modification [26, 27] of known procedures.

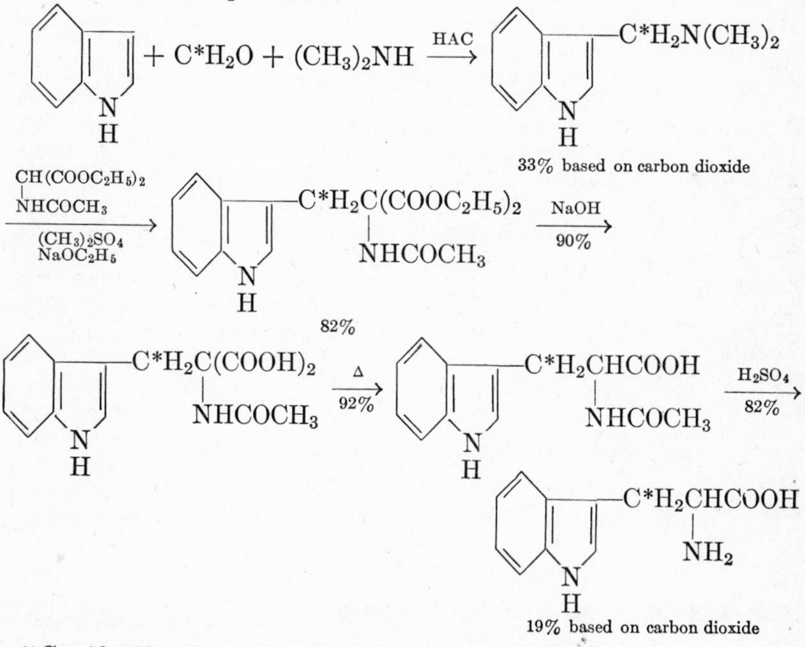

33% based on carbon dioxide

82%

19% based on carbon dioxide

---

[24] Considerable radioactivity remains in the barium sulfate.
[25] C. Heidelberger, *J. Biol. Chem.*, **175**, 471 (1948).
[26] H. R. Snyder and C. W. Smith, *J. Am. Chem. Soc.*, **66**, 350 (1944).
[27] N. F. Albertson, S. Archer, and C. M. Suter, *J. Am. Chem. Soc.*, **67**, 36 (1945).

Formaldehyde is prepared as described on page 166 and is absorbed in 0.7 ml of water with a small amount of methanol added. A cooled mixture of 1.42 grams of 33% aqueous dimethylamine and 1.42 grams of glacial acetic acid is prepared, and to it is added the cooled formalin solution. This reaction mixture is then poured onto 1.10 grams of indole in a centrifuge tube. The indole dissolves with the evolution of heat and is allowed to stand at room temperature for 18 hours. The light yellow solution is added dropwise to an ice-cold solution of 1.42 grams of sodium hydroxide in 20 ml of water. A white crystalline precipitate of gramine forms and is filtered, weight, 1.39 grams (33% based on carbon dioxide), m.p. 121–126°. The material is completely soluble in dilute hydrochloric acid, indicating that no unchanged indole is present.

Sodium, 0.18 gram, is dissolved in specially dried absolute ethanol, and to the solution is added 1.70 grams of acetaminomalonic ester and 1.29 grams of labeled gramine. The mixture is stirred mechanically, and, when solution is complete, 1.2 ml of dimethyl sulfate is added. The reaction heats up, and mechanical stirring at room temperature is continued for 4 hours. A little water is added until the sodium sulfate dissolves, and then the alcoholic solution is added dropwise to 50 ml of ice water. The crystalline precipitate is allowed to stand overnight in the refrigerator, and is filtered, washed with water, and dried, weight, 2.10 grams (82%), m.p. 131–133.5°.

The ester (2.10 grams) is refluxed for 3 hours with a solution of 1.20 grams of sodium hydroxide in 10 ml of water. On cooling and acidification, 1.57 grams (90%) of the malonic acid, m.p., 135–138° (dec.), is obtained. This compound undergoes decarboxylation when it is heated to 140°, and the resulting acetyl tryptophan is recrystallized from alcohol-water with a trace of hydrosulfite, to give a 92% yield of colorless plates, m.p. 206–208°.

Hydrolysis of the acetyl tryptophan is accomplished by boiling 0.53 gram of it for 4 hours under nitrogen, with 6 ml of 2 N sulfuric acid and a crystal of stannous chloride. About 30 ml of water is added, and the solution is heated, decolorized with charcoal, and neutralized to phenolphthalein with barium hydroxide. The barium sulfate is removed by filtration of the hot solution, which is then evaporated to dryness. The resulting tryptophan is recrystallized from 15 ml of acetic acid and 15 ml of benzene to give 0.54 gram (82%) of glistening plates of tryptophan, acetate salt, which contains one molecule of acetic acid of crystallization. This represents a yield of 19% based on carbon dioxide.

Analysis. Calculated for $C_{15}H_{20}O_6N_2$, m.w. = 324.37. C, 55.52; H, 6.15.
Found: C, 55.51; H, 6.12.

10. Aromatic Hydrocarbons and Carcinogens

Toluene-1,3,5-C^{14} [1]

$$H_3C \quad COONa$$

$$4CH_3\overset{*}{C}OCOOH + 5NaOH \longrightarrow NaOOC \overset{*}{\underset{}{}} \overset{*}{} COONa + NaOOC\overset{*}{C}OONa + 7H_2O$$

I
68%   71%

[1] D. M. Hughes and J. C. Reid, unpublished work.

To a solution of 22 grams (0.55 mole) of sodium hydroxide in 39 ml of water is added dropwise 10.6 grams (0.12 mole) of pyruvic acid-α-C^{14}. The solution is contained in a 125-ml Erlenmeyer flask which is cooled in ice during the addition and swirled to minimize local heating. The time required for the addition is about $\frac{1}{2}$ hour; if excessive local heating occurs, or if the order of mixing is reversed, the yield is lowered. After the acid has been added, the pale yellow mixture is heated 3.5 hours on a steam bath. During this time, the color becomes deep orange and a precipitate of sodium oxalate appears. The mixture is chilled, and the sodium oxalate is collected on a sintered-glass filter where it is washed with three 5-ml portions of 12 M sodium hydroxide. A typical yield is 71%, based on pyruvic acid.

Methyldihydrotrimesic Acid-1,3,5-C^{14} (I). The filtrate obtained after removal of sodium oxalate in the synthesis just described for that compound is acidified with 50 ml of concentrated hydrochloric acid. During the acidification, the solution is cooled to prevent decomposition of the methyldihydrotrimesic acid. The white precipitated solid is collected on a sintered-glass filter, where it is washed with 25 ml of water in 3- to 4-ml portions. The yield of crude acid is about 68%, based on pyruvic acid. The principal impurity in the product is sodium chloride; purification can be accomplished by one crystallization from dilute ethanol at a temperature below 60° C. The acid absorbs water from the atmosphere to form a monohydrate; the anhydrous acid can be obtained by drying the hydrate in high vacuum at room temperature.

Uvitic Acid-1,3,5-C^{14} (II).

In a 50-ml flask are placed 4.74 grams of crude dry methyldihydrotrimesic acid and 20 ml of concentrated sulfuric acid. Provision is made for passing a stream of nitrogen through the flask. The flask is immersed in an oil bath, which is gradually heated; when the temperature reaches 120°, decarboxylation commences. When the evolution of carbon monoxide [2] slackens, the temperature of the bath is raised to 150°, where it is held for 2 hours. The flask is cooled somewhat, and the contents are poured into 100 ml of water, whereupon the uvitic acid (II) separates. The mixture is allowed to become hot, for the solid which separates from a hot solution is less difficult to filter than when prepared in the cold. The dark gray crude acid is collected on a sintered-glass filter and washed free of sulfate. A typical yield is 3.53 grams, 100% based on methyldihydrotrimesic acid. The acid can be purified by crystallization from dilute ethanol, using charcoal.

Toluene-1,3,5-C^{14}. The apparatus used for the decarboxylation is shown in Fig.

[2] An interesting feature of this reaction is the loss of the carboxyl carbon atom as carbon monoxide.

83. The reaction vessel A is a 2 by 23 cm tube with a side arm attached a short distance below the mouth and terminating in a 10/30 ground joint. Provision is made for admitting nitrogen through a 24/40 ground joint, whose inner member has an extension which protrudes into the vessel to a point a few millimeters above the side arm. The tube is heated by a salt bath; a Transite disk B prevents the lubricant (silicone) in the ground joints from becoming excessively hot. The vessel is connected to the unit D, which consists of a fore trap whose capacity is about 5 ml, sealed to a second trap consisting of six turns of 7-mm Pyrex tubing, terminating in

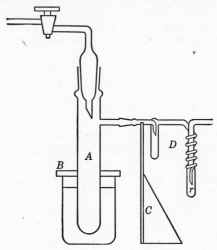

Fig. 83.   Decarboxylation apparatus.

the receptacle r. A Transite shield C protects the trap unit from the heat of an electric heater used to heat the salt bath.

Vessel A is charged with 2.03 grams of crude uvitic acid, 0.30 gram of powdered copper oxide, and 10 ml of freshly distilled synthetic quinoline, and connected to the train. The air is swept out of the system with nitrogen, then the stopcock at the entrance to A is closed. A Dry Ice-isopropanol mixture is placed around the spiral trap, and the temperature of the contents of A is raised from 150° to 265° over a period of 1 hour. The fore trap is not cooled; it collects some water and toluene and a certain amount of quinoline which distils with them. This partial removal of the extraneous substances reduces difficulty from plugs of frozen material in the coils of the spiral trap. When the bath temperature reaches 265°, a current of nitrogen (25 cc/min) is directed through the apparatus, and the temperature of the mixture is held at $265 \pm 5°$ for 3 hours. The spiral trap is watched closely, and the cooling bath is removed for brief intervals if necessary to allow plugs to melt and fall into the receptacle. Toward the end of the reaction, toluene in the fore trap is driven into r by stroking the trap with a soft flame.

The toluene is purified with the aid of the arrangement shown in Fig. 84. This consists of a high-vacuum manifold to which are attached vessels D, F, and G. A trap H is situated in the line. The unit D contains the crude toluene; the entrance to the fore trap is closed by a ground-glass plug. Vessel F contains 10 grams of phosphorus pentoxide, and G is a receptacle for purified toluene made by sealing a

3-mm straight-bore stopcock to a graduated 15-ml centrifuge tube. The stopcock and the ground joint by which the receptacle is attached to the manifold are sealed to the centrifuge tube on a lathe, to insure that all the segments are coaxial; it is then possible to insert a long capillary pipet into the tube to withdraw increments of toluene for use, and the receptacle can be used as a storage vessel.

The toluene is distilled in high vacuum (Chapter 8) into the phosphorus pentoxide tube; the last of the toluene is driven out of D by warming the vessel to 40° in a bath of water. The tube F is removed from the manifold and gently shaken to distribute

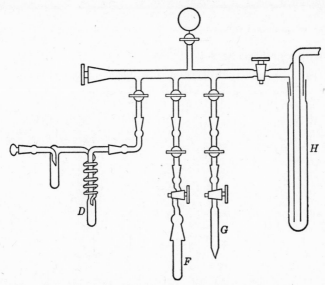

FIG. 84. Apparatus for the purification of toluene.

the toluene and phosphorus pentoxide over the entire wall area, except for the region near the stopcock. The vessel is again attached to the manifold, and the toluene is distilled into G. A soft flame is passed a few times over F to drive out the last of the toluene. A typical yield is 0.901 gram, 87% based on uvitic acid. The toluene is obtained in good purity; mass spectrometric analysis shows total impurities in the range of mass numbers 0 to 200 to be less than 0.2%.

Mesitylene-1,3,5-C^{14} and 1,3,5-Trimethylcyclohexane-1,3,5-C^{14} [3]

[3] A. V. Grosse and S. Weinhouse, *Science*, **104**, 402 (1946).

The condensation of acetone to mesitylene is brought about by the action of concentrated sulfuric acid.[4] From 1.63 grams of labeled acetone, 0.296 gram of crude mesitylene is obtained. For the purpose of purification, the crude mesitylene is converted to the monosulfonic acid; in order to minimize handling losses, it is diluted before conversion with 0.865 gram of inactive mesitylene. The crystallized sulfonic acid (m.p., 74–75° C) is decomposed with concentrated hydrochloric acid, and the mesitylene is recovered by steam distillation. The product is separated from water and collected in high vacuum over sodium. The yield of purified product is 0.672 gram; n_D^{20}, 1.4976. Of the total activity in the acetone, 10% is obtained in the purified mesitylene. Labeled 1,3,5-trimethylcyclohexane is prepared from labeled mesitylene by catalytic hydrogenation at high pressure in microbomb.

1,2,5,6-Dibenzanthracene-9-C^{14} [5]

This carcinogenic hydrocarbon has been prepared with isotopic carbon [5] by suitable modifications of the standard method of synthe-

sis.[6] The reactions employed follow. The overall yield based on barium carbonate was 11%.

The preparation of carboxyl-labeled naphthoic acid is described on page 181.

To a suspension of 0.95 gram of carboxyl-labeled naphthoic acid in 8 ml of dry benzene is added 2 ml of purified thionyl chloride, and the mixture is refluxed for 1 hour, after which the excess thionyl chloride and benzene are distilled in vacuum. A mechanical stirrer is attached to the flask containing the dark, crystalline acid chloride, and a solution of 0.95 gram of redistilled β-methylnaphthalene in 4 ml of carbon disulfide is added. Anhydrous aluminum chloride (0.95 gram) is added over a period of 15 minutes, and the dark mixture is refluxed for 1 hour. The hydrolysis

⁴ R. Adams and R. W. Hufferd, *Org. Syntheses, Coll. Vol.* I, 2nd Ed., p. 341, John Wiley & Sons, New York, 1941.

⁵ C. Heidelberger, P. Brewer, and W. G. Dauben, *J. Am. Chem. Soc.*, **69**, 1389 (1947).

⁶ L. F. Fieser, *Organic Reactions*, Vol. I, p. 151, John Wiley & Sons, New York, 1942.

is accomplished with dilute hydrochloric acid, and the carbon disulfide is removed by steam distillation. The ketone is extracted with benzene, washed with water, and distilled. A yield of 1.30 grams (80%) of yellowish, viscous oil was obtained, b.p. 212–215° (0.15 mm).

The Elbs pyrolysis is run in a small distillation flask with a sealed-on receiver, heated in a salt bath thermostatically controlled at 435°. The ketone (1.25 grams) is pyrolyzed for 3.5 hours; the gases evolved are passed directly into a combustion furnace by sweeping the entire system with nitrogen. A precipitate of 0.330 gram of barium carbonate of high specific activity is obtained. When the reaction is complete, glass wool to prevent bumping is added, the top of the flask is sealed, and the dibenzanthracene is distilled at 1 mm, bath temperature 350–400°. The yellow distillate is dissolved in hot benzene and crystallized to give 0.330 gram of yellow dibenzanthracene, m.p. 231–243°. The purification is accomplished by boiling for 1 hour a mixture of 0.330 gram of yellow dibenzanthracene and 0.07 gram of freshly prepared lead tetraacetate in 16 ml of benzene and 16 ml of acetic acid. This treatment preferentially oxidizes the linear isomer which accompanies the dibenzanthracene. The reaction mixture is concentrated to a volume of 12 ml. The colorless dibenzanthracene is removed by filtration and washed with cold acetic acid: yield, 0.230 gram; m.p., 249–253°. The product is recrystallized from benzene to give pure colorless plates of dibenzanthracene: yield, 0.207 gram; m.p., 259–262° (18%).

Radioactive dibenzanthracene of low specific activity is also mentioned [7] in connection with an investigation of radioautographic technique, but no details of its preparation are furnished.

20-Methylcholanthrene-11-C^{14}

The synthesis of this carcinogen [8] is also accomplished by means of an Elbs pyrolysis, but the intermediate ketone is prepared through the cadmium reaction.

Carboxyl-labeled 1-naphthoic acid (2.480 grams, 14 mmoles), see page 181, is heated on the steam bath for 2 hours with 10 ml of purified thionyl chloride. The excess reagent is removed at reduced pressure, and the residual acid chloride is dis-

[7] A. V. Grosse and J. C. Snyder, *Science*, **105**, 240 (1947).
[8] W. G. Dauben, *J. Org. Chem.*, **13**, 313 (1948).

solved in dry benzene, and the benzene is distilled. This process is repeated twice, and the acid chloride is dissolved in 10 ml of benzene.

A mixture of 12.3 grams (58 mmoles) of 4-bromo-7-methylhydrindene, 1.46 grams (60 mmoles) of magnesium, and a few drops of ethyl iodide in 50 ml of ether and 20 ml of benzene is refluxed under nitrogen for 24 hours. The resulting Grignard reagent is converted into the dialkylcadmium compound with 6.4 grams (35 mmoles) of anhydrous cadmium chloride. The mixture is refluxed for 1 hour, the solvents are distilled, and 25 ml of benzene is added. The solution of 1-naphthoyl chloride is added to the boiling suspension of the cadmium compound, and the resulting mixture is heated for 1 hour. The reaction mixture is decomposed with dilute hydrochloric acid, and the mixture is distilled with steam to remove benzene and volatile neutral by-products. The remaining aqueous suspension of the residual syrup is extracted with ether; the ethereal solution is washed with water, 1 N sodium hydroxide, and water, and is dried. The product distils at 223–225° at 2 mm to give a yield of 4.063 grams (98.7% based on the acid).

The Elbs reaction is run in a small distillation flask with a sealed-on receiver and is heated in a salt bath at 405–410°. The pyrolysis of 4.06 grams (14.5 mmoles) of carbonyl-labeled 4-(1-naphthoyl)-7-methylhydrindene is carried out for 40 minutes; the evolved gases are swept with nitrogen directly into a combustion furnace. A precipitate of 265 mg of highly radioactive barium carbonate is collected from the combustion. When the reaction is complete, glass wool is added to the flask, the top is sealed, and the methylcholanthrene is distilled at 1 mm, bath temperature 350–400°. The yellow distillate is dissolved in 70 ml of n-propanol, and the solution is concentrated to a volume of 45 ml. The yellow precipitate is crystallized from 50 ml of n-propanol to give 1.436 grams (38%) of yellow needles, m.p. 176.5–177.5°. The overall yield based on barium carbonate is 31%.

Phenanthrene-9-C^{14} [9]

This compound has been prepared [9] by the Wagner rearrangement of 9-fluorenylcarbinol-10-C^{14}.

The solid residue of the methyl ester prepared from 116.3 mg of 9-fluorenecarboxylic acid, see page 187, is dissolved in 5.0 ml of dry ether, and 10.0 ml (0.1508 M) lithium aluminum hydride (in ether) is added. The mixture is stirred for 15 minutes, 5.0 ml of moist ether followed by 5.0 ml of 6 N hydrochloric acid is added, and stirring is continued until both layers are clear. The ether layer is washed with 5.0 ml of

⁹ C. J. Collins, *J. Am. Chem. Soc.*, **70**, 2418 (1948).

6 N hydrochloric acid, then 5.0 ml of water, and is taken to dryness. The solid residue of carbinol is dissolved in 3.0 ml of benzene and is placed on an alumina column (Fisher 80–200 mesh) 26 cm in length and 7 mm in diameter. Benzene is passed through until 30 ml has been collected; then the alcohol is eluted with ethanol. The first 10 ml of filtrate so obtained is evaporated to dryness and dissolved in 5.0 ml of xylene which has been distilled over phosphorus pentoxide, and phosphorus pentoxide is added. (In a practice run with non-radioactive compounds, 7.7 mg of the alcohol in 5.0 ml of xylene was treated with 200 mg of phosphorus pentoxide.) This mixture is refluxed for 30 minutes and allowed to cool; to it is added 5.0 ml of water. The aqueous layer is extracted with 5.0 ml of ether, and the combined ether-xylene layer is washed with two 5-ml portions of water. Concentration yields a yellow solid which is dissolved in 1.0 ml of benzene and placed on a column 7 mm in diameter containing, from the top, 5 cm of alumina, 5 cm of a mixture of Norite and alumina, and then 8 cm of alumina. The column is developed with benzene. The first 15 ml of eluate, upon concentration, yields 80.0 mg of white crystals, m.p. 85–91° (81% crude yield based on the carboxylic acid). One further passage through an alumina column 26 cm in length and 7 mm in diameter gave an unspecified amount of material melting at 94–97°.

Benadryl Hydrochloride-C^{14} [10]

This compound has been prepared by the following series of reactions:

$$C_6H_5MgBr \xrightarrow{C^*O_2} C_6H_5C^*OOH \xrightarrow{SOCl_2} C_6H_5C^*OCl \xrightarrow[CS_2]{\substack{C_6H_6 \\ AlCl_3}}$$
$$\phantom{C_6H_5MgBr \xrightarrow{C^*O_2}} 90\%$$

$$(C_6H_5)_2C^*O \xrightarrow[i\text{-}C_3H_7OH]{Al(OC_3H_7\text{-}i)_3} (C_6H_5)_2C^*HOH \xrightarrow[C_6H_6]{CH_3COBr}$$
$$ 88\% 99\%$$

$$(C_6H_5)_2C^*HBr \xrightarrow[xylene]{HOCH_2CH_2N(CH_3)_2} (C_6H_5)_2C^*HOCH_2CH_2N(CH_3)_2 \cdot HCl$$
$$ 70\% \text{ (55\% based on carbon dioxide)}$$

No experimental details are available at time of press.

11. Steroids

The problems encountered in the total synthesis of steroidal molecules are very complex, owing to the large number of stereoisomers encountered in these hydrogenated fused-ring systems. To date, the total synthesis of two of these substances, equilenin and estrone, has been accomplished.[1,2,3] These preparations involve a considerable number

[10] R. W. Fleming and G. Rieveschl, Jr., abstract of paper presented before the American Chemical Society, New York, September 1947.

[1] W. E. Bachmann, W. Cole, and A. L. Wilds, J. Am. Chem. Soc., 61, 974 (1939).

[2] W. S. Johnson, J. W. Petersen, and C. D. Gutsche, J. Am. Chem. Soc., 67, 2274 (1945).

[3] The total synthesis of estrone has been reported by G. Anner and K. Miescher, Experienta, 4, 25 (1948).

of steps and are impractical for the preparation of isotopically labeled steroids. A method for the introduction of isotopic carbon into cholestenone [4] and testosterone [5] has been worked out. This scheme consists in the elimination of one carbon atom by ozonization and the reintroduction of the carbon labeled with C^{14}. Since only carbon atom 3 is involved, there are no complications involving stereochemical changes.

Cholestenone-3-C^{14} [4]

There was a possibility that both intermediates IV and V might be formed, and that both of them on closing would give cholestenone. However, the carbonyl group of the phenyl acetate could be incorporated into the cholestenone only if IV were the intermediate. The mechanism was checked using radioactive phenyl acetate, and from assay of the cholestenone it was shown that about 90% of the product obtained was derived from intermediate IV.

To a solution of 2.00 grams of cholestenone in a mixture of 30 ml of ethyl acetate and 30 ml of acetic acid at $-10°$ is added 2 molar equivalents of ozone. When the ozone has been passed in, 10 ml of water and 1 ml of 30% hydrogen peroxide are added, and the solution is allowed to stand overnight at room temperature. The mixture is then extracted with ether and washed with water, and the acidic material is extracted with dilute alkali. The neutral material remaining in the ether (240 mg

[4] R. B. Turner, *J. Am. Chem. Soc.*, **69**, 726 (1947).
[5] R. B. Turner, *Science*, **106**, 248 (1947).

of oil) is processed by drying and removal of the solvent in vacuum, and the residue is dissolved in 15 ml of acetic acid and treated for 4 hours at room temperature with 200 mg of periodic acid dihydrate in 1 ml of water and 5 ml of acetic acid. The mixture is then diluted with water, extracted with ether, dried, washed, and extracted with alkali. The combined alkaline extracts are acidified, and the resulting acid is filtered, dissolved in ether, and crystallized from ether-petroleum ether. Crop I, 1.66 grams, m.p. 151.5–152.5°. Crop II, 0.15 gram, m.p. 150–151° (85%). A purified sample melted at 154–157.5°. $[\alpha]_D^{26°} = +34°$. (C = 2.01 in chloroform.)

The keto acid (II) (2.00 grams) is refluxed for 44 hours with 25 ml of acetic anhydride and 10 ml of acetyl chloride. The solvents are removed in vacuum; the residue is extracted with ether, washed with water and sodium carbonate solution, and dried. The solvent is distilled, and the product is crystallized from aqueous acetone. Yield, 1.76 grams (92%); m.p., 92–93.5°. After five recrystallizations from aqueous acetone an analytical sample was obtained, m.p 94–94.5° (needles), $[\alpha]_D^{26°} = -51°$ (C = 2.07 in chloroform).

Analysis. Calculated for $C_{26}H_{42}O_2$: C, 80.77; H, 10.95. *Found*: C, 81.00, H, 10.89.

Sodium hydride (133 mg, 3 equivalents), is weighed, under nitrogen, into a flask containing 3 ml of dry benzene and 715 mg (1 equivalent) of enol-lactone, and 0.46 ml (2 equivalents) of carboxyl-labeled phenyl acetate is added. The flask is attached to a hydrogenation buret system, flushed with dry nitrogen, and stirred magnetically at room temperature for 42 hours. At the end of this time 89% of the hydrogen theoretically possible, based on the sodium hydride, has been evolved. The mixture is acidified by careful addition of dilute hydrochloric acid, and the product is extracted with ether, washed with water then saturated sodium chloride, and filtered through anhydrous sodium sulfate, and the ether is distilled. The bulk of the benzene is removed at room temperature under reduced pressure, and the residue is pumped at 100° with an oil pump with a trap for volatile substances. The residue is refluxed with 25 ml of acetic acid and 3 ml of concentrated hydrochloric acid for 27 hours in a slow stream of nitrogen. (The carbon dioxide evolved is trapped in alkali and subsequently precipitated as barium carbonate.) The solution is cooled, diluted with water, and extracted with ether. The ethereal layer is washed with water, dilute alkali, water, and saturated sodium chloride, is filtered through anhydrous sodium sulfate, and evaporated to dryness. The oily residue which weighs 638 mg is chromatographed on 12 grams of alumina, and a yield of 362 mg of cholestenone (VI), m.p. 75–77° is obtained by elution with petroleum ether and petroleum ether-benzene. This quantity represents a 51% yield based on enol-lactone (III). Crystallization from acetone gives the pure compound, m.p. 80–80.6°, with no depression on a mixture with an authentic sample of cholestenone. $[\alpha]_D^{26°} = +86°$ (C = 1.01 in chloroform. λ max., 241.5 mμ, log ε 4.22.)

Preparation of Phenyl Acetate. Carboxyl-labeled sodium acetate (2.85 grams) is covered with 10 ml of benzene and treated with 5 ml of thionyl chloride in 5 ml of dry benzene. The mixture is allowed to stand at room temperature for 1½ hours, 5 grams of phenol is added, and the mixture is refluxed for 4½ hours. The solution is cooled; diluted with ether; washed with water, dilute sodium hydroxide, water, and saturated sodium chloride; filtered through anhydrous sodium sulfate; evaporated; and fractionated through a small Podbelniak column. Yield, 4.32 grams (91%); b.p. 82.5–82°/14 mm.

Testosterone-3-C^{14} [(5)]

Testosterone benzoate (I) (2.25 grams) is ozonized (3 molar equivalents of O_3) at $-10°$ in a mixture of equal volumes of acetic acid and ethyl acetate. A mixture of 10 ml of water and 1.5 ml of 30% hydrogen peroxide is added, and the mixture is allowed to stand overnight at room temperature. The solution is then diluted with a large volume of water and extracted with ether. The acidic product is removed by extraction of the ether phase with successive ice-cold portions of 1% alkali. These extracts are immediately acidified to prevent hydrolysis of the benzoate group. Additional acidic material can be obtained by treatment of the residual neutral fraction with periodic acid. The total oily acid obtained in this way is crystallized three times from dilute methanol and gives 1.53 grams (65%) of II melting at 143–146°. Further recrystallization from methanol gave the analytical sample, m.p. 147–148°, $[\alpha]_D^{28°} = +79°$ (C = 2.11 in chloroform).

Analysis. Calculated for $C_{25}H_{32}O$: C, 72.79; H, 7.82. *Found:* C, 72.83; H, 7.84.

The keto acid (II) obtained above (1.28 grams) is refluxed for 48 hours with 10 ml of acetic anhydride and 4 ml of acetyl chloride. The solvents are removed under reduced pressure, the crystalline residue is taken up in ether-methylene chloride, and the solution is washed with dilute sodium hydroxide, water, and saturated sodium chloride. After it is dried over sodium sulfate, the solution is concentrated to a small volume and diluted with petroleum ether. A yield of 975 mg (80%) of enol-lactone (III) was obtained, m.p. 199–200°. The analytical sample was prepared by several recrystallizations from methylene chloride-petroleum ether, and melts at 202–202.5°. $[\alpha]_D^{28°} = +19°$ (C = 1.05 in chloroform).

Analysis. Calculated for $C_{25}H_{30}O_4$: C, 76.11; H, 7.66. *Found:* C, 75.98; H, 7.74.

The enol-lactone (III) (790 mg), 150 mg (3.12 equivalents) of sodium hydride, and 0.50 ml (2.00 equivalents) of carboxyl-labeled phenyl acetate are stirred in 8 ml of dry benzene under nitrogen for 4 days at room temperature. Dilute hydrochloric acid is then added, and the material is then extracted with ether-methylene chloride. After thorough washing with water, the solution is dried over anhydrous sodium sulfate and the solvents are distilled on the steam bath. The oil obtained in this way is pumped on at 100° to remove the volatile products (phenol, phenyl acetate, phenyl-acetoacetate). The non-volatile material is then refluxed under nitrogen for 18 hours with 1 gram of potassium hydroxide in a mixture of 75 ml of methanol and 25 ml of water. The solution is acidified with acetic acid, and the solvents are distilled under reduced pressure. The crude product is then dissolved in ether which is washed with dilute sodium hydroxide and water and is dried over anhydrous sodium sulfate. Removal of the solvent gives 446 mg of oil which is chromatographed on alumina. From the benzene-ether eluates there is obtained 275 mg (48% based on III) of material melting at 148–150°. Crystallization from ether-petroleum ether gives a pure product, m.p. 153–154°, which did not depress the melting point of an authentic sample of testosterone. The identity of the substance was further established by measurements of specific rotation $[\alpha]_D^{26°} = +110°$ (C = 1.52 in chloroform) and ultraviolet absorption (λ max., 241 mμ, logϵ 4.21). Testosterone acetate, m.p. 139–140°, was prepared as a derivative.

Chapter 10

CRITERIA OF PURITY

In the course of almost every investigation involving tracers it is necessary to isolate certain compounds, either from biological sources or from ordinary chemical reactions, of which the isotopic content must be determined accurately. One important matter has not been discussed as yet: criteria of absolute purity. After a compound has been isolated, in order to draw any valid conclusions it is necessary to establish rigorously the identity and especially the purity of the substance, and to show conclusively that the isotopic label that is measured actually belongs to the compound itself and is not present as a trace of contaminant.

A number of criteria for purity and identity have been used in organic chemistry for many years with completely satisfactory results. Melting points may furnish evidence of the identity of a compound, and considerable information about purity may often be gained from the sharpness of the melting point. For liquids, the density and refractive index are physical constants that are characteristic of the compounds. Quantitative analysis for carbon, hydrogen, and other elements gives considerable data on the nature of the substance and its gross purity. A number of other means are commonly used for this purpose: specific rotation, ultraviolet or infra-red absorption spectra, boiling point, x-ray diffraction, neutral or saponification equivalents, and solubility, to mention only a few. Any or all of these ordinarily sufficient criteria may be applied to an isotopic compound, and yet the results from the determination of isotopic concentration may be in serious error. This is particularly true in the use of radioactive isotopes in which a trace of contaminating material may be too small to be detected by the ordinary methods of establishing purity and yet be sufficiently radioactive to cause incorrect conclusions to be drawn.

Several cases are recorded in the literature in which the usual techniques for the separation and purification of organic compounds did not suffice to remove small amounts of these contaminants. This is particularly true if the impurity is a substance with properties closely related to those of the compound under investigation. Nevertheless, on occasion a completely different type of compound may be carried along through a considerable number of operations. This type of contamination is so likely to occur, especially when dealing with organic compounds, that one should take great pains to secure complete evidence of the purity of an important compound before its isotopic concentration is interpreted.

Crystallization

There are a number of approaches to this problem. If the compound under investigation is a solid, several crystallizations from a single solvent may fail to remove an impurity of approximately the same solubility as the compound. However, if several recrystallizations are carried out with different solvents, the chances of retaining a single impurity are rather slight. One of the best methods of establishing the purity of a compound with regard to its isotopic concentration is to recrystallize the sample to constant isotopic content. Unfortunately, even this treatment is not sufficient in a few cases to remove all impurities. For example, if labeled succinic acid contaminated with nonisotopic fumaric acid is crystallized to constant specific activity from several solvents, the fumaric acid is carried along in the same proportions, as was later proved by selective oxidation of the fumaric acid.[1]

The technique of isotope dilution, for example, is also susceptible to these hazards, and extraordinary precautions must be taken to eliminate the possibility of contamination which is particularly likely when the compounds found in a mixture have similar solubilities. This carrier technique is indispensable in dealing with minute quantities of isotopic compounds. If a non-isotopic compound is added in sufficient quantity so that it can be manipulated and purified, and if the compound is free from all contamination, then any isotope appearing in the compound must have originated from the labeled compound originally present, and, knowing the amount of carrier added and the specific activity of the original compound, one may often compute the amount of original substance. A somewhat less hazardous application of this technique is the addition of labeled compound to an unlabeled mixture followed by re-isolation and purification, and determination of loss in isotope concentration. In this process, often used for the analysis of amino acid mixtures, the only isotope present is that introduced in the compound added, and the problem of contamination by small amounts of impurities of high specific activity is not present. (For a discussion of the techniques of isotope dilution see Appendix I.)

[1] J. A. Bassham, A. Benson, and M. Calvin, unpublished experiments.

Chromatography

A considerable number of physical methods has been employed in order to purify organic compounds and remove contaminants. Some of these techniques have been adopted comparatively recently, and others have not as yet found widespread application in this field. Chromatographic methods can often be applied to the purification of certain types of compounds, particularly plant and animal pigments, and steroids. (See page 237.) The technique of paper chromatography has been applied very successfully to the separation of complex mixtures of amino acids [2] based on earlier theoretical considerations. [3] Comparative data obtained by different modifications of this type of technique, such as use of starch instead of filter paper, have been presented. [4]

This technique has already found application to work with isotopic carbon [5, 6] and will undoubtedly increase in usefulness as more complicated molecules and systems are studied. It is beyond the scope of this book to discuss fundamentals of chromatography, but an excellent text [7] is available on this subject. †

An ingenious method of partition chromatography has been developed [8] which has been used with considerable success in photosynthetic work with labeled carbon for the separation of various carboxylic acids. [9] A dry silica gel is treated with the proper amount of dilute sulfuric acid and is placed in a column. The acids to be separated are dissolved in a mixture of butanol and chloroform saturated with dilute sulfuric acid, and are developed continuously with the same solvent mixture. A continuous series of partitions of the acids between the organic solvents and the aqueous phase held in the gel takes place, and the difference in distribution coefficients of the acids causes them to be spread apart on the column, just as in ordinary chromatography. The development is continued, and the acids are eluted separately. In order to determine when the acid is eluted, a thymol blue indicator solution is allowed to drip at a

[2] R. Consden, A. H. Gordon, A. J. P. Martin, *Biochem. J.*, **38**, 224 (1944).

[3] A. J. P. Martin, and R. L. M. Synge, *Biochem. J.*, **35**, 1358 (1941).

[4] A. Polson, V. M. Mosley, and R. W. G. Wyckoff, *Science*, **105**, 603 (1947).

[5] W. H. Stein, private communication.

[6] H. Borsook, et al., *Federation Proc.*, **7**, 147 (1948).

[7] L. Zechmeister and L. Cholnoky, *Principles and Practise of Chromatography*, Chapman and Hall, Ltd., London, 1941.

[8] F. A. Isherwood, *Biochem. J.*, **40**, 688 (1946).

[9] J. A. Bassham, unpublished experiments.

† *Note added in proof.* A combination of radioautography and filter-paper chromatography has been reported by: R. M. Fink and K. Fink, *Science*, **107**, 253 (1948); R. M. Tomarelli and K. Florey, *Science*, **107**, 630 (1948); W. Stepka, A. A. Benson, and M. Calvin, *Science*, **108**, 304 (1948).

critical rate and come into contact with the dripping eluate. A red coloration of the indicator solution indicates that an acid is coming off the column. The solvents are removed under reduced pressure, and the acids are isolated. This method affords a complete separation of a mixture containing malic, fumaric, succinic, and citric acids.

Distillation

A method for the analysis and separation of mixtures of lower aliphatic acids has been developed [10] which involves azeotropic distillations with benzene and toluene. This is a very satisfactory technique for the removal of small quantities of contaminants from acids and is also excellent for the distillation of small quantities of these compounds without loss, since the azeotropes boil lower than the benzene or the toluene and hence no pot residues are left behind. The acid is easily separated from the large volume of inert hydrocarbon by alkaline extraction. Numerical data are presented which enable one to use this method as an analytical tool, as well as a means for purification of these acids. This technique has been used [11] to separate a mixture of carbon-labeled acids obtained from the fermentation of *Clostridium kluyveri*. The method does not suffer from some of the defects encountered in the Duclaux distillation procedure, [12] which often gives unreliable results in mixtures of more than two acids.

Partitions

Another technique that has been used for the separation of mixtures of aliphatic acids is a partition method. [13] This procedure utilizes the difference in partition coefficients between ether and water of the lower aliphatic acids, and by suitable extractions, followed analytically, it is possible to purify small amounts of these substances. Also, from the construction of nomograms from the data obtained from known mixtures, it is possible to obtain the quantities of known acids in an unknown mixture. This method has been applied [14] in the degradation of isotopic butyric acid produced from butyl alcohol fermentation.

[10] S. T. Schicktanz, W. I. Steele, and A. C. Blaisdell, *Ind. Eng. Chem., Anal. Ed.*, **12**, 320 (1940).

[11] H. A. Barker, M. D. Kamen, and B. T. Bornstein, *Proc. Natl. Acad. Sci. U. S.*, **31**, 373 (1946).

[12] C. Duclaux, *Ann. chim. phys.*, **2**, 289 (1874).

[13] O. L. Osburn, H. G. Wood, and C. H. Werkman, *Ind. Eng. Chem., Anal. Ed.*, **4**, 247 (1933); **8**, 270 (1936).

[14] H. G. Wood, R. W. Brown, C. H. Werkman, and C. G. Stuckwisch, *J. Am. Chem. Soc.*, **66**, 1812 (1944).

The method of utilization of partition or extraction coefficients to purify and gain considerable information about the chemical nature of radioactive samples has been widely used in studies of photosynthesis [15] and in the metabolism of dibenzanthracene.[16] This method relies on characteristic distribution of a compound between various solvents, and by a large number of extractions it may be possible to effect complete separation and purification of two very closely related compounds.

There are several advantages in the use of liquid-liquid partitions in studies of minute quantities of organic compounds even in complex mixtures. Ordinarily the ratio of volume of solution to the amounts of compound present is enormous, and thus behavior of the compound would be expected to be only slightly influenced by other constituents of a mixture. Only if actual molecular compounds exist, a rather unlikely occurrence in very dilute solutions, would the distribution coefficients be in gross error. This technique is often superior to precipitations and filtrations because there is no opportunity for losses of small amounts of material by surface adsorption effects. In addition, distribution ratios are usually more reliable than solubility measurements of solid substances, since it is often necessary to use heat and excess solvent to force some compounds into solution; these measurements become increasingly difficult as the scale is decreased.

This distribution technique is particularly useful when radioactive isotopes are used because, by determination of radioactivity, very minute amounts of substance may be studied. In general a compound or mixture of compounds in solution, or an extract from biological sources, may be distributed between two immiscible solvents; this is usually conveniently carried out in a graduated centrifuge tube. The upper layer is drawn off with a capillary pipet, the volume of each phase is measured, and an aliquot of each is taken in a micropipet and plated directly as described on page 114. In this way, in addition to the determination of distribution coefficients, a constant check is maintained on the total radioactivity and losses can be immediately noticed. Moreover, it is possible merely by following the activity in both solvents to determine whether a compound is acidic, basic, or neutral, and a mixture of compounds may be separated by this method. It is also possible to carry out a number of reactions on the microgram scale, such as acetylations, esterifications, and decarboxylations, and gain considerable insight into the chemistry of the compound. For an acidic or basic substance, one may construct an accurate titration curve by measuring the distribution coefficients of the compound between an organic solvent and a series of buffer solutions at different pH.

[15] M. Calvin, A. A. Benson, et al., unpublished data.
[16] C. Heidelberger, *Cancer*, **1**, No. 2, 261 (1948).

In conjunction with carrier techniques, liquid-liquid distribution furnishes a unique way of determining the identity and purity of a given compound. After the substance has been recrystallized to constant specific activity, several distribution coefficients may be determined by two methods. The distribution of the compound is studied by a measure of the radioactivity and also by ordinary gravimetric or colorimetric means. If the numerical values check by both methods, then one can be quite sure that the radioactivity does not arise from a contaminant. This method is probably the most satisfactory one available for the determination of identity and purity.

The use of a carrier to separate two very closely related compounds is sometimes unsatisfactory. If a mixture of aspartic and glutamic acids is to be separated, the addition of aspartic acid alone carries some of the glutamic activity with it.[17] If, however, aspartic and glutamic acids are added as carriers, and are both separated and purified, the results are then found to be reliable.

The separation of two closely related compounds by a number of distributions and extractions would be an exceedingly tedious process if it were not for the method of "counter-current" extractions,[18] which performs a large number of partitions almost automatically. By suitable use of this method, it should be possible to purify and establish the identity and homogeneity of almost any organic substance and should diminish the danger of contamination of a compound with small traces of radioactive impurities. The possibilities of this method can be extended in the case of acidic or basic compounds when one of the phases contains a buffer solution,[19] and it has been shown that the distribution coefficients are greatly affected by the pH of the medium. Since theoretical curves may be calculated on the basis of distribution coefficients, which correspond closely to those obtained experimentally, it is often possible to predict in a mixture of known components the most effective use of this technique to obtain separation. This scheme has been used [20] for the separation and characterization of some penicillins. If the constituents of the mixture are unknown, the data must be followed empirically; but, since very small quantities may be measured, the method is quite suitable for isotopic work and has already been applied in this field.[21]

[17] A. A. Benson, unpublished experiments.

[18] L. C. Craig, *J. Biol. Chem.*, **155**, 519 (1944).

[19] L. C. Craig, C. Golumbic, H. Mighton, and E. Titus, *J. Biol. Chem.*, **161**, 321 (1945).

[20] L. C. Craig, G. H. Hogeboom, F. H. Carpenter, and V. du Vigneaud, *J. Biol. Chem.*, **168**, 665 (1947).

[21] G. B. Brown, private communication.

So far only the physical methods of purification have been discussed. However, chemical processes may be extremely useful in these problems in a number of ways. In the purification of any given compound by means of recrystallization from different solvents, it is possible that traces of contaminants may be retained, as has already been discussed. If these impurities are of similar solubility but of a different chemical type from that of the original compound, they may be removed by the conversion of the compound to some derivative, which in turn may be purified, and from which the original compound could be regenerated. The chances that a contaminant, even if it were of the same chemical type as the original compound, would be carried along persistently in a derivative as well are small indeed. For example, a solid carboxylic acid may be converted to the amide, which could be purified and hydrolyzed back to the acid.

Once other criteria of purity have been satisfied, perhaps the most rigorous means of proving that the isotope actually belongs in a given compound is by the chemical degradation of the substance to locate the actual position(s) of the marked carbon within the molecule. In many studies, degradations have been widely used, not only to establish the identity of the isotopic carbon within a given molecule but also to obtain vital information about the mechanism of the process or transformation under consideration. The next chapter will be devoted to a consideration of examples of degradations that have actually been employed with compounds containing isotopic carbon.

Summary

In order to analyze for a known compound in a complex mixture the following steps are suggested as a means to establish its identity and purity:

1. A known quantity of carrier is added to the mixture.

2. By means of solvent extractions at various pH's, the compound, for example, if an acid, can be separated from neutral and basic materials.

3. Some preliminary method, if available, is used to effect a separation from other members of the same solubility class. These include chromatography, distillation, or distribution.

4. The compound, if a solid, is recrystallized from different solvents to constant isotopic concentration. If it is a liquid, it should be converted into some solid derivative.

5. After this purification, the compound is converted to a derivative, which is also recrystallized to constant isotopic concentration.

6. A comparison is made between the distribution coefficient as determined from the isotope and by conventional means. If they are identical, the compound is probably pure.

7. If desired, the compound is degraded to show the position of the labeled carbon within the molecule. If identification of an unknown compound is desired, no carrier is added at first, and steps 2 and 3 are carried out.

8. A number of chemical reactions are carried out by means of the distribution technique, and as many quantitative and qualitative data are collected as possible.

9. If the substance is present in such small quantity that ordinary physical methods, such as spectroscopy and polarography, are not applicable, and isolation is also impossible, it is often possible to make a guess as to the identity of the compound on the basis of the evidence already collected. The compound suspected can then be subjected to the same type of reactions to see whether there is close correspondence with the data obtained by isotopic measurement. If so, the compound may be added as carrier, and the steps previously outlined are carried out. If the first compound added does not carry the isotope, it may be possible to add others until success is achieved.

These procedures outlined may seem long and tedious, but only a systematic study of this type can furnish information that can be interpreted with complete confidence.

Chapter 11

DEGRADATION PROCEDURES

Acetic Acid

The most common method for the degradation of acetic acid consists in the pyrolysis of barium acetate to carbon dioxide and acetone, which is further converted into iodoform.

$$(\overset{2}{C}H_3\overset{1}{C}OO)_2Ba \overset{\Delta}{\rightarrow} Ba\overset{1}{C}O_3 + \overset{2}{C}H_3\overset{1}{C}O\overset{2}{C}H_3 \rightarrow \overset{2}{C}HI_3 + \overset{2}{C}H_3\overset{1}{C}OOH$$

This method has been used [1] to determine the distribution of label in acetic acid produced from certain fermentations. A further study of this reaction has been made [2] in which synthetic isotopic acetic acid has been degraded under a variety of conditions. It has been shown that decomposition of barium acetate in vacuum and absorption of the acetone into water is unsatisfactory, because the slowness of decomposition and water vapor in the presence of barium carbonate cause exchange to occur.

The best procedure involves sweeping with an inert gas in the apparatus shown in Fig. 85. On a degradation of synthetic methyl-labeled acetate, a temperature of

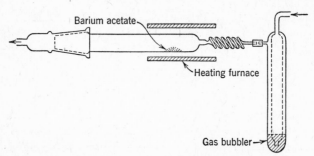

FIG. 85. Apparatus for the pyrolysis of barium acetate.

525° for 10 minutes appears to be most satisfactory, and under these conditions the yield of acetone is generally 70%. The residual barium carbonate is gray and may be purified by reprecipitation after decomposition with lactic acid. Under these

[1] H. A. Barker and M. D. Kamen, *Proc. Natl. Acad. Sci. U. S.*, **31**, 219 (1945).
[2] S. Aronoff, V. Haas, and B. A. Fries, *J. Org. Chem.*, in press.

conditions about 3.5% of the original radioactivity appears in the barium carbonate. However, when the pyrolysis is carried out at 450°, 15% of the activity is found in the barium carbonate. When carboxyl-labeled acetate was degraded, no detectable radioactivity was found in the iodoform.

To the aqueous solution containing the acetone from the pyrolysis is added a ten-fold excess of sodium hydroxide, and potassium triiodide is added in portions. The iodoform is allowed to settle, and triiodide is added until precipitation is complete. The mixture is allowed to stand for 10 minutes, and the iodoform is centrifuged, washed, and dried. The isotopic analysis may be performed directly on the iodo-form or on the barium carbonate obtained by the Van Slyke-Folch method of oxidation (page 92).

A degradation of methyl-labeled acetate was also carried out by the Kolbe electrolytic procedure.[2] The results on isotopic concentration were in agreement with those obtained by the barium acetate pyrolysis, but under the conditions used the yield of ethane was unsatisfactory.

Propionic Acid

Three reactions have been used to locate the position of isotope in propionic acid, an important problem in studies of the mode of formation of this substance by propionic acid bacteria. The reliability of reactions

$$\overset{3}{C}H_3\overset{2}{C}H_2\overset{1}{C}OONa \xrightarrow[\text{permanganate}]{\text{alkaline}} Na\overset{3}{O}O\overset{2}{C}\overset{1}{C}OONa + Na_2\overset{1}{C}O_3 \quad (1)$$

$$(\overset{3}{C}H_3\overset{2}{C}H_2\overset{1}{C}OO)_2Ba \xrightarrow[350°]{} (\overset{3}{C}H_3\overset{2}{C}H_2)_2\overset{1}{C}O + Ba\overset{1}{C}O_3 \quad (2)$$

$$\overset{3}{C}H_3\overset{2}{C}H_2\overset{1}{C}OOH \xrightarrow[H_2Cr_2O_7]{} \overset{1}{C}O_2 + \overset{3}{C}H_3\overset{2}{C}OOH \quad (3)$$

1 and 2 as means of degradation has been compared,[3] and it was found that, whereas reaction 2 produces one-half of the total isotope in the carbon dioxide, in reaction 1 only 37% of the isotope was present in the sodium carbonate, and the oxalate also contained isotope. These observations have been checked,[4] and it was also shown that oxidation with dichromate (reaction 3) is a completely reliable means for location of isotope. The oxidation of propionic, lactic, and β-hydroxy propionic acid were studied,[5] and it was concluded that the concentration of alkali markedly influences reaction 1. An increase in alkalinity increases the rate of rupture of the α-β bond, the reaction that is responsible for the presence of label in the oxalic acid.

[3] H. G. Wood, C. H. Werkman, A. Hemingway, A. O. Nier, and C. G. Stuckwisch, *J. Am. Chem. Soc.*, **63**, 2140 (1941).

[4] P. Nahinsky and S. Ruben, *J. Am. Chem. Soc.*, **63**, 2275 (1941).

[5] P. Nahinsky, C. N. Rice, S. Ruben, and M. D. Kamen, *J. Am. Chem. Soc.*, **64**, 2299 (1942).

The dry distillation of barium propionate is carried out at 460° for 1 hour in a 25-ml distilling flask submerged in an alloy bath. Dry, oxygen-free nitrogen is passed through the flask at a rate of 2 liters per hour. The diethyl ketone is collected in 45 ml of ice-cold water contained in a 22-mm test tube. The inlet is drawn to a capillary. At the conclusion of heating, the carbon dioxide is liberated from the residue of distillation with 1 N hydrochloric acid and collected for analysis. An approximate estimate of the diethyl ketone is also obtained by weighing the 2,4-dinitrophenylhydrazone prepared from an aliquot of the distillate.

Lactic Acid

The degradation of lactic acid is of considerable importance, not only for the determination of the distribution of isotope in the compound itself but also because the experiments on the distribution of isotope in glucose are based on the lactic acid obtained by fermentation.

Two closely related methods of degradation have been used. The first [6] involves the oxidation of lactic acid with permanganate to acetaldehyde and carbon dioxide. The acetaldehyde is then further degraded by means of the iodoform reaction.

$$\overset{3}{C}H_3\overset{2}{C}HOH\overset{1}{C}OOH \xrightarrow{KMnO_4} \overset{3}{C}H_3\overset{2}{C}HO + \overset{1}{C}O_2 \qquad (1)$$

$$\overset{3}{C}H_3\overset{2}{C}HO \xrightarrow{NaOI} \overset{3}{C}HI_3 + H\overset{2}{C}OOH \qquad (2)$$

The carbon dioxide in reaction 1 arises from the carboxyl group of the lactic acid; the formic acid in reaction 2, from the α position; and the iodoform, from the β position. By suitable analysis of each of these products, the distribution of isotope may be ascertained.

A slight modification of this procedure has been reported [7] in which lactic acid is oxidized to carbon dioxide and acetic acid, which is then decarboxylated.

$$\overset{3}{C}H_3\overset{2}{C}HOH\overset{1}{C}OOH \xrightarrow{CrO_3} \overset{1}{C}O_2 + \overset{3}{C}H_3\overset{2}{C}OOH \qquad (3)$$

$$(\overset{3}{C}H_3\overset{2}{C}OO)_2Ba \longrightarrow \overset{3}{C}H_3\overset{2}{C}O\overset{3}{C}H_3 + Ba\overset{2}{C}O_3 \qquad (4)$$

$$\overset{3}{C}H_3\overset{2}{C}O\overset{3}{C}H_3 \xrightarrow{NaOI} \overset{3}{C}HI_3 + \overset{3}{C}H_3\overset{2}{C}OOH \qquad (5)$$

The carbon dioxide in reaction 3 originates from the carboxyl group of lactic acid; the carbon dioxide in reaction 4, from the α position; and the iodoform in reaction 5, from the β carbon.

A solution of 10–30 mg of lactic acid in 7–8 ml of water containing 0.2 ml of concentrated sulfuric acid is placed in a test tube fitted with a 24/40 outer joint. A side arm having a vent for a stream of nitrogen is filled with 2 ml of chromic oxide

[6] H. G. Wood, N. Lifson, and V. Lorber, *J. Biol. Chem.*, **159**, 475 (1945).
[7] S. Aronoff, H. A. Barker, and M. Calvin, *J. Biol. Chem.*, **169**, 459 (1947).

in water (1:1). An open condenser is inserted in the upper portion of the tube to prevent the escape of the acetic acid. The reaction is initiated by tipping the chromic acid into the tube, and it is complete after 40 minutes on the steam bath. The acetic acid is then distilled with steam, neutralized with barium hydroxide, and decarboxylated by heat (see page 248), and the acetone is degraded by the iodoform reaction.

Ethyl Pyruvate

The mechanism of the thermal decomposition of ethyl pyruvate to give carbon monoxide and ethyl acetate has been studied.[8] Carbonyl-labeled ethyl pyruvate is heated to 130°, and the carbon monoxide liberated is oxidized to carbon dioxide, which is then counted as barium carbonate. No label is present in the carbon dioxide, proving that the carbon monoxide produced in the decomposition originates from the carbethoxyl carbon atom of the ethyl pyruvate.

$$\overset{3}{C}H_3\overset{2}{C}O\overset{1}{C}OOC_2H_5 \rightarrow \overset{1}{C}O + \overset{3}{C}H_3\overset{2}{C}OOC_2H_5$$

Pyruvic Acid

The decarboxylation of pyruvic acid may readily be accomplished with ceric sulfate; this reaction has been studied [9] and has been applied successfully to determine the isotopic content of pyruvic acid [10] in a study on the phosphoroclastic split of pyruvate in *E. coli* and also in a research [11] on the mechanism of carbon dioxide fixation in cell-free extracts of pigeon liver.

The decarboxylation is usually carried out in the Warburg apparatus, and the solution to be analyzed is acidified with 0.2 volume of 1:1 aqueous sulfuric acid. The side bulb is filled with a saturated solution of ceric sulfate in 10 N sulfuric acid. The solutions are mixed, and the evolved carbon dioxide is measured manometrically and can then be assayed for isotope. The isotopic content of the other two carbon atoms may be obtained by difference from the total isotope in a completely oxidized sample.

Butyric Acid

The degradation of butyric acid was carried out in a study [12] with heavy carbon of a previously investigated hydrogen peroxide oxidation procedure.[13] The products of the oxidation are carbon dioxide, acetic acid, acetone, and small quantities of volatile aldehydes. It was origi-

[8] M. Calvin and R. Lemmon, *J. Am. Chem. Soc.*, **69**, 1232 (1947).

[9] H. A. Krebs and W. A. Johnson, *Biochem. J.*, **31**, 645 (1937).

[10] M. F. Utter, F. Lipmann, and C. H. Werkman, *J. Biol. Chem.*, **158**, 521 (1945).

[11] H. G. Wood, B. Vennesland, and E. A. Evans, *J. Biol. Chem.*, **159**, 153 (1945).

[12] H. G. Wood, R. W. Brown, C. H. Werkman, and C. G. Stuckwisch, *J. Am. Chem. Soc.*, **66**, 1812 (1944).

[13] R. H. Allen and E. J. Witzemann, *J. Am. Chem. Soc.*, **63**, 1922 (1941).

nally presumed that the acetone originated from the α, β, and γ carbon atoms, and careful experiments [12] with synthetic carboxyl-labeled butyrate have shown this to be the fact, since no isotope could be detected in the acetone.   The acetone is degraded by the iodoform reaction.

$$\overset{4}{C}H_3\overset{3}{C}H_2\overset{2}{C}H_2\overset{1}{C}OOH \xrightarrow{H_2O_2} \overset{4}{C}H_3\overset{3}{C}O\overset{2}{C}H_3 + \overset{1}{C}O_2$$

$$\overset{4}{C}H_3\overset{3}{C}O\overset{2}{C}H_3 \xrightarrow{NaOI} \overset{2,4}{C}HI_3 + \overset{2,4}{C}H_3\overset{3}{C}OOH$$

The carbon dioxide must result largely from the carboxyl group but may also have originated from other intermediates of the oxidation. The true value for the carboxyl group has been obtained by decarboxylation of barium butyrate.[14]   The α and γ carbons of the butyric acid appear as the methyl groups of acetone, and hence the isotopic concentration in the iodoform represents the amount of isotope present in these particular atoms.   The β carbon becomes the carbonyl group of the acetone, which gives rise to the carboxyl group of the acetic acid, and, since the concentration of label in the methyl group is known from the iodoform, the concentration in the carboxyl group and hence in the β carbon of butyric acid is obtained by difference.   The isotope content of the other by-products of the oxidation is determined to furnish an overall check.

The actual procedure is carried out on ammonium butyrate and has the advantage that it may be run in dilute aqueous solution with a relatively low concentration of hydrogen peroxide.   The acetone is separated from the neutralized acids by steam distillation and is treated with acid dichromate followed by alkaline distillation to remove any aldehydes and alcohols that might be present, because those two types of compounds are oxidized to acids under these conditions.   The iodoform reaction is then carried out, and the acetic acid is shown to be pure by a partition procedure.[15] All the products are oxidized, and their label content is determined.   This reaction was studied [12] rigorously and was found to be completely reliable.

Acetoacetic Acid

The distribution of isotopic carbon in acetoacetic acid has been studied [16] in an investigation of ketone-body formation.

$$\overset{4}{C}H_3\overset{3}{C}O\overset{2}{C}H_2\overset{1}{C}OOH \xrightarrow{HgSO_4} \overset{1}{C}O_2 + \overset{4}{C}H_3\overset{3}{C}O\overset{2}{C}H_3$$

$$\overset{4}{C}H_3\overset{3}{C}O\overset{2}{C}H_3 \longrightarrow \overset{2,4}{C}HI_3 + \overset{2,4}{C}H_3\overset{3}{C}OOH$$

[14] H. A. Barker, M. D. Kamen, and B. T. Bornstein, *Proc. Natl. Acad. Sci. U. S.*, **31**, 373 (1945).

[15] O. L. Osburn, H. G. Wood, and C. H. Werkman, *Ind. Eng. Chem., Anal. Ed.*, **8**, 270 (1936).

[16] S. Weinhouse, G. Medes, and N. F. Floyd, *J. Biol. Chem.*, **155**, 143 (1944).

The solution of acetoacetate is refluxed with mercuric sulfate and dilute hydrochloric acid,[17] and the carbon dioxide is absorbed in alkali and precipitated as barium carbonate. The label content of this sample is then determined and is found to be derived from the carboxyl group of the acetoacetate. The mercuric complex of acetone (40.2 mg) is dissolved in 2 ml of 6 N hydrochloric acid, and the acetone is distilled at room temperature under reduced pressure into a cooled mixture of 2 ml of 15 N sodium hydroxide and 2 ml of a 0.1 N iodine solution. The mixture is warmed to room temperature and acidified. The iodoform is separated by centrifugation, washed thoroughly, and oxidized to carbon dioxide by the wet combustion method (see page 92). The concentration of isotope in the carbonyl group is obtained by difference of the total amount in the acetone sample and the amount in the iodoform, which originated from the methyl and the methylene groups in the acetoacetate. The decarboxylation can also be accomplished at room temperature by the use of aniline-citrate.[18]

Succinic, Fumaric, Malic, and Oxalacetic Acids

These compounds are closely related structurally and occur together in a number of biological systems. Succinic acid has been degraded [19] by a purely chemical process, whereas by combination of chemical and biological methods succinic acid has been degraded [20] with fumaric, malic, and oxalacetic acids as intermediates, so that these methods may be applied to the degradation of any of these compounds. These procedures can be used for the determination of the label concentration in the carboxyl groups and the methylene groups but obviously cannot be used to distinguish between the individual carbon atoms within a group; i.e., it is not possible to tell whether one or both of the carboxyl groups are labeled.

The first method of degradation [20] involves enzymatic conversion of succinic acid to malic acid, which is then oxidized with permanganate to carbon dioxide and acetaldehyde.

$$HOOCCH_2CH_2COOH \xrightarrow[\text{dehydrogenase}]{\text{succinic}} HOOCCH{=}CHCOOH + [2H]$$

$$H_2O + HOOCCH{=}CHCOOH \underset{\text{fumarase}}{\overset{\longrightarrow}{\longleftarrow}} HOOCCH_2CHOHCOOH$$

$$\overset{4\ 3}{HOOC}\overset{2}{CH_2}\overset{1}{CHOHCOOH} \xrightarrow{KMnO_4} (\overset{4\ 3}{HOOC}\overset{2}{CH_2}CHO) + \overset{1}{CO_2} + H_2O$$

$$\downarrow$$

$$\overset{}{CO_2} + \overset{3}{CH_3}\overset{2}{CHO}$$

$$_4$$

[17] D. D. Van Slyke, *J. Biol. Chem.*, **83**, 415 (1929).

[18] A. W. Edson, *Biochem. J.*, **29**, 2082 (1935).

[19] A. Benson, J. A. Bassham, and M. Calvin, *J. Am. Chem. Soc.* in press.

[20] H. G. Wood, C. H. Werkman, A. Hemingway, and A. O. Nier, *J. Biol. Chem.*, **139**, 377 (1941).

Both molecules of carbon dioxide originate from the carboxyl groups of the succinic acid, and the acetaldehyde, from the methylene groups. Since there is an equilibrium between malic and fumaric acid, some of the latter must be oxidized as well, but the carbon dioxide would also be derived from the carboxyl groups and hence no error is introduced. The succinic acid is extracted with ether after acid permanganate oxidation to remove lactate and other oxidizable compounds.

The extract is steam-distilled to remove volatile compounds. Enzymatic conversion is carried out in 125-ml flasks on a Warburg respirometer at 30°. The 30 ml of reaction mixture contains 20 ml of succinic dehydrogenase fumarase,[21] 0.033 M succinate, and 0.125 M phosphate buffer at pH 7.3. The mixture is incubated for 4½ hours. It is then centrifuged and oxidized with permanganate.[22]

The solution containing malic acid is placed in a 300-cc Kjeldahl flask, and the reaction mixture is carefully adjusted to neutrality, after which 1.5–8 ml of 2 M phosphoric acid is added, depending on the volume of solution. Next, 10 ml of 10% manganous sulfate, a pinch of finely powdered talcum, and sufficient water to bring the volume to 50 ml are added. The flask is then attached to a condenser, the system is aerated by suction, and the mixture is brought to boiling. To the vigorously boiling mixture, 0.01 N permanganate or colloidal manganese dioxide is added very slowly until an excess has accumulated. The addition should take about 10 minutes, and then the reaction should be aerated for 20 minutes longer. The aldehyde from the oxidation is caught in a bisulfite tower followed by an absorber containing half-saturated permanganate to remove the sulfur dioxide liberated from the bisulfite, and this absorber in turn is connected to an alkali bubbler to remove the carbon dioxide, which is analyzed for label. The acetaldehyde is recovered by distillation of a mixture of the bisulfite solution and calcium carbonate.

The second method of degradation of succinic acid consists in the enzymatic conversion of the malic acid into oxalacetic acid followed by decarboxylation with citric acid-aniline.

$$\text{HOOCCH}_2\text{CHOHCOOH} \underset{\text{dehydrogenase}}{\overset{\text{malic}}{\rightleftarrows}} \text{HOOCCH}_2\text{COCOOH} + [2\text{H}]$$

$$\overset{1\ 3\quad 2\ 1}{\text{HOOCCH}_2\text{COCOOH}} + \text{H}_2\text{NC}_6\text{H}_5 \xrightarrow[\text{acid}]{\text{citric}}$$

$$(\text{HOOCCH}_2\text{COCONHC}_6\text{H}_5 + \text{H}_2\text{O})$$
$$\downarrow$$
$$\overset{1}{\text{CO}_2} + \text{CH}_3\text{COCONHC}_6\text{H}_5$$

The carbon dioxide originates from the carboxyl groups. The malic dehydrogenase is prepared from *Micrococcus lysodeikticus*. The bacteria are washed three times with cold acetone (4°), dried, and washed six times with 50 volumes of 0.1 M phosphate buffer at pH 8.0. The centrifuged bacteria are dried on a porous plate. This preparation oxidized malate and fumarate, but not succinate; oxalacetate is oxidized slowly or not at all. The ability to oxidize oxalacetate is recovered after extended incuba-

[21] H. A. Krebs, *Biochem. J.*, **31**, 2095 (1937).
[22] T. E. Friedemann and A. I. Kendall, *J. Biol. Chem.*, **82**, 23 (1929).

tion; therefore, in converting malate to oxalacetate, the reaction is stopped when the carbon dioxide evolution approaches 60% of the oxygen uptake. The 30 ml of reaction mixture contains 20 ml of the centrifuged fumarate and malate mixture, obtained as described above, and 300 mg of the bacterial preparation. The reaction time is 1.5 hours at 30°. The mixture is cooled immediately, acidified with citric acid, and aerated vigorously for 10 minutes to remove the carbon dioxide. The citric acid-aniline is then added; the carbon dioxide formed from the oxalacetate is collected in alkali, and its isotopic concentration is determined. The results obtained on the same batch of succinate by both methods of degradation were in good agreement.

The chemical degradation [19] is carried out by means of a Curtius rearrangement according to the following scheme:

$$\overset{1\;2\quad 2\quad 1}{HOOCCH_2CH_2COOH} \xrightarrow{CH_2N_2} \overset{1\;2\quad 2\quad 1}{CH_3OOCCH_2CH_2COOCH_3} \xrightarrow{H_2NNH_2}$$

$$\overset{1\;2\quad 2\quad 1}{H_2NNHOCCH_2CH_2CONHNH_2} \rightarrow \overset{1\;2\quad 2\quad 1}{N_3OCCH_2CH_2CON_3} \rightarrow$$

$$\overset{1\quad 2\quad 2\quad 1}{C_2H_5OOCNHCH_2CH_2NHCOOC_2H_5} \xrightarrow{HBr}$$

$$HBr\cdot\overset{2\quad 2}{H_2NCH_2CH_2NH_2}\cdot HBr + 2\overset{1}{CO_2} + 2C_2H_5OH$$

Procedure. Isotopic succinate (280 mg) is converted to the methyl ester with diazomethane, and the ester is converted to the diurethane by the procedure of T. Curtius,[23] is purified by recrystallization from water followed by high-vacuum sublimation, and 145 mg (30%) is obtained. The urethane (100 mg) is placed in a small flask and heated at 120° for 2 hours with 48% hydrobromic acid. A slow stream of nitrogen is passed through the solution into a sodium hydroxide bubbler to collect the isotopic carbon dioxide. The solution of ethylenediamine hydrobromide is evaporated to dryness under reduced pressure, methanolic potassium hydroxide is added in excess, and the free amine is distilled in vacuum. The amine hydrochloride is precipitated with methanolic hydrochloric acid and is recrystallized from methanol-water and counted directly.

α-Ketoglutaric Acid

Identical methods for the determination of the isotopic content of the carboxyl carbon adjacent to the carbonyl group of α-ketoglutaric acid obtained from biological systems have been used by several workers.[24, 25] This procedure involves the permanganate oxidation of the substance and assay of the carbon dioxide evolved.

$$\overset{5\;4\quad 3\quad 2\quad 1}{HOOCCH_2CH_2COCOOH} \xrightarrow[KMnO_4]{} \overset{5\;4\quad 3\quad 2}{HOOCCH_2CH_2COOH} + \overset{1}{CO_2}$$

The α-ketoglutarate solution [24] is treated with a saturated solution of 2,4-dinitrophenylhydrazine in 2% hydrochloric acid. The hydrazone precipitates quickly and

[23] T. Curtius, *J. prakt. Chem.* (2), **52**, 222 (1895).

[24] H. G. Wood, C. H. Werkman, A. Hemingway, and A. O. Nier, *J. Biol. Chem.*, **139**, 483 (1941).

[25] E. A. Evans and L. Slotin, *J. Biol. Chem.*, **141**, 439 (1941).

is collected by centrifugation and dried in vacuum at 100°. An aliquot of the compound is oxidized, and its total label concentration is determined. About 50 mg is dissolved in 5 ml of dilute alkali; the solution is acidified with 3 ml of 50% sulfuric acid, 10 ml of saturated potassium permanganate is added, and the resulting carbon dioxide is swept with nitrogen into an alkaline bubbler and assayed.

Citric Acid

The degradation of citric acid has been carried out by the following series of reactions.[26]

$$\overset{5\ 4}{\text{HOOCCH}_2}\overset{\overset{\displaystyle\text{OH}}{|}}{\underset{\underset{\displaystyle 6}{|}}{\overset{3\ 2}{\text{CCH}_2}}}\overset{1}{\text{COOH}} \xrightarrow[\text{H}_2\text{SO}_4]{} \overset{6}{\text{CO}} + \overset{5\ 4}{\text{HOOCCH}_2}\overset{3}{\text{CO}}\overset{2}{\text{CH}_2}\overset{1}{\text{COOH}} + \text{H}_2\text{O}$$

$$\underset{\displaystyle\text{COOH}}{}$$

$$\overset{5\ 4}{\text{HOOCCH}_2}\overset{3}{\text{CO}}\overset{2}{\text{CH}_2}\overset{1}{\text{COOH}} \xrightarrow{\Delta} \overset{1,5}{2\text{CO}_2} + \overset{2}{\text{CH}_3}\overset{3}{\text{CO}}\overset{4}{\text{CH}_3}$$

The carbon monoxide originates from the tertiary carboxyl group, and the carbon dioxide, in the second step, from the terminal carboxyl groups. The acetone is derived from the other carbon atoms, and degradation of this compound shows the distribution of activity among these three atoms.

The citric acid is isolated from the complex reaction mixture as the quinidine salt, which is carefully purified. Then 40 mg of the salt is placed in a glass tube carrying a side bulb containing 1 ml of concentrated sulfuric acid. The tube was attached to the vacuum line through an adapter fitted with a stopcock so that the tube may be removed without breaking the vacuum. After evacuation, the assembly is detached and cooled to −10°, and the sulfuric acid is tipped in. The tube is cooled and shaken until the quinidine citrate has dissolved and is then allowed to stand at room temperature for 3 hours until visible bubble evolution has ceased. The tube is attached to the vacuum line, and the evolved gas is transferred by means of a Topler pump to a sample tube for mass spectrometric determination. The gas consists of 91.8% carbon monoxide, 1.5% carbon dioxide, and 5.7% air. The tube is then re-evacuated and heated for 2 hours at 100°. The carbon dioxide evolved is condensed into the vacuum line and sublimed into a tube for isotope analysis. The acetone is isolated from a separate portion of citric acid by a permanganate oxidation.

Glucose

Glucose has been degraded [27] in order to ascertain the distribution of label in rat liver glycogen. One method consists in fermentation of glucose to lactic acid by *Lactobacillus casei*, followed by degradation of the lactic acid as described on page 250.

[26] S. Weinhouse, G. Medes, and N. F. Floyd, *J. Biol. Chem.*, **166**, 691 (1946).
[27] H. G. Wood, N. Lifson, and V. Lorber, *J. Biol. Chem.*, **159**, 475 (1945).

$$\overset{1}{\text{CHOH}}\overset{2}{\text{CHOH}}\overset{3}{\text{CHOH}}\overset{4}{\text{CHOH}}\overset{5}{\text{CHCH}}\overset{6}{\text{CH}_2\text{OH}} \xrightarrow{\text{L. casei}}$$

$$\overset{1}{\text{CH}_3}\overset{2}{\text{CHOH}}\overset{3}{\text{COOH}} + \text{HOO}\overset{4}{\text{C}}\overset{5}{\text{CHOH}}\overset{6}{\text{CH}_3}$$

$$\downarrow \text{KMnO}_4$$

$$\overset{1,6}{\text{CH}_3}\overset{2,5}{\text{CHO}} + \overset{3,4}{\text{CO}_2}$$

$$\downarrow \text{NaOI}$$

$$\overset{1,6}{\text{CHI}_3} + \overset{2,5}{\text{HCOOH}}$$

This procedure has been modified slightly [28] so that the lactic acid is oxidized to acetic acid and carbon dioxide as described on page 250. This method of degradation gives the isotope concentration in pairs of carbons and not of individual positions.

The fermentations are conducted with a suspension of *Lactobacillus casei*, which is centrifuged from a three-day growth, at 37°, in 1% glucose and 0.5% Bactoyeast extract. The cells are washed three times with 20 volumes of distilled water. The fermentation is carried out under carbon dioxide at 37° in 150-ml Warburg flasks. The reaction mixture contains 2% wet bacteria, 0.06 M sodium bicarbonate, and the glucose solution. The final volume is 30 ml. When the fermentation is complete as judged by the cessation of gas evolution, the bacteria are removed by centrifugation and the lactic acid is recovered by ether extraction. To remove miscellaneous impurities, the alkaline solution is continuously extracted with ether for 24 hours. This extraction is discarded, and the lactic acid is extracted from the acidified residue, which is then distilled with steam to remove volatile impurities; the lactic acid is degraded as described on page 250.

The following chemical degradation was carried out [27] in order to determine the distribution of isotope in the individual carbons.

$$\text{CH}_3\text{O}\overset{1}{\text{CH}}\overset{2}{\text{CHOH}}\overset{3}{\text{CHOH}}\overset{4}{\text{CHOH}}\overset{5}{\text{CHCH}}\overset{6}{\text{CH}_2\text{OH}} \xrightarrow{\text{HIO}_4}$$

$$\text{CH}_3\text{O}\overset{1}{\text{CH}}\text{—}\overset{2}{\text{CHO}} \qquad \overset{4}{\text{CHO}}\overset{5}{\text{CH}}\overset{6}{\text{CH}_2\text{OH}} + \text{HCOOH}$$
$$_3$$

$$\downarrow \overset{\text{HIO}_4}{\Delta}$$

$$\overset{2}{\text{CHO}}\overset{1}{\text{CHO}} + \overset{4}{\text{CHO}}\overset{5}{\text{CHOH}}\overset{6}{\text{CH}_2\text{OH}} + \text{CH}_3\text{OH}$$

$$\downarrow$$

$$\underset{1,2,4,5}{3\text{HCOOH}} + \underset{6}{\text{HCHO}} + \text{CH}_3\text{OH}$$

By this periodic acid procedure [29] carbons 3 and 6 may be distin-

[28] S. Aronoff, H. A. Barker, and M. Calvin, *J. Biol. Chem.*, **169**, 459 (1947).

[29] For a review of the applications of this reaction see E. L. Jackson in *Org. Reactions*, Vol. II, p. 341, John Wiley & Sons, New York, 1944.

guished.   Methylation of the dried glucose is carried out in the test tube.[30]

To the dry glucose is added 2 ml of anhydrous methanolic hydrochloric acid (0.25% HCl), and the mixture is refluxed for 30–45 minutes with frequent shaking. The test tube is then sealed and placed in an öven at 100° for 50 hours, after which charcoal is added.   The mixture is shaken, is allowed to stand half an hour, and is filtered with repeated methanol washings into a small weighed flask.   Concentration to a thick syrup is carried out under a current of air at 60–70°.   The flask is seeded with a minute crystal of methyl glucoside and is rotated in an ice-water bath while crystallization takes place, permitting the formation of a thin film of crystals on the walls of the container.   After they have stood in the icebox overnight, the crystals are covered with ether and permitted to stand with one change of ether for 24 hours. This treatment usually removes the faint yellowish discolorations from the crystals. The glucoside is dried in an oven at 50° and weighed.   Yields of about 75% were obtained by this method.

The solid methyl glucoside (1 mmole) is oxidized for 2 hours at room temperature by dissolving it in 0.25 M periodic acid (free acid, not acidified salt) equivalent to 2 mmoles of periodic acid per mmole of glucoside.   The reaction mixture is diluted to 20 ml, 3 grams of mercuric oxide is added, and the mixture is boiled and aerated for 20 minutes.   The resulting carbon dioxide is obtained from the formic acid of the first oxidation (carbon 3).   The mercury salts are removed by filtration into a steam-distillation flask, and 25 ml of 0.25 M periodic acid is added: the total volume is now approximately 70 ml.   Steam distillation is not begun until the volume is reduced to 15 ml.   A total of 250 ml of distillate is collected.   By simultaneous oxidation and steam distillation, the formaldehyde is removed as it is formed in order to reduce secondary oxidation.   Some carbon dioxide is produced in this step; its source is unknown.   To the distillate is added 20 mg of mercuric oxide, the mixture is boiled for 20 minutes, then 2 ml of 1.7 M phosphoric acid is added and this mixture is boiled and aerated for 15 minutes.   The resulting carbon dioxide originates from the formic acid of the second oxidation.   The mercuric salts are removed by filtration, and 25 ml of 1 N NaOH is added to the filtrate followed by 30 ml of 0.05 N iodine.   The ice-cold mixture is acidified after 10 minutes with 0.1 ml excess 2 N sulfuric acid, and the excess iodine is titrated with standard thiosulfate.   The formaldehyde is converted to formic acid by this oxidation.   To the above solution 20 ml of 0.3 M mercuric acetate and 5 ml of 1 N acetic acid are added, and the mixture is boiled and aerated for 20 minutes.   The resulting carbon dioxide is derived from the formic acid obtained from the formaldehyde of the second oxidation (carbon 6).   The conversion of authentic formaldehyde to carbon dioxide by hypoiodite oxidation followed by mercuric acetate oxidation is found to be quantitative.

Uric Acid

In a study on its biological precursors, uric acid was extracted from the feces of pigeons and was degraded [31] by an earlier procedure.[32] Two samples of the compound were utilized in the degradations.

[30] E. Fischer, *Ber.*, **28**, 1145 (1895).

[31] J. C. Sonne, J. M. Buchanan, and A. M. Delluva, *J. Biol. Chem.*, **166**, 395 (1946); *J. Biol. Chem.*, **173**, 69, 81 (1948).

[32] E. Fischer and F. Ach, *Ber.*, **32**, 2745 (1899).

$$
\begin{array}{c}
\overset{1}{N}-\overset{6}{C}-OH \\
\end{array}
$$

uric acid structure with MnO₂ arrow:

$$\xrightarrow{\text{MnO}_2} \overset{6}{CO_2} + \underset{\text{urea}}{H_2N\overset{2,8}{C}ONH_2} + \underset{\text{glyoxalic acid}}{\overset{4}{C}H\overset{5}{O}COOH}$$

$$\downarrow \text{urease}$$

$$\overset{2,8}{CO_2} \qquad \text{semicarbazone}$$

$$\downarrow \text{KClO}_3 \qquad \qquad \downarrow \text{KMnO}_4$$

$$\overset{5}{CO_2} + \overset{4}{HCOOH}$$

$$\downarrow \text{HgO}$$

$$\overset{4}{CO_2}$$

$$
\underset{\text{urea}}{\begin{array}{c} H_2N \\ | \\ \overset{8}{C}=O \\ | \\ NH_2 \end{array}} +
\underset{\text{alloxan}}{\begin{array}{c} \overset{6}{NH}-CO \\ | \quad\quad | \\ \overset{2}{CO}\;\;\overset{5}{CO} \\ | \quad\quad | \\ NH-\overset{4}{CO} \end{array}}
\xrightarrow{H_2S}
\underset{\text{alloxantin}}{\begin{array}{c} NH-CO \quad CO-NH \\ | \quad\;\; |\;\;\overset{OH}{|}\quad | \\ \overset{2}{CO}\;\;\overset{}{C}-O-CH\;\;\overset{2}{CO} \\ | \quad\quad | \quad\quad | \quad\quad | \\ NH-CO \quad\;\; CO-NH \end{array}}
$$

$$\downarrow \text{PbO}_2$$

$$CO_2 + \overset{2}{CO}\overset{H_2N}{\diagdown}$$
$$\underset{NH_2}{|}$$

Adrenaline

Adrenaline, obtained biologically from a rat given labeled phenyl-alanine, has been degraded [33] to show the location of the isotopic carbon atom.

$$\text{HO}\underset{\text{HO}}{\diagup}\!\!\!\left\langle\;\;\right\rangle\!\!-CHOH-C^*H_2NHCH_3 \xrightarrow{\text{HIO}_4}$$

$$\text{HO}\underset{\text{HO}}{\diagup}\!\!\!\left\langle\;\;\right\rangle\!\!-CHO + C^*H_2O \rightarrow HC^*OOH$$

The adrenaline sample is submitted to oxidation with a slight excess of periodic acid in $2.5\,N$ sulfuric acid. In strong acid the formation of the usual red oxidation products is at the minimum. After the solution has stood for 4 hours, the formaldehyde is steam-distilled and absorbed in cold alkaline hypoiodite. After acidification and removal of excess iodine with sodium thiosulfate, the resulting formic acid is oxidized by refluxing the solution with mercuric acetate in dilute acetic acid. The evolved carbon dioxide is absorbed in sodium hydroxide and is tested for radioactivity.

Propylene

The propylene obtained by various conditions from propanol-1-C^{14} has been degraded [34] in order to determine the distribution of labeled carbon.

The degradation is accomplished by permanganate oxidation; acetic acid, carbon dioxide, and some oxalic acid are formed. This procedure

[33] S. Gurin and A. M. Delluva, *J. Biol. Chem.*, **170**, 545 (1947).
[34] B. A. Fries and M. Calvin, *J. Am. Chem. Soc.*, **70**, 2235 (1948).

has been checked by ozonization and the results are in excellent agreement.

$$\overset{3}{C}H_3\overset{2}{C}H=\overset{1}{C}H_2 \xrightarrow{KMnO_4} \overset{1}{C}O_2 + \overset{3}{C}H_3\overset{2}{C}OOH + \overset{1,2}{(C}OOH)_2$$

The acetate has been further degraded as described on page 248. Studies on the labeled propylene show that the oxalic acid originates from carbons 1 and 2 by rupture of the carbon-carbon single bond.

When propanol-1-C^{14} is dehydrated over metaphosphoric acid or alumina at high temperatures, the label is equally distributed between carbons 1 and 3, indicating a symmetrical intermediate in the reaction. If, however, the propylene is obtained by decomposition of n-propyl-trimethylammonium hydroxide (prepared by the action of methyl iodide on the corresponding bromide), the label is found only in the 1 position.

Approximately 3 mmoles of propylene is distilled into an evacuated 400-cc three-neck flask. Fifty milliliters of 0.1 M phosphoric acid is added through a separatory funnel. The mixture is agitated with an induction stirrer (see Appendix IX), and the reaction is carried out at room temperature. An amount of 0.4 N potassium permanganate calculated to be exactly sufficient to oxidize the propene to propylene glycol is added over 45 minutes. This is followed by the addition, over 45 minutes, of 110% of the amount of 2 N permanganate required for the oxidation of propylene glycol to acetic acid and carbon dioxide. The solution is stirred for 15 minutes, and an acid solution of ferrous sulfate is added to reduce manganese to the manganous state and to liberate the carbon dioxide. The flask is connected to a sodium hydroxide bubbler and swept with nitrogen. The residual solution is steam-distilled to recover acetic acid, which is titrated with sodium hydroxide and evaporated to dryness. The acetate is then degraded as described on page 248.

Decarboxylation of α-Amino Acids

All α-amino acids are smoothly and quantitatively decarboxylated by the action of triketohydrindene hydrate (ninhydrin). This reaction has been used [35] in a study of protein synthesis in which the mixture of amino acids from a protein hydrolysate is subjected to this degradation, and the carbon dioxide is assayed for labeled carbon. Alanine isolated from photosynthetic experiments has been degraded, and both the carbon dioxide and acetaldehyde have been assayed. [36]

[35] I. D. Frantz, R. B. Loftfield, and W. W. Miller, *Science*, **106**, 544 (1947).
[36] A. Benson, unpublished experiments.

RCHCOOH | NH$_2$ + [phthalic/ninhydrin structure: C=O, C(OH)(OH), C=O] →

[structure: C=O, CHOH, C=O] + NH$_3$ + RCHO + CO$_2$

A mixture [36] of 15 mg of alanine and 100 mg of Van Slyke's citrate-citric acid buffer (pH 2.5) in a small flask is frozen, and 150 mg of ninhydrin is added. The flask is fitted with a stopcock and is evacuated and heated in a boiling water bath for 10 minutes. The flask is then attached to one arm of the apparatus shown in Fig. 31; the system is evacuated; and the water, carbon dioxide, and acetaldehyde are distilled into the sodium hydroxide solution in the other arm. Barium chloride is added to precipitate barium carbonate, which is collected by centrifugation. The acetaldehyde solution is then treated with iodine, and is degraded to iodoform; see page 250.

Alternatively, the mixture after decomposition can be distilled into a solution containing a saturated solution of one equivalent of 2,4-dinitrophenylhydrazine in acetic acid. The flask is warmed, and the acetaldehyde phenylhydrazone crystals may be recovered. This type of degradation should be general for all α-amino acids.

Decarboxylation of Carboxylic Acids

All ordinary carboxylic acids may be decarboxylated by boiling in quinoline with copper oxide or copper chromite as catalysts. The yields vary from 60 to 95% of theoretical.[37]

An equal weight of carboxylic acid and copper chromite catalyst is placed in a small flask fitted with a reflux condenser and a gas inlet tube. A suitable volume of purified quinoline is added, and the mixture is heated to 260° (salt bath) and is swept vigorously with carbon dioxide-free nitrogen. The gas stream is passed through the top of the condenser into a sodium or barium hydroxide bubbler, and the carbonate is then assayed for isotope. The reaction is heated for ½ hour and is allowed to cool while being swept for an additional half hour.[38]

[37] W. G. Dauben, J. C. Reid, P. E. Yankwich, and M. Calvin, *J. Am. Chem. Soc.*, **68**, 2117 (1946).

[38] The decarboxylation of labeled benzoic and mandelic acids has been carried out by means of the Schmidt reaction by W. v. E. Doering, T. I. Taylor, and E. F. Schoenewaldt, *J. Am. Chem. Soc.*, **70**, 455 (1948).

Chapter 12

BIOSYNTHETIC METHODS

There are many compounds of great biochemical interest which cannot as yet be synthesized in the laboratory by the ordinary methods of organic chemistry. These include not only the macro molecules—proteins, polysaccharides, nucleic acids, and the like—but also many of the simpler molecules whose structures are believed to be fully known, such as some of the vitamins and hormones, naturally occurring porphyrins, and sucrose. Even the simple monosaccharides, which are of great importance, such as glucose and fructose, require extremely inefficient synthetic methods, and, although a number of laboratories are at present engaged in the problem, neither of these two compounds has as yet been totally synthesized with a carbon isotope. It has, of course, been widely recognized that all these compounds could be made by living organisms using isotopically enriched substrates. The compounds could be isolated and purified, their isotopic constitution determined, and then they could be used in further metabolic experiments. Actually, a great deal of work has been done with isotopically labeled substrates demonstrating the course of their incorporation into a variety of molecules by living organisms.[1] However, most of this work has been directed toward the elucidation of a metabolic path and not toward the preparation of a biologically important compound to be isolated later and used in further experiments.

The problems involved in the development of biosynthetic methods for preparative purposes are somewhat different from those encountered in the use of isotopes to elucidate a metabolic process. Where a specific compound is desired, there are a number of general conditions which one must seek to fulfill. First of all is the selection of the organism to be used. This choice must be made in accordance with the compound desired and the labeled substrates available, as well as with regard for the remaining two conditions which ought to be fulfilled, namely, that the label should go into the desired compound with the highest yield and with the minimum of dilution, and finally that the desired compound should be capable of being isolated and subjected to a high degree of purification.

[1] J. M. Buchanan and A. B. Hastings, *Physiol. Revs.*, **26**, 120 (1946); H. G. Wood, *Physiol. Revs.*, **26**, 198 (1946).

There is another point of view which may be taken in relatively large laboratories where the facilities are available, and that is to select some suitable living organism and merely allow it to grow an appreciable length of time on a nutrient containing large amounts of isotopic carbon. This produces a generally labeled organism in which practically all the constituent compounds are labeled to varying degrees. Compounds can then be isolated as needed for further work. This type of "isotope farm" has been suggested in a variety of places, but, in addition to the obvious disadvantages of isolation and isotope distribution, there is the additional problem, at least in connection with animal work, that only a relatively small fraction of the injected or ingested isotope is incorporated into the animal tissues; a very large fraction is expired as respiratory carbon dioxide in a very short time, especially when the material is given by injection. This expired carbon dioxide can, of course, be recovered, but it is diluted. Although in general it is advisable to use a chemical synthetic method for making a compound when this can be done, in special circumstances particular laboratories may find a biosynthetic method more convenient, when such a method is highly efficient, as it is, for example, in the bacterial synthesis of certain fatty acids.

Since all the carbon isotopes are available as carbon dioxide ($BaCO_3$), it would seem highly desirable to find organisms that can use the carbon efficiently in this form as substrate. This consideration leads directly to photosynthesis as the method par excellence for biosynthesis with carbon dioxide. Although it has been demonstrated that non-photosynthetic organisms, both animal- and micro-organisms, can incorporate carbon dioxide into a variety of compounds by exchange reactions, it does not appear that this method can lead to a very efficient production of labeled compounds in terms of the utilization of the isotope and the dilutions involved. There are, of course, a number of heterotrophic micro-organisms which derive their energy from sources other than photosynthesis and which can incorporate carbon dioxide efficiently. They will be discussed specifically later.

Photosynthetic Methods [2]

Radioactive starch, glucose, fructose, and sucrose can be isolated from green leaves in good yields after the leaves have been exposed to an atmosphere of radioactive carbon dioxide in the presence of light. At

[2] The following procedures were kindly supplied to us by Professor W. Z. Hassid of the Division of Plant Nutrition of the College of Agriculture of the University of California, Berkeley. Another procedure for the preparation of starch labeled with C^{13} is to be found in the publication of L. G. Livingstone and G. Medes, *J. Gen. Physiol.*, **31**, 75 (1947).

the end of the photosynthetic period, the leaf or leaves are extracted with dilute alcohol. The alcohol-insoluble fraction contains the starch which can be isolated; hydrolysis of the starch with acid produces glucose, which can be obtained in crystalline form. The alcohol extract contains glucose, fructose, and sucrose; in order to increase the yield of the monosaccharides, the sucrose is hydrolyzed with acid, thus producing additional glucose and fructose. The separation of fructose from glucose is accomplished by precipitation of the former with calcium hydroxide. The calcium complex is then decomposed, and the fructose is liberated. Sucrose is prepared by fermenting a mixture of glucose, fructose, and sucrose with *Torula monosa*. The two monosaccharides are decomposed to carbon dioxide and ethanol while the sucrose remains unaffected and can be concentrated and crystallized.

Apparatus. The photosynthesis chamber is made of a Pyrex glass tube (Fig. 86) 21 cm in length and 5.5 cm in inside diameter. The lower end consists of a drawn-down recurved entry tube fitted with a stopcock a and a 10/30 tapered joint. The upper end bears a 60/50 joint A_1 to which a cover is fitted carrying an exit tube

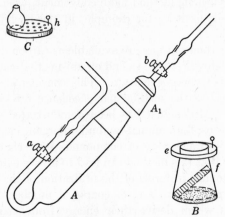

Fig. 86. Photosynthesis apparatus. (A, photosynthesis chamber; B, carbon dioxide generator; C, leaf chamber and stand.)

which is also fitted with a stopcock b and 10/30 joint. The volume between the stopcocks a and b is 500 ml.

When conducting an experiment, about 500 mg of barium carbonate containing approximately 0.25 millicurie of C^{14} is introduced into a 25-ml Erlenmeyer flask B from which the neck has been removed. A cork disk e, slightly smaller than the inside diameter of the chamber A, is fitted to the top of the flask so that its position is fixed when it is placed in the chamber. The barium carbonate is then mixed with about 5 ml of water, and a few drops of paraffin oil are added to prevent excessive foaming. One milliliter of 80% lactic acid is placed in a small test tube f, cut off so that it rests at about a 45° angle when placed in flask B. This flask, containing the barium carbonate slurry and the test tube of lactic acid, is then placed in an upright position in the photosynthesis chamber A, which was previously rinsed with water to assure a humid atmosphere. (Enough water should also be left in the recurving portion of the entry tube to serve as an indicator when the internal and external pressures are equalized.)

A Florence flask C from which the neck has been removed is attached to a plywood disk h bored through with numerous holes. The flask is filled with water, and the petiole of the leaf, which has previously been kept in the dark for 24 hours, is inserted so that it reaches the bottom of the flask. The leaf and its container are placed in a vacuum desiccator which is evacuated to about 20 cm. After the initial

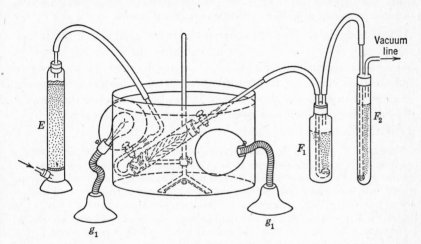

FIG. 87. Photosynthesis apparatus. (E, soda-lime tower; g_1, lamp; F_1, F_2, sodium hydroxide traps.)

flow of gas bubbles from the petiole of the leaf ceases, the pressures are equalized and the water displaced in flask C is replaced. The leaf and container are then placed in the photosynthesis chamber A on top of the cork ring e. A piece of moistened filter paper is placed over the plywood disk to prevent spattering of acid into the upper part of the vessel. The greased upper-end ground taper A_1 is fitted on, and with the entry tube a closed the chamber is partially evacuated through the exit tube which is then closed with stopcock b. With the chamber tilted about $30°$ the acid is dumped into the barium carbonate slurry. (This should be done slowly so as to avoid excessive foaming.) When the reaction has subsided and all the barium carbonate has reacted, with liberation of the carbon dioxide, atmospheric pressure is restored by opening stopcock a. The chamber is then immersed in a cylindrical Pyrex water bath, 10 inches high and 18 inches in diameter, held in position by a condenser clamp on a heavy ring stand in the bath as shown in Fig. 87.

Illumination is effected by two 100-watt bulbs in desk lamps g_1 and g_2 placed opposite each other on the outside of the bath. A small fan (not shown in Fig. 87) is placed above the water bath so that a current of air passes over the surface of the bath. This maintains the bath temperature $3°$ to $4°$ above the prevailing room temperature. Illumination is continued for 18 to 24 hours. A relatively long period of illumination is used in order to insure complete utilization of the available carbon dioxide and to increase the probability of obtaining uniformly labeled compounds.

During the last hour of illumination a soda-lime tower E is attached to the entry tube of the photosynthesis chamber, and two carbon dioxide traps F_1 and F_2 are attached in series to the exit tube. During this period about 5 liters of carbon dioxide-free air is pulled through the system by application of a vacuum at F_2. Trap F_1 consists of a 500-ml jar fitted with a sintered-glass aerator containing 335 ml of 0.1 N sodium hydroxide; trap F_2 consists of a 100-ml test tube also equipped with an aerator and 65 ml of 0.1 N sodium hydroxide.

Titration of a 25-ml aliquot of the alkali in the traps F_1 and F_2 with 0.1 N hydrochloric acid after addition of 1 ml of 10% barium chloride, using phenolphthalein as an indicator, usually gives the same value as the alkali control.

Plant Materials. Turkish tobacco leaves are good starch producers. A high rate of synthesis can be achieved after the leaves are placed in the dark for approximately 24 hours to use up the reserve carbohydrate, and are then subjected to photosynthesis in an atmosphere containing initially 10 to 15% carbon dioxide. It has been observed that, under the experimental conditions described, about 20% of the dry weight of the alcohol-extracted leaf residue consists of starch.

The plants are grown in Hoagland's solution [3] or sand culture. The leaves, weighing from 3.0 to 3.5 grams and from 15 to 18 cm in length, are taken from the middle portion of the stem of plants about 2.5 feet high. Leaves of plants grown in culture solution are harvested in the morning and placed in water in the dark until the following morning. Plants grown in pots of sand are placed with the container in the dark for a similar period of time and the leaves are harvested just before the experiment. On a fresh-weight basis the starved leaves usually contain about 0.25% reducing sugars (glucose and fructose) and 0.15% sucrose. The residue does not give a blue color with iodine, indicating the absence of starch. After 24 hours of illumination in the chamber in an atmosphere of carbon dioxide derived from 0.5 gram of barium carbonate, about 0.85% reducing sugars, 0.65% sucrose, and 2.5% starch are obtained.

Starch

Radioactive starch can be prepared by the following technique: A Turkish tobacco leaf is harvested in the morning and allowed to remain in the dark for 24 hours to exhaust the starch. The leaf is then placed in the photosynthesis chamber in an atmosphere of radioactive carbon dioxide, as previously described, and is illuminated for 24 hours. At the conclusion of the photosynthetic period and after the chamber has been swept out with carbon dioxide-free air, the leaf is killed by immersion in boiling 80% alcohol. It is then cut into small pieces and placed in a Soxhlet extraction thimble. The alcohol used in killing the leaf is transferred to the boiling flask of a Soxhlet extractor. The extractor is assembled and the extraction continued for 6 to 8 hours, after which the alcoholic extract containing the soluble sugars (glucose, fructose, and sucrose) is set aside.

After the 80% alcohol extraction, the residue remaining in the Soxhlet thimble is dried at 50° in a vacuum oven for a period of 18 to 24 hours (0.3 to 0.4 gram of dry

[3] D. R. Hoagland and D. I. Arnin, *Calif. Agr. Expt. Sta. Circular* 347, December 1938.

material is obtained), 25% of its weight of magnesium carbonate is added, and the mixture is ground fine in a mortar under a hood. The ground material is extracted [4] as follows: It is transferred to a heavy-duty 50-ml centrifuge tube to which an amount of 100- to 150-mesh ground glass, equivalent to 7.5 times the weight of the plant material, is added. This is followed by the addition of 5 ml of water, and a heavy stirring rod is placed in the tube. The tube is immersed in a steam bath, and the mixture is stirred vigorously for 15 minutes to gelatinize the starch. Seven milliliters of 46% calcium chloride solution, previously heated on the same water bath, is added, and stirring is continued for 10 minutes. The tube is centrifuged, the supernatant liquid decanted into a 100-ml centrifuge tube, and the residue ground again for about 5 minutes. The tube is returned to the steam bath, 3 ml of boiling water and 5 ml of 46% calcium chloride solution at 100° are added, and stirring is continued for 10 minutes. The tube is centrifuged and the supernatant liquid decanted into the 100-ml tube containing the first extract. After four such extractions, the last drop of the fourth supernatant liquid is acidified with a drop of 0.5 N acetic acid and tested with dilute iodine solution. If no blue starch-iodine color is observed, the extraction of starch is assumed to be complete and the residue is washed twice with 15 ml of hot water. If the starch-iodine test is positive, the extraction procedure is continued until a negative test is obtained. Seven or eight extractions are sometimes necessary to completely free the residue of starch.

The extract (60 to 120 ml) in the 100-ml centrifuge tube (or tubes) is treated with 1 ml of 2.3 N hydrochloric acid and 2 ml of 20% sodium chloride per each 10 ml of extract. The starch is then precipitated by the addition of 0.5 ml of iodine-iodide solution (30 grams of iodine and 50 grams of potassium iodide diluted to 250 ml) per 10 ml of extract. The tube is stoppered loosely and allowed to stand for 10 minutes, after which it is placed in a steam bath for 15 minutes. The tube with contents is cooled and centrifuged, the supernatant liquid is decanted, and the starch-iodine complex is well washed with 60% alcohol. The complex is then decomposed with 2 to 4 ml of 0.25 N alcoholic sodium hydroxide and washed three times with 60% alcohol. The crude starch is dissolved in 5 ml of water, filtered through paper into a centrifuge tube, and reprecipitated with 1.5 volumes of 95% alcohol. When precipitation is complete, the starch is centrifuged and washed with 60% alcohol, [5] twice with 95% alcohol, twice with absolute alcohol, and finally twice with ether. After the ether has evaporated and the starch is ground to a powder, it is placed in a vacuum oven and dried at 50° for 24 hours.

(Several starch preparations made by this method with approximately 230 μc of C[14] in 0.5 gram barium carbonate yielded from 20 to 25% starch calculated on dry basis of the alcohol extracted plant material. The specific activity of the starch was from 0.48 μc/mg to 0.72 μc/mg.)

Glucose from Starch

The radioactive starch is hydrolyzed to glucose by dissolving it in sufficient water to make a 0.2% solution and at the same time adding an amount of inactive glucose carrier necessary to provide enough material to crystallize conveniently (0.3 gram was usually added). An equal volume of 2 N sulfuric acid is added to this solution,

[4] G. W. Pucher and H. B. Vickery, *Ind. Eng. Chem., Anal. Ed.*, **8**, 92 (1936).

[5] If the starch is to be used immediately for the preparing of radioactive glucose, the drying is unnecessary; it can be immediately hydrolyzed with sulfuric acid after washing with 60% alcohol.

and the mixture is refluxed for 30 minutes on a hot plate. After cooling, the theoretical amount of powdered barium carbonate needed to neutralize the acid is added and the precipitate is centrifuged and washed. The supernatant liquid and the washings are then passed through Duolite ion exchange columns, C-3 and A-3, having 25-ml bed volumes. Each column is washed with 100 ml of water. The demineralized solution, about 300 ml, is concentrated to a small volume *in vacuo* at 50°, is transferred to a 25-ml beaker, and is taken to a thick syrup in the vacuum oven at 50°. The syrup is warmed on the steam bath, and approximately 4 volumes of hot absolute alcohol is stirred in. Into the resultant viscous mass, 50 mg of finely powdered crystalline glucose is stirred and the beaker is allowed to cool in a desiccator. Crystallization of the glucose is complete within 24 hours. The crystals are transferred to a sintered-glass funnel with cold absolute alcohol, sucked dry, washed with ether, and placed in the vacuum oven at 50°. After 24 hours the sugar is ground in a mortar, weighed, and assayed for radioactivity.

In a typical experiment an 85-mg starch sample, having a specific activity of 0.57 μc/mg, yielded, after addition of 350 mg of inactive glucose, 406 mg of glucose with a specific activity of 0.09 μc/mg. In another experiment, a 71-mg starch sample with a specific activity of 0.48 μc/mg yielded, after addition of 350 mg of inactive glucose, 383 mg of glucose of specific activity 0.1 μc/mg.

Fructose

The 80% alcohol plant extract contains glucose, fructose, and sucrose. Most of the labeled glucose can be crystallized out by the addition of inactive glucose to the mixture after acid hydrolysis of the sucrose. The fructose, which does not readily crystallize and remains in solution, can be separated from glucose by forming the insoluble calcium-fructose complex, which is later decomposed.

The technique used in the preparation of fructose is as follows: The 80% alcoholic extract is concentrated on the steam bath with occasional additions of water until all the alcohol is removed. The aqueous solution is cooled and extracted twice, with one-fourth of its volume of ether, using a separatory funnel to remove pigments and tarry matter. The ether is then washed with water, and the washings are added to the original aqueous phase. This latter solution is returned to the steam bath and heated to remove the dissolved ether. About 400 mg of inactive glucose carrier is added, and after the solution is cooled it is passed through Duolite ion exchange columns, C-3 and A-3 of 25-ml bed volume capacity, to remove the organic acids and amino acids. Approximately 100 ml of wash water is used for each column, and the resulting neutral solution is concentrated under reduced pressure at 50° to a volume of 8 ml. Two milliliters of 5 N sulfuric acid is added, and the solution is heated in a water bath at 80° for 10 minutes to invert the sucrose. After cooling and diluting to about 50 ml, the solution is passed through the anion exchange column A-3 to remove the acid used for hydrolysis. The resulting neutral solution of glucose and invert sugar is concentrated under vacuum at 50° to a volume of 10 ml, transferred to a small beaker, and concentrated to a thick syrup in the vacuum oven. The glucose is then crystallized as previously described. When the mother liquor is concentrated, a second crop of crystalline glucose is obtained. (The specific activity of this glucose is about 25% greater than that of the first crop, indicating radioactive contamination. Two hundred milligrams of inactive glucose is added to the mother liquor in order to reduce the activity of the residual glucose. Upon crystallization, 221 mg of glucose is recovered with a specific activity equivalent to one-third of that of the second crop. Considering the dilution with inactive glucose, approximately one-tenth of the previous activity would be expected. The higher activity indicates that some radioactive fructose is likely to be carried down with the inactive glucose.)

TABLE XXIV

	Weight, mg	Specific Activity, $\mu c/mg$	Total Activity, μc
1st crop of glucose	426	0.089	38
2nd crop of glucose	79	0.113	9
3rd crop of glucose	221 *	0.037	8.1

* Includes 200 mg carrier.

The radioactive glucose obtained from the mixture with fructose was contaminated with about 1 to 2% of radioactive fructose. It could be freed almost completely from the radioactive contaminant by the addition of inactive fructose and by recrystallization.

The calcium-fructose complex is prepared according to the following procedure: [6] One gram of fructose carrier is added to the mother liquor after practically all the radioactive glucose has been crystallized by the addition of inactive glucose, and the alcohol present is removed by evaporation on the steam bath. In order to precipitate this quantity of fructose, an amount of calcium oxide equivalent to half of the weight of the fructose should be added. A 19% milk of lime suspension is made up from 0.76 gram of calcium hydroxide powder and 3.25 ml of water, making a total weight of about 4 grams. The calcium hydroxide used was shown to contain 66% calcium oxide, as determined by titration with 0.1 N hydrochloric acid. The sugar solution containing the radioactive fructose is diluted with 11.7 ml of water, so that the fructose would constitute 6% by weight of the total reaction mixture.

The fructose solution and the calcium oxide slurry are placed in a refrigerator at 0°. When the fructose solution is cooled to 0°, one-fourth of the lime slurry is poured into a 50-ml centrifuge tube in an ice bath, and then one-fourth of the sugar solution is slowly added with vigorous mechanical stirring. (After 15 minutes fine crystalline needles of calcium-fructose can be observed under the microscope.) The second quarter of the slurry is added with continuous stirring, followed by the slow addition of the second quarter of the sugar solution. The third and fourth portions are added at 20-minute intervals, and after another 20 minutes' stirring the mixture is placed in a refrigerator overnight. The next day the precipitate is centrifuged in a chilled centrifuge cup and washed twice with 2-ml portions of ice-cold saturated calcium hydroxide.

The calcium-fructose complex is then treated with an excess of 1 M oxalic acid, using phenolphthalein as an indicator, with mechanical stirring. The calcium oxalate is centrifuged and washed twice with 25-ml portions of water. The supernatant liquid and washings are then passed over ion exchange columns, Duolite C-3 and A-3, concentrated to a small volume in vacuum below 50°, and finally taken to a syrup in a vacuum oven.

[6] F. J. Bates et al., "Polarimetry, Saccharimetry and Sugars," National Bureau of Standards, Circular C-440 (1942), p. 92.

This syrup, containing practically all fructose, is crystallized as follows: [7]   It is taken up in a small amount of warm absolute alcohol, a few milliliters of dry benzene are added, and the mixture is taken to dryness under reduced pressure while a stream of dry air blows over the surface of the liquid.   After repetition of this procedure four times, the residue is taken up in a minimum quantity of hot absolute methyl alcohol, cooled in a desiccator, and seeded with 50 mg of finely powdered crystalline fructose; the fructose is precipitated by the slow dropwise addition of absolute ether. The crystals are allowed to remain in a desiccator for 24 hours and are then filtered off and washed with ether.   A yield of 0.925 gram of fructose is recovered, having a specific activity of 0.0325 μc/mg.

Initially there is a total of 132 μc in the sugar solution, to which 2.125 grams of inactive glucose and fructose is added.   The radioactive sugars synthesized in the plant probably amount to about 100 mg.   These preparations are made from the combined 80% alcoholic extracts of two tobacco leaves.

TABLE XXV

Recovered Sugar	Amount, mg	Total, μc
Glucose	726	55
Fructose	925	30
Calcium-fructose complex supernatant solution, calculated from reducing value	61	16.4
Calcium-fructose complex wash water calculated from reducing value	29	6.5
	1,741	107.9

The extent to which the glucose and fructose are contaminated with one another has been investigated in a control experiment performed as follows: A tobacco leaf, previously placed in the dark and then illuminated in the presence of inactive carbon dioxide for 24 hours, is extracted with alcohol, the alcoholic extract is clarified, and the sucrose hydrolyzed.   The solution containing glucose and fructose is divided into two halves.   To one half of the solution, labeled fructose is added and the glucose is crystallized as previously described.   The other half is treated with labeled glucose, and the fructose is isolated from the mixture by the calcium precipitation method.

The results indicate that the glucose crystallized from the mixture with labeled fructose contained 1.3% fructose.   The fructose is found to be contaminated with glucose to the extent of 2.5%.   The glucose is almost completely freed from the radioactive fructose contaminant by dissolving the sugar in water, adding inactive fructose, and recrystallizing.   The glucose contaminant in the fructose is reduced to a negligible amount by dissolving the sample and oxidizing with barium hypoiodite solution as described, [8] passing the solution through ion exchange columns, and recovering the fructose by concentrating the solution and recrystallizing.

Sucrose

For the production of sucrose a leaf from the *Canna indica* plant is used.   Leaves from this plant do not form any detectable starch but do produce a considerable amount of sucrose.   Photosynthesis is carried

---

[7] H. O. L. Fisher and E. Baer, *Helv. Chim. Acta*, **19**, 519 (1936).

[8] W. F. Goebel, *J. Biol. Chem.*, **72**, 809 (1927).

out at 17°, since it has been observed that the "sucrose/reducing sugar" ratio is more favorable at that temperature than at 28°. (The ratio of sucrose to reducing sugars was 1.0 at 17°, whereas it was 0.7 at 28°.)

Canna leaves with blades from 12 to 15 cm long are picked from new shoots on the rhizome, the petioles being cut to 2 cm. These young leaves contain nearly enough anthocyanin pigments to mask the green color of the leaf. Under the conditions of the experiment, when 500 mg of barium carbonate is used at 17° with a 24-hour illumination period, all the carbon dioxide is utilized. On a wet weight basis, the final level of reducing sugars is 1.4%, and that of sucrose 1.8%.

The wet weight of the leaf after it has been placed in the dark for 24 hours and then infiltrated with water through the petiole is 4.92 grams. The leaf is placed in the photosynthesis chamber containing carbon dioxide from 500 mg of radioactive $BaCO_3$. After 24 hours of illumination at 15°, the leaf is killed with alcohol as previously described and then is allowed to reflux overnight with 80% alcohol.

The extract is concentrated on the steam bath, water being added from time to time to maintain volume, and the aqueous solution is extracted with ether in a separatory funnel. Two hundred milligrams of sucrose carrier is added, the excess ether is evaporated on the steam bath, and the resultant aqueous solution is passed over ion exchange columns. The neutral solution is concentrated to about 7 ml, and the reducing sugars are fermented out with *Torula monosa*.

Torula monosa ferments glucose, fructose, and mannose but does not attack sucrose or other disaccharides. The organism is grown aerobically for 24 hours at 28° on agar plates containing 0.5% yeast extract and 1% glucose. The cells are washed twice by centrifugation and resuspended in 0.033 M, pH 5, phosphate buffer. A yeast suspension prepared in this way will decompose approximately 15 mg of glucose per hour per 100 mg of dry yeast under anaerobic conditions at 37°. The initial glucose concentration should not be above 3%.

The mixture of sucrose, yeast, and acid phosphate buffer is centrifuged, and the supernatant sugar solution is again passed over the ion exchange columns after the addition of another 100 mg of sucrose carrier. The neutral fraction is concentrated again and finally reduced to an immobile syrup in the vacuum oven. Upon the addition of warm absolute alcohol with stirring, the sucrose immediately crystallizes. The crystals are placed in a desiccator and after 24 hours are filtered onto a sintered-glass funnel, washed with absolute alcohol, and dried with ether. The material is then ground in a mortar and assayed for radioactivity. The yield of sucrose is 360 mg. (When the quantity of carrier specified in the foregoing description is used, the specific activity of the sucrose is about three-fourths that of the barium carbonate. Of the initial activity, about 55% is recoverable as sucrose.)

Microbiological Methods

A number of microbiological procedures have been used for the preparation of several carbon-labeled fatty acids, namely, doubly labeled acetic acid; 1,3-C^{14}, 2,4-C^{14}, and 1,2,3,4-C^{14} butyric acids; and a variety of labeled caproic acids.[9]

---

[9] The following procedures were kindly supplied to us by Professor H. A. Barker of the Division of Plant Nutrition, College of Agriculture, University of California, Berkeley.

Acetic Acid-1,2-C^{14}

Clostridium thermoaceticum ferments glucose approximately according to the equation
$$C_6H_{12}O_6 = 3CH_3COOH \qquad (1)$$

It has been shown [10,11,12] that this conversion involves an oxidation of glucose to acetic acid and carbon dioxide (equation 2), coupled with a condensation and reduction of carbon dioxide to acetic acid (equation 3). Approximately two-thirds of the acetic acid originates from the

$$C_6H_{12}O_6 + 2H_2O = 2CH_3COOH + 2CO_2 + 8H \qquad (2)$$

$$8H + 2CO_2 = CH_3COOH + 2H_2O \qquad (3)$$

glucose molecule directly, and one-third is from carbon dioxide. If the fermentation is carried out in the presence of labeled bicarbonate, doubly labeled acetic acid is formed. Since no other volatile acid is produced, the isolation of the labeled acetic acid by steam distillation is very simple.

A basal medium of the following composition (in grams per 100 ml) is used: glucose 0.5, tryptone 0.5, yeast extract 0.5, $(NH_4)_2SO_4$ 0.1, $MgSO_4 \cdot 7H_2O$ 0.02, $CaSO_4 \cdot 2H_2O$ 0.001, $FeSO_4 \cdot 7H_2O$ 0.0005, sodium thioglycollate 0.05, made up in glass-distilled water and adjusted to pH 6.5. The medium is sterilized by autoclaving.

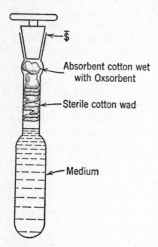

Absorbent cotton wet with Oxsorbent

Sterile cotton wad

Medium

FIG. 88.   Culture vessel.

As a culture vessel, a large Pyrex test tube provided with a standard taper joint and a glass stopper is convenient to use (Fig. 88). The tube should be large enough to hold 30 ml of medium, a sterile cotton plug, and a small wad of absorbent cotton, as illustrated in the figure.

The labeled carbon dioxide must be added to the medium after sterilization; otherwise, most of it would be lost. The most convenient procedure is to sterilize the labeled carbon dioxide in the form of sodium carbonate containing a slight excess of sodium hydroxide, in the culture vessel, which is closed with a cotton plug. Approximately 0.25 mmole of sodium carbonate, made by the absorption of the carbon dioxide from 40 to 50 mg of labeled barium carbonate in 0.6 ml of 1 N carbon dioxide-free NaOH, is used. Twenty-five milliliters of the basal medium is sterilized in a separate vessel, and to this is added 1.5 ml of 1 M sterile phosphate buffer, pH 6.6. By the usual bacteriological technique, the buffered medium is then added to the culture vessel containing the sterile, labeled carbonate. The quantities of buffer and carbonate are chosen so that the final pH is 6.8–7.2. The medium is immediately inoculated with 0.5 ml of an active culture of *Cl. thermoaceticum* grown in the same medium with unlabeled carbon dioxide. The sterile cotton plug is then pushed down

[10] H. A. Barker, *Proc. Natl. Acad. Sci. U. S.*, **30**, 88 (1944).

[11] H. A. Barker and M. D. Kamen, *Proc. Natl. Acad. Sci. U. S.*, **31**, 219 (1945).

[12] B. Volcani and H. A. Barker, unpublished experiments.

into the tube, as illustrated in Fig. 88, a wad of absorbent cotton is placed on top of the sterile plug, and 0.5 ml of Oxsorbent [13] is pipetted into the cotton wad. The tube is immediately closed with a well-greased glass stopper to prevent loss of carbon dioxide and entrance of oxygen. The culture is incubated at 55° C until growth ceases and the bacteria begin to settle to the bottom of the tube. This process usually requires 2 to 3 days.

When the fermentation is completed, a saturated solution of barium hydroxide is added to the medium until it is alkaline to thymol blue (pH 9.5). The precipitated barium salts of phosphate, sulfate, and carbonate are centrifuged and carefully washed. The labeled carbon dioxide may be recovered from the precipitate by the usual procedures. The combined supernatant liquors containing the labeled acetic acid are concentrated to a small volume on a steam bath and acidified to pH 2 with 25% sulfuric acid. The precipitated barium sulfate is centrifuged, carefully washed, and discarded. The supernatant solution is then steam-distilled in an all-glass apparatus, and the acetic acid is titrated with 0.1 N sodium hydroxide in successive fractions of the distillate until no more comes over. The recovery should be 1.5–2.0 mmoles of acetic acid, equivalent to about 2.6 mmoles per mmole of glucose fermented. A small additional amount of labeled acetic acid of lower specific activity can be recovered by the addition of a little carrier acetic acid to the residue and continuation of the distillation. The acetate, obtained by steam distillation, can be used for most purposes without further purification.

The acetic acid so prepared is labeled in both positions. Published data [11] show that the distribution of the isotope may be uniform or somewhat in favor of the carboxyl position; a 40:60 distribution between the methyl and carboxyl groups was observed in one preparation.

The recovery of the isotope in acetic acid is 80–85% based on the labeled carbon dioxide utilized and 70–80% based on the labeled carbon dioxide added. From 5 to 15% of the isotope can be recovered as carbon dioxide at the end of the fermentation. The labeled carbon is diluted 15 to 20 times. This is not a serious disadvantage when using high-activity C^{14}. If sodium carbonate containing 2 mc/mmole is used, the acetic acid will contain over 0.2 mc/mmole. The dilution factor and the isotope recoveries may be increased or decreased by alteration of the ratio between the amounts of carbonate and glucose added.

The maximum amount of C^{14} that can be used in a single preparation on the above scale has not been determined but is in excess of 1 mc.

Another biological method for making doubly labeled acetic acid has been developed [12] which is more complicated but has the advantages of a lower dilution factor (1–2 fold) and a higher yield (90–95%). It makes use of the reaction

$$4H_2 + 2CO_2 \rightarrow CH_3COOH + 2H_2O \tag{4}$$

catalyzed by *Clostridium aceticum*.[14]

---

[13] Oxsorbent is an acid solution of a chromous salt which absorbs oxygen without absorbing carbon dioxide. Sold by Burrell Technical Supply Co., Pittsburgh, Pa.

[14] K. T. Wieringa, *Antonie van Leeuwenhoek, J. Microbiol. Serol.*, **3**, 1 (1936); **6**, 251 (1940).

The Butyric Acids

B. rettgeri ferments lactate to carbon dioxide, acetic acid, butyric acid, and a trace of caproic acid.[15]　The following reactions occur during the fermentation:

$$CH_3CHOHCOOH + H_2O \rightarrow CH_3COOH + CO_2 + 8H \qquad (5)$$

$$2CO_2 + 8H \rightarrow CH_3COOH + 2H_2O \qquad (6)$$

$$2CH_3COOH + 4H \rightarrow CH_3CH_2CH_2COOH + 2H_2O \qquad (7)$$

Reactions 6 and 7 make possible the synthesis of completely labeled acetic and butyric acids from labeled carbon dioxide.　By the use of unlabeled carbon dioxide and labeled acetic acid, it is possible to make variously labeled butyric acids as follows:

SUBSTRATE	PRODUCT
CH_3C^*OOH	$CH_3C^*H_2CH_2C^*OOH$
C^*H_3COOH	$C^*H_3CH_2C^*H_2COOH$
$C^*H_3C^*OOH$	$C^*H_3C^*H_2C^*H_2C^*OOH$

Since acetic, butyric, and caproic acids are always present in the fermented medium, it is necessary to separate them by an azeotropic distillation [16] or some other suitable method.[17]

Procedure 1: Preparation of $C^*H_3C^*OOH$ and $C^*H_3C^*H_2C^*H_2C^*OOH$ from C^*O_2.　A medium containing the following constituents (in grams per 100 ml) is used: sodium lactate 1.0, Difco yeast extract 0.5, $(NH_4)_2SO_4$ 0.05, $1 M$ pH 6.4 KH_2PO_4—Na_2HPO_4 buffer 2.5, $MgSO_4 \cdot 7H_2O$ 0.02, cysteine hydrochloride 0.05, $CaSO_4 \cdot 2H_2O$ 0.01, and $FeSO_4 \cdot 7H_2O$ 0.0005, made up with glass-distilled water. Labeled sodium carbonate made from 0.6 ml of $1 N$ carbon dioxide-free sodium hydroxide and 40 to 50 mg of isotopic barium carbonate is sterilized in the culture tube shown in Fig. 88.　To this is added 25 ml of the sterile medium described above. The final pH should be between 6.8 and 7.4.　The medium is inoculated with 0.5 ml of an active culture of *B. rettgeri*, and then the culture tube is provided with an Oxsorbent anaerobic seal and immediately closed.　The tube is incubated at 30 to 37° for 3 to 4 days until growth ceases.

In the separation of the products, the residual labeled carbon dioxide is first removed from the medium by adding an excess of a 10% barium chloride solution and making the medium alkaline to thymol blue with sodium hydroxide.　The precipitated barium salts are centrifuged, carefully washed, and used for the recovery of labeled carbon dioxide by the usual methods.　The combined supernatant solutions are concentrated, acidified with sulfuric acid, and steam-distilled to recover the

[15] H. A. Barker and V. Haas, *J. Bact.*, **47**, 301 (1944); H. A. Barker, M. D. Kamen, and V. Haas, *Proc. Natl. Acad. Sci. U. S.*, **31**, 355 (1945).

[16] S. T. Schiktanz, W. I. Steeles, and A. C. Blaisdell, *Ind. Eng. Chem., Anal. Ed.*, **12**, 320 (1940).

[17] S. R. Elsdeu, *Biochem. J.*, **40**, 252 (1946).

volatile acids. These acids are titrated and concentrated to a small volume on a steam bath, transferred to a continuous extraction apparatus, adjusted to pH 2 with sulfuric acid, and extracted for at least 5 hours with ethyl ether. The extracted ethereal solution of fatty acids is dried overnight by addition of anhydrous sodium sulfate, which must be alkali-free. The ether solution is then filtered into a 100-ml distillation flask fitted with a ground-glass joint, and the sodium sulfate is carefully washed with ether to recover all the acid. The flask is attached to a Podbielniak-type fractionating column about 100 cm long and 6 mm in internal diameter, fitted with a single glass spiral having an efficiency of about 30 theoretical plates. The ether is first distilled, and then 75 ml of anhydrous benzene is added. Acetic acid is carried over as an azeotrope with the benzene and is titrated in successive 10-ml fractions of the distillate, with phenolphthalein as an indicator. (As the titration end point is approached, the benzene solution must be shaken vigorously to transfer all the acid to the aqueous phase.) When the volume of liquid in the still has been reduced to about 20 ml, another 50 ml of benzene is added. This addition usually must be repeated at least once before all the acetic acid has distilled. To be certain that no labeled acetic acid remains with the butyric acid in the residue, 0.5 mmole of unlabeled acetic acid is now added and the distillation is continued. When the distillate contains less than 0.01 milliequivalent of acid per 10 ml, toluene is added to the still to replace the benzene and the distillation is continued as before. Butyric acid is carried over as an azeotrope with toluene. The caproic acid in the residue is negligible in amount and may be discarded.

The aqueous solutions of acetate and butyrate are separated from the benzene and toluene in a separatory funnel, and the last traces of the solvents are removed by evaporation of the alkaline aqueous solutions on a steam bath. The solutions are then transferred separately to an all-glass distillation apparatus, acidified with sulfuric acid, and again steam-distilled.

The acetic and butyric acids so obtained are quite pure, as can be demonstrated by Duclaux distillation. The yield is approximately 0.6 mmole of acetic acid and 0.5 mmole of butyric acid. Sixty to seventy per cent of the isotope added as carbonate is converted into organic compounds; about one-fourth of this is in the acetic acid and one-half is in the butyric acid. The labeled carbon is diluted about 20-fold during the transformation from carbon dioxide to butyric acid. The distribution of the isotope in acetic acid is slightly in favor of the carboxyl group; a carboxyl-methyl ratio of 57:43 was observed in two preparations. In the butyric acid, the isotope content is highest in the carboxyl group and appears to decrease progressively along the chain; the isotope content of the terminal methyl group is about 30% less than that of the carboxyl group. The C^{14} tolerance of the bacteria is probably in excess of 0.5 mc/25 ml culture.

Procedure 2: Preparation of $C^*H_3CH_2C^*H_2COOH$ from C^*H_3COOH. Procedure 1 is followed except in the following respects: No carbonate is added to the medium, but instead 0.5 mmole of methyl-labeled sodium acetate is supplied. This can be autoclaved together with the rest of the medium. A pH 7.4 phosphate buffer is substituted for the more acid buffer used in procedure 1. The Oxsorbent anaerobic seal is replaced by a mixture of 0.3 ml of 40% pyrogallol and 0.2 ml of 10% potassium carbonate. This removes oxygen and supplies carbon dioxide. In the isolation procedure it is not necessary to carry out the barium precipitation, since the carbon dioxide will not contain a significant amount of labeled carbon.

Approximately 0.5 mmole of α, γ-labeled butyric acid containing 60 to 70% of the added isotope is obtained. Most of the remainder can be recovered as acetic acid.

The Caproic Acids

Cl. Kluyveri[18] catalyzes the following reactions under anaerobic conditions:

$$CH_3CH_2OH + CH_3COOH \rightarrow CH_3CH_2CH_2COOH + H_2O$$

$$(8)$$

$$CH_3CH_2OH + CH_3CH_2CH_2COOH \rightarrow CH_3(CH_2)_4COOH + H_2O$$

$$(9)$$

When an excess of ethanol is supplied in the culture medium, very little butyric acid accumulates; the main product is caproic acid. By the use of variously labeled acetic and butyric acids as substrates with ethanol, the following types of labeled caproic acid can be prepared in good yields:

SUBSTRATE	PRODUCT					
CH_3C^*OOH	$CH_3C^*H_2CH_2C^*H_2CH_2C^*OOH$					
C^*H_3COOH	C^*	C	C^*	C	C^*	$COOH$
$C^*H_3C^*OOH$	C^*	C^*	C^*	C^*	C^*	C^*OOH
$CH_3CH_2CH_2C^*OOH$	C	C	C	C^*	C	$COOH$
$C^*H_3C^*H_2C^*H_2C^*OOH$	C^*	C^*	C^*	C^*	C	$COOH$

In order to prepare pure caproic acid it is necessary to remove residual acetic and butyric acids by an azeotropic distillation as described on page 275.

Procedure 1: Preparation of $C^*H_3C^*H_2C^*H_2C^*H_2C^*H_2C^*OOH$ from $C^*H_3C^*OOH$. A medium of the following composition (in grams per 100 ml) is used: ethanol 0.6, carboxyl-labeled sodium acetate 3H$_2$O 0.4, 1 M pH 7 KH$_2$PO$_4$—Na$_2$HPO$_4$ buffer 2.5, (NH$_4$)$_2$SO$_4$ 0.05, MgSO$_4$·7H$_2$O 0.02, CaSO$_4$·2H$_2$O 0.001, FeSO$_4$·7H$_2$O 0.0005, Difco yeast extract 0.075, and sodium thioglycollate 0.05, made up in distilled water. Twenty-five milliliters of the medium is autoclaved in the culture vessel shown in Fig. 88. The medium is inoculated with 0.5 ml of an active culture of *Cl. kluyveri* in the same medium with unlabeled acetate, and then an anaerobic seal is applied as shown in Fig. 88, except that the Oxsorbent is replaced by 0.3 ml of 40% pyrogallol and 0.2 ml of 10% potassium carbonate. Carbon dioxide from the mixture of pyrogallol and carbonate is necessary for the growth of the bacteria. The culture is incubated at 30–37° C until growth ceases and the bacteria begin to settle to the bottom of the tube. Two to four days is usually sufficient.

The fatty acids are removed from the fermented medium by steam distillation, concentrated as the sodium salts, and acidified and extracted with ether. After removal of the ether they are subjected to an azeotropic distillation with toluene as previously described. The toluene distillation removes the acetic and butyric acids,

[18] H. A. Barker, M. D. Kamen, and B. T. Bornstein, *Proc. Natl. Acad. Sci. U. S.*, **31**, 373 (1945); B. T. Bornstein and H. A. Barker, *J. Biol. Chem.*, in press; B. T. Bornstein and H. A. Barker, *J. Bact.*, in press.

which contain not more than 10% of the added isotope. To be sure of the elimination of the last traces of labeled acetic and butyric acids, about 0.25 mmole of each acid (unlabeled) is added to the distillation flask and the distillation is continued until no more acid comes over. The residual solution of caproic acid in toluene is then shaken with 10 ml of water and titrated with alkali to the thymol blue end point. The aqueous solution is separated from the toluene in a separatory funnel, concentrated on a steam bath, acidified, and steam-distilled to recover the labeled caproic acid, which is titrated and kept as the sodium salt.

The yield of caproic acid is about 0.7 mmole; it should contain at least 75% of the isotope added as acetic acid. The caproic acid is labeled in all carbon atoms; however, the distribution of the isotope is not entirely uniform. The carboxyl and α carbon atoms have an appreciably lower isotope content than the remaining four carbon atoms, because they are added last and are more highly diluted by carbon from the unlabeled ethanol. The dilution of the added radiocarbon is not more than threefold. The C^{14} tolerance of the bacteria has not been determined but probably exceeds 0.5 mc/25 ml culture.

Procedure 2: Preparation of $CH_3CH_2CH_2C^*H_2CH_2COOH$ from $CH_3CH_2CH_2$-C^*OOH. The carboxyl-labeled acetate of procedure 1 is replaced by 0.1 gram of unlabeled sodium acetate hydrate and 0.4 gram of carboxyl-labeled sodium butyrate per 100 ml; otherwise, procedure 1 is followed.

Approximately 1.1 mmoles of caproic acid containing 80% of the isotope added as butyrate is obtained in this fermentation. The remainder of the isotope is present in the residual butyrate; the acetate is unlabeled.

Appendix I

ISOTOPE DILUTION METHODS

Experimental Techniques

When a multicomponent mixture is to be analyzed for one of its constituents and when the properties of several of these components are very similar, the purification of any one fraction is a delicate and tedious process. In general it will be impossible to obtain a *quantitative* analysis for the desired constituent because purity and recovery under these conditions are mutually exclusive. This analysis can, however, be accomplished through the agency of tracers.[1]

For example, consider a situation in which a radioactive isotope is to be used as the tracer. Let a quantity of the component for which analyses are to be made be synthesized containing the radioactive isotope in some stable part of the molecule. Suppose, further, that a milligrams of the tracer material having a specific activity of A counts per minute per milligram is added to the crude sample; the total activity added is aA counts per minute. The unlabeled compound serves as inactive diluting substance. If there are b milligrams of this inactive material, then there will be $a + b$ milligrams total of the compound in the mixture. Now the mixed sample is carefully analyzed for the desired component, a very small amount finally being isolated. Let us call the specific activity of this final sample C counts per minute per milligram. The total amount of activity added was aA counts per minute, and clearly it is equal also to $(a + b)C$ counts per minute. The ratio of the two specific activities is given by the relation

$$\frac{\text{Specific activity of tracer}}{\text{Specific activity of total sample}} = \frac{aA/a}{aA/(a+b)} = \frac{(a+b)}{a} \quad (1)$$

In this example b is the desired quantity. If the ratio of the specific activities is called Z, then

$$b = a(Z - 1) \quad (2)$$

[1] F. A. Paneth, *Radioelements as Indicators*, McGraw-Hill Book Co., New York, 1928; D. Rittenberg and G. L. Foster, *J. Biol. Chem.*, **133**, 737 (1940); S. Graff, D. Rittenberg, and G. L. Foster, *J. Biol. Chem.*, **159**, 431 (1945); D. Shemin, *J. Biol. Chem.*, **159**, 439 (1945); A. S. Keston, S. Udenfriend, and M. Levy, *J. Am. Chem. Soc.*, **69**, 3151 (1948); K. Bloch and H. S. Anker, *Science*, **107**, 228 (1948); N. S. Radin, *Nucleonics*, **1**, No. 2, 48 (1947).

The only requirement which must be met is that an amount of the mixture sufficient for radioactivity analysis must be isolated successfully.[2]

Occasionally the situation may be such that the investigator desires to follow a very small amount of some substance through a complicated scheme of some sort. In such a case the material is synthesized with a radioactive atom and treated as the normal compound. For purposes of analysis a known amount of inactive material, which may be very large compared with the amount of tracer material used, is added to the sample; again, a portion of pure mixed compound large enough for radioactivity analysis is isolated and its specific activity determined. In this instance the figure a is desired, the ratio Z is computed, b is known, and

$$a = \frac{b}{Z - 1} \tag{3}$$

A modification of the first method has been applied to the microanalysis of mixtures, in the research cited, of protein hydrolysates.[3] The mixture is treated with a labeled reagent forming quantitatively a stable derivative of the desired component. A very large excess of unlabeled derivative is added to the mixture, and a portion is purified to constant activity. If b milligrams of inactive derivative are added to the mixture containing a milligrams of the labeled derivative, then a and b are related as in equation 3, where Z is the specific activity of the labeled derivative (computed from that of the reagent) divided by the specific activity of the purified mixed derivative. In most cases $Z \gg 1$ and $a = b/Z$. The method can be used with either radioactive or stable labels. In analyses of this type it is necessary that the sample isolated be pure and completely free of labeled contaminants. The question of purity as related to tracer measurements is discussed in Chapter 10.

Mathematical Treatment

All the above relations assume that the amount of tracer present in the labeled material is too small to exert any effect on its molecular weight. The assumption is quite justified in nearly all experimentation with the radioactive isotopes but may be in serious error when compounds are marked with high concentrations of the stable isotopes.[4]

[2] A complete analysis of a three-component mixture is described by F. C. Henriques, Jr., and Charles Margnetti, *Ind. Eng. Chem., Anal. Ed.*, **18**, 420 (1946).

[3] A. S. Keston, S. Udenfriend, and R. K. Cannan, *J. Am. Chem. Soc.*, **68**, 1390 (1946).

[4] For instance, if methane is prepared with hydrogen which is $\frac{1}{4}$ deuterium, the molecular weight of the compound is 17.049 instead of the value 16.042 obtained when the contribution of the heavier isotope is neglected.

The general problem of isotope dilution, in which a number of mixtures of several isotopes are themselves mixed, has been treated.[5] Equations were derived for the final concentration of a particular isotope. Suppose that a number of batches containing various proportions of label are mixed. If Aa_n is the atom percentage [6] of isotope a in batch n, M_n is the real molecular weight,[7] and W_n the mass of compound in the nth batch, the final atom percentage of a in the mixture of all batches is given by the expression:

$$Aa_{\text{final}} = \frac{[(Aa_1W_1/M_1) + (Aa_2W_2/M_2) + \cdots + (Aa_nW_n/M_n)]}{[(W_1/M_1) + (W_2/M_2) + \cdots + (W_n/M_n)]} \quad (4)$$

If the atom per cent excess, C, is defined $C = A - A_{\text{standard}}$, then

$$Ca_{\text{final}} = \frac{[(Ca_1W_1/M_1) + (Ca_2W_2/M_2) + \cdots + (Ca_nW_n/M_n)]}{[(W_1/M_1) + (W_2/M_2) + \cdots + (W_n/M_n)]} \quad (5)$$

In the most frequently encountered situations, in which two batches are mixed and only two isotopes of the chosen element are abundant enough to be considered, equations 4 and 5 reduce to

$$A_{\text{final}} = \left(\frac{A_1W_1}{M_1} + \frac{A_2W_2}{M_2}\right) \div \left(\frac{W_1}{M_1} + \frac{W_2}{M_2}\right) \quad (6)$$

$$C_{\text{final}} = \left(\frac{C_1W_1}{M_1} + \frac{C_2W_2}{M_2}\right) \div \left(\frac{W_1}{M_1} + \frac{W_2}{M_2}\right) \quad (7)$$

[5] H. Gest, M. D. Kamen, and J. M. Reiner, *Arch. Biochem.*, **12**, 273 (1947).

[6] The atom per cent of a in the compound is defined as 100(number of a atoms) $\div$ (total number of atoms of this element). Suppose that propionic acid is carboxyl-labeled with carbon which is 60% C^{13}; the normal concentration of the isotope is 1%. Considering the average constitution of a single molecule, in the carboxyl group there are 0.60 C^{13} atom and 0.40 C^{12} atom; the α and β carbons are each 0.01 C^{13} atom and 0.99 C^{12} atom. Thus the atom per cent of C^{13} in the molecule is

$$100 \times \frac{0.60 + 2(0.01)}{0.40 + 0.60 + 2(0.99 + 0.01)} = 100 \times \frac{0.62}{3} = 20.7$$

[7] The real molecular weight, M_n, is defined as [fraction of labeled molecules $\times$ labeled-molecule weight + fraction of normal molecules $\times$ normal molecule weight]. For example, propylene is carbon labeled at the methylene position with 40% C^{13}. The molecular weight of normal propylene is 42; a mole of propylene labeled with C^{13} in the methylene position would have a molecular weight of 43. Thus

$$M_n = [0.4 \times 43 + 0.6 \times 42] = 42.4$$

Ordinarily one of the batches is of normal isotopic constitution; let $C_2 = 0$, and equation 7 can be put in the form

$$W_2 = W_1 \frac{M_2}{M_1}\left(\frac{C_1}{C_{\text{final}}} - 1\right) \qquad (8)$$

If the tracer element is present in such small amounts that there is an unimportant difference between M_1 and M_2, equation 8 reduces to

$$W_2 = W_1 \left(\frac{C_1}{C_{\text{final}}} - 1\right). \qquad (9)$$

This condition is nearly always satisfied when radioactive tracers are used, in which case the C's represent specific activities.

It is often difficult to visualize the interdependence of the various methods of expressing mass abundance data. In Table XXVI are given the values for several data when 1 mmole of propionic acid which is carboxyl labeled with 50% C^{13} is diluted with 9 and 99 mmoles of inactive acid. It is assumed that the normal abundance of C^{13} is 1%.

TABLE XXVI

EFFECTS OF DILUTION WITH UNLABELED IDENTICAL CARRIER

	Original Acid	10-Fold Diluted	100-Fold Diluted
Atom % C^{13} in COOH	50	5.9	1.49
Atom % excess C^{13} in COOH	49	4.9	0.49
Atom % C^{13} in molecule	17.33	2.633	1.163
Atom % excess C^{13} in molecule	16.33	1.633	0.163
C^{13}/C^{12}, CO_2 from decarboxylation	1.00	0.0627	0.0151
C^{13}/C^{12}, CO_2 from combustion	0.2095	0.02705	0.01177

A more general computation is that in Table XXVII where certain data are given for the case in which 1 mmole of this same labeled propionic acid is diluted with varying amounts of benzoic acid during combustion. The products in rows 5 and 7 are obtained in a manner analogous to that often used in radioactivity measurements in which total activity is computed from the specific activity and the weight of sample material. Such a product is useful in work with stable isotopes, for it suggests an "activity" unit such as milligrams of C^{13} excess per milligram of sample material. The weight excess per mole of labeled material is 13 times the atom per cent excess in the labeled carbon atom; the "activity unit" can then be computed. The advantage of such units is that they can be used to clarify the results of experiments in which the original label is distributed among several molecular species; thus, one obtains for each final sample substance the actual excess weight of isotope, the sum of all such figures equaling the total actual excess with which the experiment was begun. The actual atom per cent excess figures do not lend themselves directly to such use.

TABLE XXVII

EFFECTS OF DILUTION WITH UNLABELED NON-IDENTICAL CARRIER

	Mmoles Benzoic Acid per Mmole Propionic Acid				
	0	0.2	1.0	5.0	20.0
(1) Atom $\%$ C^{13} in CO_2 from combustion	17.33	12.13	5.90	2.29	1.343
(2) Atom $\%$ excess C^{13} in CO_2 from combustion	16.33	11.13	4.90	1.29	0.343
(3) C^{13}/C^{12} in CO_2 from combustion	0.2095	0.1254	0.0627	0.02345	0.01361
(4) Total mmoles carbon	3	4.4	10	38	143
(5) (2) $\times$ (4)	49	49	49	49	49
(6) $\dfrac{\text{mgCO}_2 \text{ from diluent}}{\text{mgCO}_2 \text{ from propionic acid}}$	0	0.4667	2.333	11.67	46.67
(7) $3 \times [(6) + 1.000] \times (2)$	49	49	49	49	49

NOTE: The figures in row 7 indicate that the exact nature of the diluent need not be known.

Appendix II

STATISTICAL TREATMENT OF COUNTING DATA

General Considerations

All physical measurements are subject to error, and it is usually desirable that the magnitude of this possible deviation of the observed result from the "true" one be known. Measurements of tracer carbon are performed with three types of instruments—counters, ionization chambers, and mass spectrometers—and the results obtained by each technique require different types of error analysis. Thus, the errors associated with counter-tube radioactivity measurements on a gaseous sample of carbon dioxide, other than error in the pressure reading, are due largely to the random nature of the disintegration and background processes. The same is approximately true of ionization-chamber measurements except that there is a greater chance that instrumental error may affect the observed result. Mass spectrometer measurements involve techniques similar to those employed in measuring small ion currents, but the effect due to a selected isotope must be separated from those of other isotopes of about the same mass number, and this type of resolution error is not found in any measurement of radiations from the carbon nuclides.

Perhaps the most useful error formula is that for the standard deviation of a series of observations; the figure obtained is a measure of the relative precision of all the measurements and of their internal consistency. If n determinations of a certain quantity V are made, then the standard deviation of the mean value of V [1] is given by the relation:

$$\text{Standard deviation} = \sqrt{\frac{\sum_{i=0}^{n}(V_{\text{mean}} - V_i)^2}{n(n-1)}} \tag{1}$$

[1] For example: A sample is counted six times for various lengths of time; the observed activities are: 72.2, 68.6, 70.0, 64.5, 71.1, and 72.4 counts per minute. The mean activity is 69.8 c/min. Then:

$$\text{S.D.} = \sqrt{\frac{(2.4)^2 + (1.2)^2 + (0.2)^2 + (5.3)^2 + (1.3)^2 + (2.6)^2}{(6)(5)}}$$

$$= \sqrt{\frac{43.78}{30}} = 1.23$$

Therefore the activity is expressed as 69.8 ± 1.2 c/min.

Counters and ion chambers measure ionizing events, and except for errors due to the measuring instrument, such as the finite time of resolution of a counter tube (see Appendix III), the statistical behavior of the data obtained is due to the random nature of the disintegration process (see page 16). Since individual nuclei decay independently of each other, the laws of probability can be applied to the observed results. Errors due to the measuring instrument can be noted because they cause large or erratic departure from the errors calculated on the assumption of a random disintegration process.

Let us consider the measured activity of a sample of such long half-life that its disintegration rate is not sensibly affected by decay during the time of observation. A series of similar determinations on this sample results in a number of values which, in general, will all be different and distributed about an average value in a random manner. The statistical treatment applied to these results enables one to estimate how well the average of any given set of determinations approximates the true average.

Suppose that $\bar{n}$ is the average number of particles detectable in a given time interval, determined by a long period of counting; the probability P_n that n particles will actually be detected in this interval is given by the Poisson relation [2]

$$P_n = \frac{(\bar{n})^n e^{-\bar{n}}}{n!} \tag{2}$$

If the error ϵ in a single determination which involves the detection of n particles is defined as $\epsilon = \sqrt{\sum_0^\infty (\bar{n} - n)^2 P_n}$, application of equation 2 yields $\epsilon = \sqrt{\bar{n}}$. Thus, the error is proportional to the square root of the number of particles detected, and the relative accuracy which one can obtain increases in this manner with the number of events observed. The information usually desired is the probability that the error in a given determination is greater than the product of the square root of n and some constant k. This probability is obtained by evaluation of the integral

$$P_k = \sqrt{\frac{2}{\pi n}} \int_{k\sqrt{n}}^\infty e^{-\frac{1}{2}(\epsilon/\sqrt{n})^2} \, d\epsilon \tag{3}$$

In Table XXVIII are collected a number of values of k and the corresponding probability that $\epsilon > k\sqrt{n}$ will be observed.

[2] H. Bateman, *Phil. Mag.*, **20**, 704 (1910); K. W. F. Kohlrausch, *Ergeb. exakt. Naturw.*, **5**, 192 (1926). See also L. J. Rainwater and C. S. Wu, *Nucleonics*, **1**, No. 2, 60 (1947); **2**, No. 1, 42 (1948).

In practice one does not assume an error and then compute the probability that such a deviation will be observed. Rather, one selects a limit for the probability and then calculates the limits of error in the observed result so that the observed deviations of a large number of determinations scatter in the manner predicted. Thus, if 10,000 disintegrations are measured in a certain time interval, the error will be proportional to $(10,000)^{\frac{1}{2}} = 100$. If the k for "probable error" error is chosen, then there is a 50–50 chance that the true number of disintegrations is greater than $10,000 + 67.5$ or less than $10,000 - 67.5$; however,

TABLE XXVIII

VALUES OF THE PROBABILITY CONSTANT, k

k	Probability that $\epsilon > k\sqrt{n}$
0	1.0000
0.6745	0.5000 (probable error)
1.0000	0.3173 (standard error)
1.6449	0.1000 ("reliable" error)
1.4600	0.0500 ("95/100" error)
2.0000	0.0455
2.5758	0.0100 ("99/100" error)
3.0000	0.0027
3.2905	0.0010

if k for "reliable error" is used, the results would be expressed as $10,000 \pm 165$ disintegrations, which would be interpreted that there is only 1 chance in 10 that the true number of disintegrations is more different from 10,000 than by 165.[3]

Combination of Errors

From the relation $\epsilon = \sqrt{n}$, certain rules can be formulated concerning the manipulation of experimentally derived quantities. If the error in the quantity A is represented by a, etc., then:

Error of a sum

$$(A \pm a) + (B \pm b) \cdots = (A + B + \cdots) \pm \sqrt{a^2 + b^2 + \cdots}$$

Error of a difference $\quad (A \pm a) - (B \pm b) = (A - B) \pm \sqrt{a^2 + b^2}$

Error of a product $\quad (A \pm a)(B \pm b) = (AB) \pm \sqrt{a^2 B^2 + b^2 A^2}$

Error of a quotient $\quad (A \pm a)/(B \pm b) = (A/B) \pm \sqrt{a^2/A^2 + b^2/B^2}$

[3] See: F. Rasetti, *Elements of Nuclear Physics*, Prentice-Hall, New York, 1936, pp. 32–35; H. V. Neher, in J. Strong, *Procedures in Experimental Physics*, Prentice-Hall, New York, 1938, pp. 298–304.

A simple timesaver when combining by multiplication or division errors which are expressed in different units, such as c/min, cm Hg, and °K, is the expression of the errors in terms of per cent of the measured quantities. The per cent (or fractional) error of any product or quotient of measured quantities is equal to the square root of the sum of the squares of the various percentage (or fractional) errors.

Radioactivity determinations ordinarily yield rate data; a sample will have an activity of so many counts per minute, or the balance of a current collected in an ion chamber requires the application of a certain number of millivolts per second. Two factors limit the sensitivity and precision of any counting method (so far as true random behavior of the activity is concerned); one of these is the natural background of the instrument, and the other is any limitation placed upon the time that may be expended to get a certain result. The usual procedure in counting is to measure the activity due to the sample and background combined and then to subtract from this the activity due to the background alone. In the sections below are collected a number of useful relations which are derivable from the formulas stated above.

N	counts	t	time (any unit)
b	background	R	rate
s	sample plus b	E	error
x	s minus b	E_R	error of a rate
k	probability constant	$E\%$	percentage error

Formulas for Use with G-M Counter Data

1. The error of a given number of counts is $E = k\sqrt{N}$, regardless of the length of time necessary to make the determination.[4]

2. The error of a net activity is

$$E_x = \sqrt{E_b{}^2 + E_s{}^2} = k\sqrt{N_b + N_s}$$

provided $t_b = t_s$.[5]

[4] Example: What is the reliable error in the detection of 6,400 disintegration events?

$$E = 1.65(6,400)^{\frac{1}{2}} = \pm 132$$

[5] Example: What is the standard error of the net activity when 5,400 counts are detected from the sample (plus background) in 10 minutes and 1,000 counts due to the background alone are detectable in the same time?

$$E_x = 1.00\sqrt{5,400 + 1,000} = \pm 80 \text{ counts}$$

$$N_x = 4,400 \pm 80, \; R_x = 440 \pm 8 \text{ c/min}$$

3. The percentage error of a net activity thus determined [6] is

$$E_x = \frac{100k\sqrt{N_b + N_s}}{N_s - N_b}$$

4. The error of a rate, $E_R = E/t$, is given by the relations [7]

$$E_R = k\frac{\sqrt{N}}{t} = k\sqrt{\frac{R}{t}}$$

5. The percentage error when an approximately known activity is counted for a time t is

$$E\% = 100k\frac{\sqrt{N}}{N} = \frac{100k}{\sqrt{Rt}}$$

6. The counting time necessary to get a certain percentage error [8] is

$$t = \frac{10^4 k^2}{R(E_R\%)^2}$$

7. The error of the difference of two rates when each activity is measured for a different length of time is given by the relation [9]

$$E_{Rx} = k\sqrt{\frac{R_s}{t_s} + \frac{R_b}{t_b}}$$

8. The per cent error of a rate difference is

$$E_{Rx}\% = \frac{100k\sqrt{\dfrac{R_s}{t_s} + \dfrac{R_b}{t_b}}}{R_s - R_b}$$

[6] See R. D. Evans and R. A. Mugele, *Rev. Sci. Instruments*, **7**, 441 (1936).

[7] What is the "ninety-nine hundredths" error of the rate when 6,400 disintegration events are detected in 10 minutes?

$$E_R = \frac{2.58(6,400)^{1/2}}{10} = \pm 20.64 \text{ events per minute}$$

[8] Example: How long must an activity of about 120 c/min be counted so that it will be known to a "standard error" of 1.5%?

$$t = \frac{10^4(1.00)^2}{120(1.5)^2} = 37.0 \text{ minutes}$$

[9] A 5-minute background count indicates a rate of 60 c/min, while the sample plus background, from a 10-minute count, is apparently 150 c/min. What is the 999/1,000 error of the sample rate?

$$E_{Rx} = 3.29\sqrt{\frac{150}{10} + \frac{60}{5}} = 3.29\sqrt{27} = \pm 17.0 \text{ c/min}$$

9. The error due to the presence of the background can be minimized by dividing properly the total counting time between the counts for background and sample plus background. The most efficient distribution is

$$\frac{t_s}{t_b} = \sqrt{\frac{R_s}{R_b}}$$

In Table XXIX are listed values of t_s/t_b for various "standard errors" and values of R_s/R_b where R_b is 30 c/min.

TABLE XXIX

COUNTING TIMES FOR A GIVEN STANDARD ERROR OF NET ACTIVITY

$$R_b = 30 \text{ c/min} \quad R_x = R_s - R_b$$

(Short times are rounded off to nearest minute greater than zero)

Standard Error in R_x

R_s/R_b	1%		2%		5%		10%	
	t_b(min)	t_s(min)	t_b	t_s	t_b	t_s	t_b	t_s
1.1	68,300	71,700	17,100	18,000	2,730	2,870	683	717
1.2	17,500	19,100	4,360	4,780	698	764	175	191
1.4	4,550	5,380	1,140	1,350	182	215	46	54
1.7	1,570	2,050	393	513	63	82	16	21
2.0	804	1,140	201	284	32	46	8	11
2.5	383	606	96	152	15	24	4	6
3.0	228	395	57	99	9	16	2	4
3.5	153	286	38	72	6	11	2	3
4.0	111	222	28	56	4	8	1	2
5.0	68	151	17	38	3	6	1	2
6.0	46	113	12	28	2	5	1	1
7.0	34	89	8	22	1	4	1	1
8.0	26	74	7	18	1	3	1	1
9.0	21	62	5	16	1	3	1	1
10.0	17	54	4	14	1	2	1	1

Calculation: $R_s = \gamma R_b$

$$t_s = t_b\sqrt{\gamma}$$

$$t_b = \frac{10^4(\sqrt{\gamma} + 1)k^2}{(\gamma - 1)^2 E\%^2 R_b}$$

Formulas Pertinent to Ionization Chamber Measurements

The formulas just given were illustrated with data from Geiger-Müller counter determinations of activity, since it was convenient to consider the recording of individual ionizing events. The integrating ion chambers ordinarily employed respond differently to various types of ionizing radiations.

Cosmic-ray events, except when they result in shower production in the walls of the chamber, produce only a small number of ion pairs per unit path length. The ionization produced by a β particle is of somewhat greater density, and chambers must be designed so that their dimensions are commensurate with the particle range when β events are measured, because of their relatively long path lengths. α Particles have very short paths, a few centimeters in air at the most, and the ionization produced along these tracks is very intense. Thus, each kind of particle makes a different relative and total contribution to the total ion current.

Let the rates of the various kinds of events be F for sample disintegration events, G for cosmic rays, and H for α-particle events; if f, g, and h are the respective average numbers of ion pairs produced in the chamber per event, and if t is measured in seconds, the two currents observed will be

$$V_b = (gG + hH) \text{ ion pairs/sec} = \text{background}$$

$$V_s = (fF + gG + hH) \text{ ion pairs/sec} = \text{sample plus background}$$

The null method of measurement, in which the drift of the electrometer is balanced by the application of a small potential through a capacitance, is often used. If θ is the number of ion pairs per coulomb and C is the capacitance of the auxiliary condenser in farads, the expressions above become

$$V_b = \frac{10^3}{C\theta} (gG + hH)$$

and

$$V_s = \frac{10^3}{C\theta} (fF + gG + hH) \text{ mv/sec}$$

The corresponding error formulas are

$$E_b = \frac{1}{\sqrt{t_b}} \sqrt{g^2G + h^2H}$$

$$E_s = \frac{1}{\sqrt{t_s}} \sqrt{f^2F + g^2G + h^2H} \text{ ion pairs/sec}$$

and

$$E_b = \frac{10^3}{C\theta} \sqrt{\frac{g^2G + h^2H}{t_b}}$$

$$E_s = \frac{10^3}{C\theta} \sqrt{\frac{f^2F + g^2G + h^2H}{t_s}} \text{ mv/sec}$$

Then, since

$$V_x = V_F = V_s - V_b$$

and

$$E_x = E_F = \sqrt{E_s{}^2 + E_b{}^2}$$

Standard deviation of the net activity $\left.\right\} = E_x = \frac{10^3}{C\theta} \sqrt{\frac{f^2F}{t_s} + \frac{1}{t_s} + \frac{1}{t_b}(g^2G + h^2H)} \text{ mv/sec}$ [10]

Rejection of Suspected Observations

Many variables are associated with activity measurements, and occasionally a result will be obtained which differs greatly from a group of observations as a whole. Such an occurrence might be caused by failure of an automatic clock to turn off at exactly the right time, by a large fluctuation in the line voltage, or by a sudden increase in background due to the shield door being ajar, etc. If this variant result is one of a small number of determinations, it may exert an unduly large influence on the average value of the measurements, and some method is desirable for deciding whether the suspected observation shall be included in the average determination or shall be rejected as improbable of normal occurrence. [11]

The Chauvenet criterion [12] provides that any result of a series containing n such observations shall be rejected when the magnitude of its deviation from the mean of all measurements is such that the probability of occurrence of all deviations as large or larger is less than $1/2\,n$. In Table XXX are shown values of the maximum allowable deviation in terms of the standard error for various values of n.

Example: Five 4-minute counts of a certain sample were made. The observed activities were 2,280, 2,297, 2,276, 2,301, and 2,350 c/min. The mean counting rate is 2,301 c/min. Should the value 2,350 have

[10] R. D. Evans, *Rev. Sci. Instruments*, **4**, 229 (1933); R. D. Evans and H. V. Neher, *Phys. Rev.*, **43**, 144 (1934).

[11] See K. Pearson, *Phil. Mag.*, **50**, 157 (1900).

[12] See A. de F. Palmer, *Theory of Measurements*, McGraw-Hill Book Co., New York, 1912, p. 127 et seq.

been included? The standard error of a single determination having the mean counting rate is $(2,301/4)^{1/2} = 24$. The deviation from the mean of the suspected result is $2,350 - 2,301 = 49$. The ratio of this devia-

TABLE XXX

FIGURES FOR USE WITH THE CHAUVENET CRITERION

n = number of activity determinations.
P = ratio of the deviation acceptable to the standard error.

n	P	n	P
2	1.15	12	2.04
3	1.38	15	2.13
4	1.54	20	2.24
5	1.65	30	2.40
6	1.73	40	2.50
7	1.80	50	2.58
8	1.86	100	2.81
9	1.91	200	3.02
10	1.96	500	3.29

tion to the standard error just calculated is 2.04. For 5 determinations the maximum acceptable value is 1.65; the suspected observation should, therefore, be rejected.

Appendix III

DETERMINATION OF COINCIDENCE CORRECTIONS

All instruments of detection have a finite resolving time which limits their ability to respond separately to events occurring close together. In G-M counters the resolving time is usually of the order of 10^{-5} minute, and correction for coincidence effects must be made on all observed activities over a thousand or so counts per minute. The behavior of counters is such that there is a time interval τ after the registration of an event during which the instrument is insensitive to further events. Several authors have reviewed the techniques available for determining the value of τ.[1,2]   Of the many methods available, three are of sufficient interest to be mentioned here. These are, in order of increasing accuracy and difficulty: (1) single paired-source measurements, (2) measurement of sources of known relative intensities, and (3) multiple paired-source measurements with least-squares analysis of the data.

Single Paired-Source Measurements [3]

Two radioactive samples of approximately equal strength are counted separately and together; the time τ is evaluated from the observed activities and the computed loss on combination. Several formulas for τ have been developed, [1,2,4] but one of the simplest is from reference 1. If the observed counting rates of the separated samples (including background) are R_A and R_B, and their counting rate when combined is R_C, then

$$\tau = \frac{R_A + R_B - R_C - b}{R_C{}^2 - R_A{}^2 - R_B{}^2} \tag{1}$$

where b is the background rate. This formula assumes that the observed counting rate R and the true rate N are related by the expression

$$N = R + \tau R^2 \tag{2}$$

[1] T. P. Kohman, Ph.D. Dissertation, University of Wisconsin, 1943.

[2] Y. Beers, *Rev. Sci. Instruments*, **13**, 72 (1942).

[3] P. B. Moon, *J. Sci. Instruments*, **14**, 189 (1937).

[4] D. E. Hull, *Rev. Sci. Instruments*, **11**, 404 (1940); D. E. Hull and H. Seelig, *Phys. Rev.*, **60**, 553 (1941); A. E. Ruark and F. E. Brammer, *Phys. Rev.*, **52**, 322 (1937); L. I. Schiff, *Phys. Rev.*, **50**, 88 (1936).

Such an assumption is valid for many counters at rather high activities and coincides well with experiments on most instruments when the activities measured are under 2,000–3,000 c/min. Most samples encountered in tracer work are no stronger than this, and the single paired-source method is probably of wide application.[5]

Measurement of Sources of Known Relative Intensities

Probably the first technique suggesting itself as a method for coincidence correction determination involves successive determinations of the activity of a sample that is decaying with a moderate half-life.

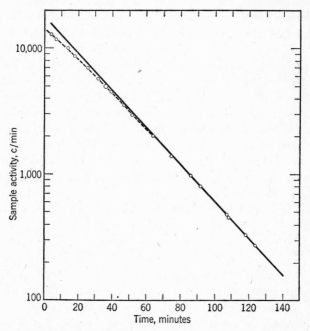

Fig. 89.   Determination of coincidence loss by following the decay of a sample containing C^{11}.   (The large circle represents a count where 5260 c/min were expected, solid line, but 5000 c/min were observed, broken line.)

After the activity has fallen to a low value, the coincidence loss is assumed to be negligible and a correction curve is obtained by plotting the activity expected at certain times against that actually observed. The basis is illustrated by Fig. 89. The greatest source of error asso-

[5] The procedure for taking the data is the same as that used with the multiple paired-source technique and is found on page 298.

ciated with such a technique lies in the fact that an unusually accurate knowledge of the half-life of the particular radioelement used is required, since the decay must be followed through several half-life periods; [6] the half-lives of Rn^{222} and I^{128} are known accurately enough for this purpose.

A variation of this method, in which samples of very long life are counted, has been widely used. A number of sources are prepared from active material of high specific activity, in such a manner that their relative strengths are accurately known. Care must be exercised in the preparation of the samples to eliminate self-absorption of the radiations and other mounting effects. (RaD + E can be used.) As in the technique just described, the correction curve can be obtained by plotting against each other the expected and the observed activities. [7]

In order that the curve be properly located with respect to the coordinate axes, it is necessary to assume that the activity of the weakest sample can be measured with no coincidence loss; other errors are the statistical errors in the actual counting and deviations produced by imperfect mounting of the sources. The uncertainties due to all but the last-mentioned contribution cannot be made negligible simultaneously. The effect of these errors can be minimized if the experimental data are properly handled; one such procedure is described below. [8]

Let F be the relative source strength unit and A the true specific activity such that $N = FA + b$ is the true counting rate, where b is the background. In general, A is not known, so some provisional value A' is selected and a tentative fractional correction C' is computed from the relation

$$C' = \frac{FA' + b - R}{R} \tag{3}$$

where R is the observed counting rate. C' is plotted against R, and the best smooth curve through the points is drawn. This curve should approach a straight line asymptotically as R approaches zero, but it will not pass through the point $C' = 0$ unless accidentally $A = A'$. Call the intercept of the curve C_0'; the correct value of A can be obtained from the equation

$$A = \frac{A'}{1 + C_0'} \tag{4}$$

[6] See A. Flammersfeld, Z. Physik, **112**, 727 (1939); K.-E. Zimens, Trans. Chalmers Univ. Technol. (Gothenburg), No. 54 (1946).

[7] W. F. Shepherd and R. O. Haxby, Rev. Sci. Instruments, **7**, 425 (1936); H. Volz, Z. Physik, **93**, 539 (1935); M. D. Kamen, Radioactive Tracers in Biology, Academic Press, New York, 1947, p. 82. See also O. S. Duffendack, H. Lifschutz, and M. M. Slawsky, Phys. Rev., **52**, 1231 (1937).

[8] This method was developed by T. P. Kohman, Institute for Nuclear Studies, University of Chicago.

The true fractional correction C is calculated for several values of R by equation 3 by the substitution of A for A'. The final curve can be located by raising or lowering the provisional one, but better results are obtained if the final values of C are computed from equation 5:

$$C = C' - \frac{C_0'}{1 + C_0'}(1 + C') \tag{5}$$

The application of this method is illustrated by the data in Tables XXXI and XXXII and by Fig. 90.

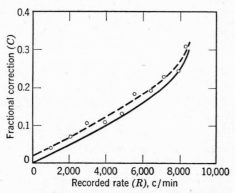

FIG. 90.   Coincidence correction curves from multiple single-source data; provisional curve is broken, final curve is solid.   (T. P. Kohman.)

TABLE XXXI

METHOD OF LOCATING PROVISIONAL CURVE

	Data		Provisional Curve		
F	R (c/min)	FA'	$FA' + b$	$FA' + b - R$	C' (per cent)
1	1,075	1,100	1,120	+45	+4.2
2	2,075	2,200	2,220	145	7.0
3	3,007	3,300	3,320	313	10.4
4	3,999	4,400	4,420	421	10.5
5	4,891	5,500	5,520	629	12.9
6	5,603	6,600	6,620	1,017	18.1
7	6,485	7,700	7,720	1,235	19.1
8	7,192	8,800	8,820	1,628	22.6
9	7,988	9,900	9,920	1,932	24.2
10	8,394	11,000	11,020	2,626	31.4

$b = 20$ c/min. $A' = 1,100$ c/min.

TABLE XXXII

TRANSPOSITION OF PROVISIONAL CURVE

From Fig. 90, $C_0' = +1.8\%$; therefore, $\dfrac{C_0'}{(1 + C_0')} = 0.0177$.

R	C'	$0.0177(1 + C')$	C
0	+0.018	−0.018	0.000
2,000	0.066	0.019	+0.047
4,000	0.117	0.020	0.097
6,000	0.176	0.021	0.155
7,000	0.213	0.021	0.192
8,000	0.265	0.022	0.243
8,500	0.313	0.023	0.290

Multiple Paired-Source Measurements

This technique differs from the first described only in the amount of data which can be used to carry out a correction relation determination; several years' experience in the use of the least-squares treatment described below has convinced the authors of its general applicability and accuracy.[9]

Derivation of the Equations. Principles of the Method

Let us consider a pair of samples which have been counted separately and together. The activity of either one or the combined activity of both can be represented by an equation of the form

$$N = R + \tau R^2 + \nu R^3 + \cdots + \omega R^n \tag{6}$$

where R is the observed counting rate and N is the corrected or "true" rate; both rates include the activity of the background. The values of the parameters $\tau, \nu, \cdots$ etc., are determined by the characteristics of the detector. If these parameters are correctly evaluated, then

$$\delta = N_A' + N_B' - N_C' = 0 \tag{7}$$

where $N_A' = N_A - b$, etc. (b is the background activity), and the subscripts A and B refer to the separate samples while C refers to their combination. The quantity δ is the algebraic sum of the errors in the corrections to the observed activities, R_A, R_B, and R_C; in general, $\delta \neq 0$ since it is not possible to make all the corrections perfect. It may be assumed that δ is a measure of the error in the correction to R_C, since

[9] This method was developed by T. P. Kohman while at the Hanford Engineer Works. See Atomic Energy Commission, MDDC 429, June 13, 1945; *Phys. Rev.*, **72**, 181 (1947).

of the several quantities $(N_x - R_x)$ that concerning the combined samples will generally be the largest. The fractional residual $\epsilon = \delta/R_C$ may be taken as a measure of the fractional error in the correction applied. For the data derived from a series of measurements with separated, then paired, samples, the best values of the parameters τ, ν, etc., are those for which the sum of all ϵ^2 is minimal; i.e.,

$$\frac{\partial}{\partial \tau} \Sigma \epsilon^2 = 0$$

$$\frac{\partial}{\partial \nu} \Sigma \epsilon^2 = 0, \text{ etc.} \tag{8}$$

The number of parameters for which values must be obtained depends upon the performance of the particular instrument in question. In any case, values for two parameters should be obtained when it is known that the value of τ is greater than 1×10^{-5} minute or that the corrections to be used may be greater than 5–10% of the observed rate. Since the two-parameter equation is perhaps of most general usefulness, its derivation will be carried out in some detail.

The fractional residual is given by the following expressions:

$$\epsilon = \frac{\delta}{R_C} = \frac{N_A' + N_B' - N_C'}{R_C} = \frac{N_A + N_B - N_C - b}{R_C} \tag{9}$$

$$= \frac{\left\{\begin{matrix}(R_A + R_B - R_C - b) + \tau(R_A{}^2 + R_B{}^2 - R_C{}^2) \\ + \nu(R_A{}^3 + R_B{}^3 - R_C{}^3)\end{matrix}\right\}}{R_C} \tag{10}$$

Substituting in equation 5 for the various powers of R's, one obtains

$$\epsilon = \frac{D + \tau E + \nu F}{R_C} \tag{11}$$

For a series of determinations

$$\Sigma \epsilon^2 = \Sigma \left(\left[\frac{1}{R_C{}^2}\right]\left[D + \tau E + \nu F\right]^2\right) \tag{12}$$

Expanding equation 7 and collecting terms

$$\Sigma \epsilon^2 = \Sigma \frac{D^2}{R_C{}^2} + 2\tau \Sigma \frac{DE}{R_C{}^2} + 2\nu \Sigma \frac{DF}{R_C{}^2} + 2\tau\nu \Sigma \frac{EF}{R_C{}^2} + \tau^2 \Sigma \frac{E^2}{R_C{}^2} + \nu \Sigma \frac{F^2}{R_C{}^2} \tag{13}$$

The extended summation in 13 can be simplified by the substitution of other symbols for the individual summations:

$$\Sigma\epsilon^2 = G + 2\tau H + 2\nu J + 2\tau\nu K + \tau^2 L + \nu^2 M \tag{14}$$

Now, the conditions for minimal error in the corrections are

$$\frac{\partial}{\partial\tau}\Sigma\epsilon^2 = 2H + 2\nu K + 2\tau L = 0 \tag{15}$$

$$\frac{\partial}{\partial\nu}\Sigma\epsilon^2 = 2J + 2\tau K + 2\nu M = 0 \tag{16}$$

Solution of the two simultaneous equations 15 and 16 for τ and ν gives

$$\tau = \frac{JK - HM}{LM - K^2} \tag{17}$$

$$\nu = \frac{HK - JL}{LM - K^2} \tag{18}$$

(The result of the single parameter calculation is $\tau = -H/L = -D/E$.)

Procedures for Taking Data

Each set of paired-source measurements requires four determinations involving two samples approximately equal in activity, R_A, R_B, R_C, and the background. There must be taken at least as many sets of data as there are constants in the desired correction equation. For accuracy, the activities measured should cover the whole range of the instrument for which corrections are desired; no less than two sets of data should be taken even for a single-parameter computation. A number of pairs of active samples may be used, or the activity of a very active pair may be diminished by interposing a graduated series of absorbers between the sources and the detector.

Counters Which Use Active Carbon Dioxide or Methane. A series of samples containing a constant amount of carbon dioxide but varying amounts of activity is measured. The series is made up of pairs of samples, the included activity of one being exactly double that of the other (i.e., for a system of constant volume $p_{A,B}C^*O_2 = \frac{1}{2}p_C C^*O_2$). Then $R_A = R_B$, and in the computation $2R_A^n$ is substituted for $(R_A^n + R_B^n)$.[10] In order that this technique be successful, the partial pressures of the radioactive gas must be measured with considerable accuracy; this necessity is the principal difficulty associated with the

---

[10] A similar technique can be used with the method of radioactive decay. If the activities are measured at intervals of exactly one half-life, then $R_A = R_B$ = the lower activity and R_C = that observed one half-life earlier.

application of the method to sample-filled counters.   There is an alternative procedure, namely, the use of a set of completely external sample pairs which emit penetrating radiations; for this type of determination, the counter tube is filled with inactive carbon dioxide.   The counting characteristics and, therefore, the coincidence losses in gas-filled counters are somewhat dependent on the nature of the filling gas.   Present methods allow considerable choice in the matter of the partial pressure of carbon dioxide in the mixture.   Where relatively high activities are to be encountered, it may be necessary to employ fillings at several different total gas pressures, and determinations should be made at each.   One of the most unusual features of the paired-source methods is their complete lack of dependence upon measurements of any property other than radioactive strength; in order that full advantage be taken of this independence, the determinations should not involve weighings, pressure measurements, etc., except where unavoidable.   Thus, external samples for coincidence-loss evaluation are to be favored wherever such a technique can be applied.

Counters Which Use External Samples. (Example: an end window counter used with solid samples containing C^{14}.)

A shellac-bound plate is made by the procedure outlined on page 120. The plate and a blank disk are carefully cut in half; the halves of the

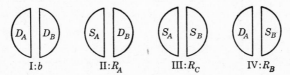

Fig. 91.   Sequence of counting for paired-source methods.

blank are used as dummies.   The sequence of counting is shown in Fig. 91, where D is a dummy and S is an active half.

Accuracy in the Rate Determinations

Calculation of coincidence loss corrections involves small differences from large numbers.   Therefore, the counting rates must be very accurately determined.   A convenient way of dividing the counting time is

$$t_A : t_B : t_C : t_b = 1 : 1 : \sqrt{2} : \sqrt{b/R_A} \tag{19}$$

This arrangement results in very nearly the greatest statistical accuracy for a given total expenditure of time.[2]   However, if all the counting times are made equal, little accuracy is lost, and certainly such an arrangement is more convenient.   The actual times necessary for counting depend upon the accuracy desired in the corrections.   If all counting times are made equal, then t, the length of the interval, can be evaluated approximately from the relation

$$t \approx \frac{8k^2}{P^2 R_C} \tag{20}$$

where k is the probability constant (see Appendix II) and P is the fractional error desired in R_C.[11]

In general, counters should not be used except in rare circumstances, for counting rates where the corrections to be applied are more than 25–35% of the observed rate. As some G-M tubes are damaged by

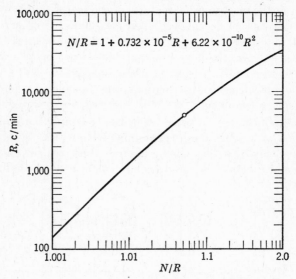

$$N/R = 1 + 0.732 \times 10^{-5}R + 6.22 \times 10^{-10}R^2$$

R, c/min

N/R

FIG. 92. Coincidence correction curve. (Example: N/R for $R = 5000$ c/min is 1.052; thus an observed activity of 5000 c/min represents an actual activity of 5000 $\times$ 1.052 = 5260 c/min.)

even short counting at high rates, care must be exercised in this regard.

In order to illustrate the application of this method to an actual counting instrument, and so that the procedure for calculation may be shown, a sample computation is worked out in Table XXXIII. The correction curve obtained is plotted in Fig. 92.

[11] For example: Suppose that $\tau \approx 10^{-5}$ minute and its actual value is to be determined from a single pair of sources, the approximate counting rates involved being 1,000, 1,000, and 2,000 c/min. A "reliable error" of 1% is desired at 2,000 c/min. At this value of R_C the coincidence correction is approximately $(2,000)^2 \times 10^{-5} = 40$ c/min; the accuracy desired is $0.01 \times 2,000 = 20$ c/min. From equation 20,

$$t \approx \frac{8 \times (1.65)^2}{(0.01)^2 \times 2,000} \approx 109 \text{ minutes}$$

TABLE XXXIII

	Pair 1	Pair 2
R_A	4,711	14,102
R_B	4,523	12,840
R_C	8,657	22,198
b	60	60
$R_A + R_B - R_C - b = D$	517	4,684
R_A^2	2.21935×10^7	1.98866×10^8
R_B^2	2.04575×10^7	1.64866×10^8
R_C^2	7.49436×10^7	4.92751×10^8
$R_A^2 + R_B^2 - R_C^2 = E$	-3.22926×10^7	-1.29019×10^8
R_A^3	1.04554×10^{11}	2.80441×10^{12}
R_B^3	0.92529×10^{11}	2.11688×10^{12}
R_C^3	6.48787×10^{11}	10.93809×10^{12}
$R_A^3 + R_B^3 - R_C^3 = F$	-4.51704×10^{11}	-6.01680×10^{12}
$DE/R_C^2 = h$	-2.22771×10^{12}	-1.22643×10^3
$DF/R_C^2 = j$	-3.11609×10^6	-5.71946×10^7
$EF/R_C^2 = k$	1.94636×10^{11}	1.57540×10^{12}
$E^2/R_C^2 = l$	1.39146×10^7	3.37816×10^7
$F^2/R_C^2 = m$	2.72253×10^5	7.34689×10^{16}
$\Sigma h = H$		-1.44920×10^3
$\Sigma j = J$		-6.03107×10^7
$\Sigma k = K$		1.77004×10^{12}
$\Sigma l = L$		4.76962×10^7
$\Sigma m = M$		7.61914×10^{16}
JK		-1.06752×10^{20}
HM		-1.10417×10^{20}
HK		-2.56514×10^{15}
JL		-2.87659×10^{15}
LM		3.63404×10^{24}
K^2		3.13304×10^{24}

$JK - HM = 3.665 \times 10^{18}$

$HK - JL = 3.1145 \times 10^{14}$

$LM - K^2 = 5.0100 \times 10^{23}$

$$\frac{JK - HM}{LM - K^2} = \tau = 0.7315 \times 10^{-5}$$

$$\frac{HK - JL}{LM - K^2} = \nu = 6.217 \times 10^{-10}$$

Examination of the Data

Before working out the values of the various parameters, compute $-D/E$ for each set of data. If the values do not differ by more than 5–10%, it is usually unnecessary to calculate ν for rates lower than the highest R_C taken. If the spread in the values of $-D/E$ is as great as 100%, or if the trend in these numbers is not monotonic, three parameters are needed to describe adequately the behavior of the instrument at high counting rates. If the values calculated for ϵ, for more than four sets of data, are all of the same sign, show a significant trend, or are large compared to the desired fractional error in R_C, either an additional parameter is required or a mistake has been made in arithmetic.

Appendix IV

DETERMINATION OF COUNTER EFFICIENCY

The numerical absolute efficiency of a given counting arrangement is defined as the quotient of the number of particles registered by the detector and the number emitted by the source. The value of the absolute efficiency is always of interest but is a *necessity* when clinical work is being carried out in several different laboratories. If a small sample of very penetrating radiation is mounted on a thin film, the absolute efficiency of the counting array of which it is a part is the product of the ionization efficiency of the detector for the radiations involved and the fraction of the total solid angle about the sample which is subtended by the sensitive volume of the detector; the second factor is called the "geometry" of the system and is often given as a percentage. This simple picture is usually not even closely approached in actual practice. Even very thin films scatter back to the detector an appreciable fraction of the particles originally directed away from it; radiations of any but the highest energies are appreciably absorbed and scattered in the windows of counters and the air path between the sample and the window; etc.

Unitized Determinations of Absolute Efficiency

One sure method for efficiency determination is based upon a knowledge of the absolute disintegration rate of a sample of the isotope to be employed. Two data are required: the weight of the measured isotope, and the half-life of the observed radiation. The source which is prepared for counting must be of the same size and located identically with respect to the detector as the samples which will be obtained during routine operation. In addition, the standard source, if solid, must be very thin or the investigator must have accurate self-absorption data at hand. By the use of such a procedure all scattering, absorption, and geometry effects are duplicated in the standard source and routine sample measurements, and the absolute efficiency is given by the quotient of the activity observed and that calculated. This method is the only one applicable to ion-chamber counting of gaseous carbon dioxide.

The method of coincidence counting enables one to determine in one experiment, with a sample emitting β and γ radiations simultaneously, the absolute disintegration rate of the source used, as well as the absolute efficiency for the particular γ rays of one counter and that for the β particles of another. The only quantities involved are the γ counting rate of one counter, N_γ, the β counting rate of the other N_β, and the rate of β-γ coincidences between the two, $N_{\beta\gamma}$.[1] None of the radioactive carbons decay with coincident γ emission, and, since conversion of data obtained with other elements depends upon a knowledge of scattering and other effects, the coincidence-counting method will not be detailed here.

Semi-Empirical Methods for Efficiency Calculation

The quantity E, the overall efficiency for a given counter and sample arrangement, is the product of four factors, if it is assumed that the corrections for self-absorption and coincidence losses have been made.

$$E = G \times B \times A \times I \tag{1}$$

G is the geometric efficiency of the arrangement, B is the backscattering correction, A is the absorption correction factor, and I is the ionization probability.

Determination of Geometric Efficiency

Direct Measurements

The simplest method for evaluation of G involves the direct counting of a sample whose absolute activity is known, whose area and distance from the counter are the same as those to be used for samples made up during the course of experimentation, whose radiations are not appreciably absorbed or scattered by the window of, or air path to, the counter (or whose absorption can be accurately calculated), and whose radiations are not significantly backscattered by the mount. Most of these conditions can be satisfied, at least approximately. One difficulty lies in the determination of the absolute disintegration rate. Several isotopes are suited for this type of geometry determination; nearly always they are members of one of the natural radioactive series, the absolute activities of which can be determined from the known decay relationships of the particular active family, although I^{128} has been used.

---

[1] For a complete presentation of the method see J. V. Dunworth, *Rev. Sci. Instruments*, **11**, 167 (1940); also J. Rotblat, *Proc. Roy. Soc. London*, **A177**, 260 (1941); M. L. Wiedenbeck, *Phys. Rev.*, **72**, 974 (1947); further applications can be found in: A. Roberts, J. R. Downing, and M. Deutsch, *Phys. Rev.*, **60**, 544 (1941); J. R. Downing, M. Deutsch, and A. Roberts, *Phys. Rev.*, **61**, 686 (1942); W. Peacock, *Phys. Rev.*, **66**, 160 (1944); E. Bleuler and W. Zünti, *Helv. Phys. Acta*, **19**, 375 (1946); A. C. G. Mitchell, L. M. Langer, and P. W. McDaniel, *Phys. Rev.*, **57**, 1107 (1940); A. C. G. Mitchell, *Revs. Modern Phys.*, **20**, 296 (1948).

The hard β radiations of UX_2 (Pa^{234}) are often employed as well as those of Radium E (Bi^{210}).

Samples of UX_2 are made of some accurately weighable form of an aged uranium salt. Usually the ignited oxide U_3O_8 is counted in the form of a very fine powder, or certain uranium compounds which can be electrodeposited on metal foils. The sample is covered with at least 20 mg/cm^2 of aluminum to cut out the soft radiations from UX_1 (Th^{234}) ($E_{max} = 0.108$ Mev). The maximum energy of the UX_2 radiation is 2.32 Mev.[2] The foil absorption can be determined from the work of several authors.[2,3] For a foil of 20 mg/cm^2 thickness, one estimates a transmission of 0.94 from the data in references 3 and 4. (It must be remembered that there is an effect of relative sensitivity in the determination and use of transmission coefficients, especially for particles of high energy, since a given detector may be more sensitive to radiations of one energy than to those of higher or lower energy.) From the weight of uranium in the sample, the backscattering power of the mounting, the transmission of the foil (and window, if thick), and the known activity of UX_2, 734 β/min/mg U, the number of particles per minute available from the side of the sample toward the counter can be calculated. The ratio of the observed activity to that expected is approximately equal to the geometric efficiency.[5]

Calculation of Geometries

Absolute disintegration rate data are usually more often desired in work carried out with C^{14} than with C^{11}. Carbon 14, when counted externally, is usually determined in the form of a thin disk coaxial with a cathode of circular cross section. If the radius of the sample is small compared with the radius of the cathode (or where this relation is only approximately true but the distance between source and detector is relatively large), the sample may be assumed to behave as if it were a point source, and the geometric efficiency is given by the relation

$$G = \tfrac{1}{2}(1 - \cos \alpha) \tag{2}$$

[2] B. W. Sargent, *Proc. Roy. Soc. London*, **A139**, 659 (1933).

[3] N. Feather, *Proc. Cambridge Phil. Soc.*, **34**, 599 (1938).

[4] N. Feather, and E. Bretscher, *Proc. Roy. Soc. London*, **A165**, 530 (1938).

[5] Samples of UX_2 can be prepared conveniently from the U_3O_8 obtained by the ignition of ammonium diuranate. The ammonium salt is precipitated from a solution of aged uranyl nitrate by the addition of carbonate-free concentrated ammonium hydroxide.

Another preparation involves carrying UX_2 with lanthanum fluoride; the precipitate is formed when a dilute nitric acid solution of ammonium diuranate containing a small amount of lanthanum salt is made 2 M in hydrofluoric acid. (Plastic vessels must be used.)

where α is the angle subtended at the center of the source by the radius of the sensitive volume of the detector.[6]

Since the samples to be measured are usually of extensive area, and since the counter-sample separation is so small that point-source relationships do not hold, some more general method of calculation is required.[7,8] The calculation is further complicated because particles off the counter-sample axis do not "see" a circular opening. A rigorous treatment of the general case for coaxial circular sample and cathode has been developed.[9] In the formulas below, R_1 is the radius of the sensitive volume, R_2 is the radius of the sample, and h is the perpendicular distance between the sample and the cathode (sensitive volume). r is the length of any path between the source and detector and is given by the relation

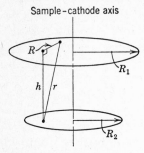

Sample-cathode axis

FIG. 93. Notation for equations 3 to 13.

$$r^2 = R^2 + h^2 \tag{3}$$

where R (see Fig. 93) is a distance in the plane of the cathode which varies between $R_1 + R_2$ and $R_1 - R_2$, where $R_1 > R_2$. For the generally existing situation R_1 greater than R_2, the following relation holds:

$$
\begin{aligned}
G = \frac{1}{2}\Bigg[&1 - \frac{1}{2}\left(\frac{h}{\sqrt{h^2 + (R_1 - R_2)^2}} + \frac{h}{\sqrt{h^2 + (R_1 + R_2)^2}} \right) \\
&+ \frac{2h}{\pi R_2^2} \int_{R_1-R_2}^{R_1+R_2} \left\{ \frac{R_1^2}{2} \cos^{-1}\left(\frac{R^2 + R_1^2 - R_2^2}{2RR_1} \right) \right. \\
&- \frac{R_2^2}{2} \sin^{-1}\left(\frac{R^2 + R_2^2 - R_1^2}{2RR_2} \right) \\
&\left. - \frac{1}{4}\sqrt{4R^2R_1^2 - (R^2 + R_1^2 - R_2^2)^2} \right\} \frac{R\,dR}{r^3} \Bigg]
\end{aligned} \tag{4}
$$

[6] $\cos \alpha = \dfrac{h}{\sqrt{R_1^2 + h^2}}$ (see Fig. 93).

[7] A. A. Wohlauer, *J. Franklin Inst.*, **231**, 49 (1941).

[8] A. F. Reid, *Preparation and Measurement of Isotopic Tracers*, Edwards Bros., Ann Arbor, Mich., 1947; A. F. Reid, A. S. Weil, and J. R. Dunning, *Anal. Chem.*, **19**, 824 (1947).

[9] The relations to be quoted were worked out by L. R. Henrich, Theoretical Group, Radiation Laboratory, University of California (Berkeley).

The last part of this expression is most conveniently integrated numerically. Even at very high geometric efficiencies, the contribution of this third part is relatively small, so that only a few terms, say $R/dR = 5$ to 8, are necessary for 1 to 3% accuracy.[10, 11]

Certain other relations derived in the same manner are of interest in actual laboratory practice. If R_p is the distance from the common axis of a single radiating point, then the efficiency with which the radiations from the point are detected is given by:

$$R_1 > R_p \qquad G = \frac{1}{2}\left[1 - \frac{h}{\sqrt{(R_1 - R_p)^2 + h^2}}\right]$$

$$+ \frac{h}{2\pi} \int_{R_1 - R_p}^{R_1 + R_p} \cos^{-1}\left[\frac{R^2 + R_p^2 - R_1^2}{2RR_p}\right] \frac{R\,dR}{(R^2 + h^2)^{3/2}} \tag{6}$$

When the particle is on the axis ($R_p = 0$), this expression reduces to the simple one often given for approximate calculation:

$$G = \frac{1}{2}\left[1 - \frac{h}{\sqrt{R_1^2 + h^2}}\right] \tag{7}$$

[10] The first two terms are from expressions integrable by formula, i.e.:

$$G = \frac{1}{2}\left[\frac{h}{2}\int_0^{R_1 - R_2} \frac{R\,dR}{r^3} + \frac{h}{2}\int_0^{R_1 + R_2} \frac{R\,dR}{r^3} + \frac{2h}{\pi R_2^2}\int \text{etc.}\right]$$

[11] For the case $R_1 < R_2$ the limits of R are $R_2 - R_1$ and $R_2 + R_1$, and equation 4 becomes

$$G = \frac{1}{2}\left[\frac{R_1^2}{R_2^2}\left(1 - \frac{h}{\sqrt{h^2 + (R_2 - R_1)^2}}\right)\right.$$

$$+ \frac{1}{2}\left(\frac{h}{\sqrt{h^2 + (R_2 - R_1)^2}} - \frac{h}{\sqrt{h^2 + (R_2 + R_1)^2}}\right)$$

$$+ \frac{2h}{\pi R_2^2}\int_{R_2 - R_1}^{R_2 + R_1}\left\{\frac{R_1^2}{2}\cos^{-1}\left(\frac{R^2 + R_1^2 - R_2^2}{2RR_1}\right)\right.$$

$$- \frac{R_2^2}{2}\sin^{-1}\left(\frac{R^2 + R_2^2 - R_1^2}{2RR_2}\right)$$

$$\left.\left. - \frac{1}{4}\sqrt{4R^2R_1^2 - (R^2 + R_1^2 - R_2^2)^2}\right\}\frac{R\,dR}{r^3}\right] \tag{5}$$

In Fig. 94 are plotted values of the calculated geometric efficiency as a function of h. For purposes of computation, R_1 was taken to be

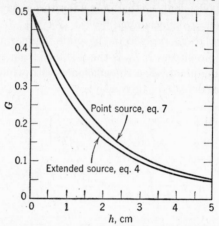

FIG. 94. Geometric efficiency (G) as a function of cathode-sample separation (h). ($R_1 = 2.46$ cm; $R_2 = 0$ and 1.91 cm.)

2.46 cm. Two curves are shown, one for an extended source, $R_2 = 1.91$ cm, and the other for an essentially point source coaxial with the cathode.

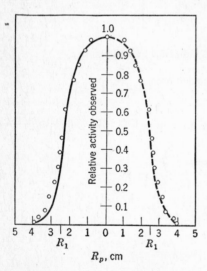

FIG. 95. Variation of counting efficiency with the lateral position of a point source. (Circles are experimental data; solid line is calculation based on mean value of r; broken line is calculation based on mean value of $e^{-\mu r}$.)

For a constant h and R_1, equation 6 defines the manner in which the observed activity varies as a radiating point is moved across a diameter of the sample disk. In Fig. 95 are shown calculated and observed data for a representative counter-sample arrangement. For the regions where $R_p > R_1$, only the integral term in equation 6 remains, and its lower limit becomes $R_p - R_1$. Since corrections were not applied for the variation with point position of B, the agreement is surprisingly good.

Backscattering Corrections

It has been mentioned earlier that backscattering directs into the detector particles whose original directions were not such that they would have passed through the sensitive volume. There is a certain amount of this type of scattering in the paths of the β particles through the air and the counter filling, but these deflections of particles in and out of the beam are relatively few and just about balance each other. The principal sources of scattering error are in the window of the counter, the sample material, and the sample mount. The error due to the window can be minimized by placing the window as close to the sensitive volume as possible. If it cannot be so placed, there may be an effect attributable to scattering of more particles into the beam than out of it.[12, 13]

By far the greatest component of the backscattered radiation is due to particles originally directed away from the detector. The magnitude of the backscattering effect is, therefore, dependent upon the nature of the sample and mounting and upon the energy of the radiations involved. When thick samples or mounts are used the effect observed increases with their increasing atomic number and with increasing β-particle energy. The contribution due to the sample materials can be neglected if the observed activities are corrected for self-absorption by a method in which data are obtained by extrapolating observed specific activities to zero sample thickness. The activity increase due to the mount can be kept small by using backings such as paper, glass, aluminum, beryllium, quartz, cellophane, and nylon which contain the lighter elements. Accurate determinations of backscattering factors as functions of the solid angle subtended by the detector at the source have not been made. It is known that the magnitude of the observable effect is dependent upon the geometry of the detection system, increasing with increasing geometric efficiency.[14]

[12] The magnitude of this phenomenon depends upon the geometric efficiency of the counting array, the nature and energy of the radiations, and the thickness of the absorbing layers and sample mounts. For example (E. Strajman, unpublished experiments): a sample containing P^{32} was mounted on a thick layer of polystyrene; when a 6 mg/cm^2 polystyrene absorber was interposed between the sample and (thin window) counter the observed activity increased $\sim 2\%$.

[13] Air scattering is difficult to measure; one group (L. R. Zumwalt, private communication) has carried out such determinations by observing the change in activity when a thin absorber of polystyrene (whose mean atomic number is near that of air) is placed in various positions between the sample and counter. The experiments indicate that air scattering at low geometries may increase C^{14} activities as much as 10%. The effect apparently increases with decreasing geometry and decreasing particle energy.

[14] For a discussion of this dependence see E. Rutherford, J. Chadwick, and C. D. Ellis, *Radiations from Radioactive Substances*, Cambridge University Press, 1930, pp. 392–397, 419–423. Experimental data elucidating the problem are recorded by B. F. J. Schonland, *Proc. Roy. Soc. London*, **A104**, 235 (1923), and **A108**, 187 (1925); W. Wilson, *Proc. Roy. Soc. London*, **A87**, 321 (1912); H. W. Schmidt, *Ann. Physik*, **23**, 678 (1907); A. F. Kovarik, *Phil. Mag.*, **20**, 849 (1910); J. L. Saunderson and O. S. Duffendack, *Phys. Rev.*, **60**, 190 (1941). There is a general discussion of the effect by W. Bothe in Vol. XXII-2 of *Handbuch der Physik*, Julius Springer, Berlin, 1933. For additional information see K. G. Emeleus, *Proc. Cambridge Phil. Soc.*, **22**, 400 (1924).

Since experiments of this type have yet to be performed, the best way to estimate the backscattering due to the mount is to measure the activity of a very thin source, with and without a thick backing, in the actual arrangement to be used. The source is mounted on a very thin support—mica, collodion, or stretched nylon—and care is taken to keep objects of appreciable scattering power away. (Mica sheet can be easily split to 0.2 mg/cm^2 in small-sized pieces, but collodion films can be made as thin as 0.01 mg/cm^2 by dropping amyl acetate solutions of collodion on clean water.[15]) It may be assumed that there is no appreciable backscattering from these thin films.

- If mica is used, an extended source can be prepared by one of the mounting techniques described on pages 117–121. When collodion or nylon films are used, the preparation of uniform and thin extended sources is difficult both because of the delicacy of these thin supports and because they are easily distorted or destroyed by contact with the usual suspension media. In any case, the sample preparation employed should be as thin as possible, whether it is extended or just a "point." In order that this requirement be met, one must select material of high specific activity. If a point source is used, its position can be varied over the area to be covered by the sample and an approximation to the extended source measurement can be achieved by weighting suitably the various observed activities.

After the activity of the source has been thus determined, it is remeasured with the actual sample mount carefully placed behind the supporting film and as close as possible to the active area. This enhanced activity divided by that first observed is equal to the backscattering factor (reflection coefficient) B.

In Table XXXIV are collected the results of some backscattering experiments carried out with C^{14} at two different geometric efficiencies.[16] The data are referred to air. With these data it is possible to make certain statements about a phenomenon involving multiple scattering of β particles from within sample materials. For convenience in discussion call backscattering from the sample mount "exterior reflection" and that from the sample itself "internal reflection." Consider first a sample

---

[15] J. Backus, *Phys. Rev.*, **68**, 59 (1945); L. M. Fry and R. T. Overman, Atomic Energy Commission, AECD 1800.

[16] P. E. Yankwich and J. Weigl, *Science*, **107**, 651 (1948). A 4-μg sample of active barium carbonate was mounted over an area of 0.040 cm^2 on a plastic film 0.07 mg/cm^2 thick. The sample particle layer was not thicker than 0.15 mg/cm^2. The equivalent thickness of counter window and air path was 3.4 mg/cm^2 at the lower geometry (12%) 2.3 mg/cm^2 at the higher (30%).

of radioactive barium carbonate mounted on aluminum and counted at 30% geometry. If one envisions the sample as made up of many thin layers it is apparent that the observed activity of the first lamina (counting from the mount) is 1.16 times its intrinsic activity because the aluminum mount contributes an additional radiation flux to the measurement by exterior reflection. The activity observable from the next lamina is increased by slightly more than 1.16 for, although fewer radiations can reach the mount, they are more powerfully reflected by the first barium carbonate layer. Thus as the sample thickness is increased the activity observed rises from 1.16 to 1.35 times that observed when all reflection processes are neglected. If samples of active

TABLE XXXIV

BACKSCATTERING OF C^{14} β PARTICLES

(Thin-window counter data)

Scatterer	Relative Observed Activity (backscattering factor or reflection coefficient)	
	12% geometry	30% geometry
Air	1.00	1.00
Platinum	1.43 ± 0.02	1.51 ± 0.02
Barium carbonate	1.30 ± 0.01	1.35 ± 0.01
Glass	1.16 ± 0.01	1.17 ± 0.01
Aluminum	1.15 ± 0.01	1.16 ± 0.01
Paper⎱ Wax ⎰	1.04 ± 0.015	1.07 ± 0.015

wax were used the activity observable would fall from 1.16 to 1.07 times that expected because the interior reflecting power of wax is less than the exterior reflecting power of the aluminum. It must be emphasized that ordinarily these reflection effects are never noted directly but are impressed upon the experimental self-absorption relations. For this reason all backscattering effects, at least as far as they affect self-absorption corrections, are canceled out when the self-absorption correction curves are derived from data obtained experimentally under conditions identical with those which will be used in routine counting.

Backscattering effects saturate very rapidly because they involve double transit of radiations through absorbing layers, and the effect of the weak radiations is thus emphasized. The maximum penetration of C^{14} β particles in matter is about 28 mg/cm², yet the reflection effects reach 80% of their maximum at a sample thickness of 6 mg/cm², and 97% at 12 mg/cm².

Several authors [17] have given values for the absorption coefficient of the C^{14} β radiations. These values are usually derived from the slope at zero sample thickness of a plot of activity observed against thickness of sample layer, or from direct foil-absorption measurements. The result quoted in the first paper [17] was accompanied by no experimental data relative to reflection effects; that in the second was obtained from samples mounted on aluminum; in the third, from a curve derived from counting data with sources on stainless steel (whose reflecting power is somewhat greater than that of aluminum).

It has been assumed by many investigators that the effective self-absorption corrections for several sample substances are very nearly the same as those for barium carbonate, for which most such determinations have been made. That this is not so can be seen by reference to Fig. 34 (page 105), where data for wax and barium carbonate samples, all mounted on aluminum, are graphed. A consideration of the reflection enhancement of the observed radiation leads one to expect that at sample thicknesses where the backscattering effects are saturated the curves for the two sample materials will be related to each other by the quotient of the proper reflection coefficients. The value predicted is $\dfrac{1.35 \pm 0.01}{1.07 \pm 0.015} =$ 1.26 ± 0.02; that observed is 1.27 (thin-window counter data).

Absorption Corrections

Especially with C^{14}, corrections must be applied to allow for the partial absorption of the disintegration electrons in the air path, window, and filling gas path. Calculation is most easily made from a foil absorption curve taken with the counting arrangement actually used since compensation is thus automatically made for the fact that only a small fraction of the particles travel in approximately perpendicular paths through the absorbing layers, and for the external reflection effect described above.

The relation between source-detector arrangement and geometric efficiency has been given on page 306. One can obtain the mean path length, $\bar{r}$, by weighting by r the integrals from which the geometry is derived and dividing by G (mean value theorem). Since the factor to be applied to the absorber thicknesses is $\bar{r}/h$, that quantity will be calculated.

[17] A. F. Reid, J. R. Dunning, S. Weinhouse, and A. V. Grosse, *Phys. Rev.*, **70**, 431 (1946); 0.257 cm²/mg; P. E. Yankwich, T. H. Norris, and J. Huston, *Anal. Chem.*, **19**, 439 (1947), 0.285 ± 0.008 cm²/mg; A. K. Solomon, R. G. Gould, and C. B. Anfinsen, *Phys. Rev.*, **72**, 1097 (1947), 0.29 cm²/mg.

For the usual case where R_1 is greater than R_2 the expression obtained is:

$$\frac{\bar{r}}{h} = \frac{1}{2G}\left[\frac{1}{2}\log_e \frac{\sqrt{(R_1 - R_2)^2 + h^2}}{h}\right.$$

$$+ \frac{1}{2}\log_e \frac{\sqrt{(R_1 + R_2)^2 + h^2}}{h}$$

$$+ \frac{2}{\pi R_2{}^2}\int_{R_1 - R_2}^{R_1 + R_2}\left\{\frac{R_1{}^2}{2}\cos^{-1}\left(\frac{R^2 + R_1{}^2 - R_2{}^2}{2RR_1}\right)\right.$$

$$- \frac{R_2{}^2}{2}\sin^{-1}\left(\frac{R^2 + R_2{}^2 - R_1{}^2}{2RR_2}\right)$$

$$\left.\left.- \frac{1}{4}\sqrt{4R^2R_1{}^2 - (R^2 + R_1{}^2 - R_2{}^2)^2}\right\}\frac{R\,dR}{r^2}\right] \qquad (8)$$

The equation which gives $\bar{r}/h$ for $R_2 > R_1$ is similarly derivable. The expressions given in equations 6 and 7 yield $\bar{r}/h$ formulas as follows:

Point source off the axis, equation 6.

$$\frac{\bar{r}}{h} = \frac{1}{2G}\left[\ln\frac{\sqrt{(R_1 - R_p)^2 + h^2}}{h}\right.$$

$$\left.+ \frac{1}{2\pi}\int_{R_1 - R_p}^{R_1 + R_p}\cos^{-1}\left(\frac{R^2 + R_p{}^2 - R_1{}^2}{2RR_p}\right)\frac{R\,dR}{R^2 + h^2}\right] \qquad (9)$$

Point source on the axis, equation 7.

$$\frac{\bar{r}}{h} = \frac{1}{2G}\left[\ln\frac{\sqrt{R_1{}^2 + h^2}}{h}\right] \qquad (10)$$

Now $\bar{r}/h$ is dimensionless and can therefore be applied to the measured absorber thickness as well as to the actual distances involved. If the apparent (perpendicular) absorber thicknesses total t_w mg/cm^2, then the effective absorber thickness is $t_w \times \bar{r}/h = t$ mg/cm^2.

C^{14} β particles are absorbed approximately exponentially, for at least 10 mg/cm^2. Since counter windows used for the measurement of this isotope are always much thinner, the exponential relation can be used to simplify the computation of absorption corrections. Briefly, if a beam of C^{14} β particles passes through an absorber t mg/cm^2 thick, the initial and final intensities are related according to the expression

$$\frac{I_t}{I_0} = e^{-\mu t} \qquad (11)$$

where μ is the absorption coefficient expressed in units of surface density. It is often convenient to express the absorption coefficient in terms of the "half-thickness," $t_{\frac{1}{2}}$, that thickness of absorber which will reduce by one-half the intensity of an incident beam. For such cases equation 11 reduces to

$$\frac{I_t}{I_0} = 2^{-t/t_{\frac{1}{2}}} = 2^{-\left(\frac{\bar{r}}{h} \cdot \frac{t_w}{t_{\frac{1}{2}}}\right)} \qquad (12)$$

The half-thickness for absorption of C^{14} β rays, corrected to perpendicular absorption, is 2.1 mg/cm^2; that for C^{11} positrons is 54 mg/cm^2; [18]

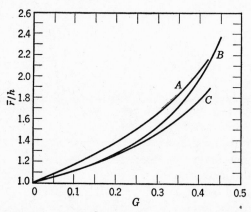

FIG. 96.   Variation of $\bar{r}/h$ with G.   (R_1 2.46 cm. A: extended source, R_2 1.91 cm, equation 8; B: point source, equation 10; C: point source, calculation after A. F. Reid, et al., reference 8.)

that for C^{11} annihilation radiation 8.4 gm/cm^2 in Al, 4.1 gm/cm^2 in Pb, and approximately 19.5 gm/cm^2 in water [19] (see also Table V, page 27).

In Fig. 96 are plotted values of the calculated $\bar{r}/h$ as a function of G for $R_1 = 2.46$ cm.   Two curves are shown, one for an extended source, $R_2 = 1.91$ cm, and the other for an essentially point source coaxial with the cathode.

The calculation by other methods of the obliquity correction is simple and accurate but too often extended.   A limitation is placed on a calculation of this type which does not apply to the geometry computation. Consider, for example, the case where a thin mica window is stretched

[18] W. F. Libby, *Ind. Eng. Chem., Anal. Ed.*, **19**, 2 (1947); for a general discussion see E. Bleuler and W. Zünti, *Helv. Phys. Acta*, **19**, 375 (1946).

[19] W. Heitler, *The Quantum Theory of Radiation*, Clarendon Press, Oxford, 1936 pp. 215–216; W. Gentner, *J. phys. radium*, **6**, 274 (1935); *Physik. Z.*, **38**, 836 (1937).

over the end of a glass envelope filled with helium at about 74 cm pressure. The window curves inward as shown in Fig. 97. The calculation for the obliquity of paths through the absorbing layers, the greater part of which is the window, is valid only so long as this curvature does not greatly affect the interpretation of the calculation, which assumes absorption in a layer parallel to the sample; at certain distances the perpendicular and oblique paths will approach each other closely. It may be helpful to record here two rules of the thumb useful in deciding the validity of an $\bar{r}/h$ calculation. If d is the distance by which the center of the window is depressed from the plane of its mount and D is the diameter of the window, then $\bar{r}/h$ as calculated from equation 8 is in-

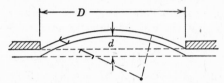

FIG. 97.   A source of error in the use of $\bar{r}/h$.

accurate when the distance of the sample from the center of the window, h, is of the same order of magnitude as the quantity $(D^2 + 4d^2)/8d$. The result is also inaccurate when h is less than $4d$. Effects due to violation of the second condition are the more important, though the actual errors in either case are often small enough to be ignored.

Some calculations for G and $\bar{r}/h$ (see reference 8, for example) have have been made by including, in certain integrals, weighting factors for the approximately exponential absorption of the β particles. The calculation of absorption corrections by the methods just described is probably accurate to 5% for $\bar{r} < 2t_{1/2}$. When this condition cannot be satisfied, it is probably better to evaluate $(e^{-\mu r})_{\text{mean}}$ instead of $\bar{r}/h$.

Thus, $(e^{-\mu r})_{\text{mean}} = \dfrac{\displaystyle\int e^{-\mu r}F(r)\,dr}{\displaystyle\int F(r)\,dr}$.   One branch of the curve in Fig.

95 was calculated with the use of such a refinement.

Probability for Ion Production

Suppose that a given particle, in passing through a certain gas at 1 atmosphere pressure, produces along its path i electrons per centimeter. Then for a path l centimeters in length there will be produced li electrons

The probability that the particle will produce no electrons in this path length is e^{-li}, and the probability that one electron, capable of causing a discharge which will register the passage of the ionizing particle, will be produced is $1 - e^{-li}$. For the general case where i is the specific ionization, ions per centimeter per atmosphere, l the path length in centimeters, and p the pressure of the filling in atmospheres, the probability that the ionizing particle will be detected is

$$I = 1 - e^{-lpi} \qquad (13)$$

The specific ionization i decreases with increasing particle energy and increases with gas density.[20] The values for i in air at various electron energies have been determined.[21, 22] From i for air and the relations for other gases [23] very approximate values have been computed for several other gases of interest in carbon counting; these are listed in Table XXXV.

TABLE XXXV

APPROXIMATE SPECIFIC IONIZATION CONSTANTS FOR SEVERAL GASES

Particle	i:air	He	CO_2	A
$C^{14}\ E_{max.}$	105	35	160	140
$C^{14}\ E_{ave.}$	220	70	300	270
$C^{11}\ E_{max.}$	55	20	80	70
$C^{11}\ E_{mean}$	70	25	100	90

Suppose that a counter filled with helium at 1 atmosphere pressure counts C^{11} positrons. It is desired to compute the average distance which must be traveled by a positron of maximum energy before the probability that it will have produced a "count" is 95%. From Table XXXV, we find that i for helium is 20, very approximately. Then $0.95 = 1 - e^{-20l}$ and l is 0.15 cm. In fact, then, a counter of even moderate dimensions would count better than 99% of the positrons incident when filled with 1 atmosphere of helium. As a contrast, l would be 1.15 cm if the helium pressure were 10 cm.[24] Thus, for nearly all counters of ordinary size using fillings at moderate pressures, the ionization probability is nearly unity.

[20] P. T. Smith, *Phys. Rev.*, **38**, 1293 (1930).

[21] C. T. R. Wilson, *Proc. Roy. Soc. London*, **A104**, 192 (1923).

[22] P. Lenard, *Quantitative über Kathodenstrahlen*, Heidelberg, 1918; E. Buchmann, *Ann. Physik*, **87**, 509 (1928).

[23] R. D. Kleeman, *Proc. Roy. Soc. London*, **A79**, 220 (1907); E. Buchmann, *Ann. Physik*, **87**, 509 (1928); M. Cosyns, *Bull. Tech. Ing., École Polytech. (Brux.)*, 1936; W. E. Danforth and W. E. Ramsey, *Phys. Rev.*, **49**, 854 (1936); W. E. Hazen, *Phys. Rev.*, **63**, 107 (1943).

[24] For comparison: If a tube filled with 10 cm argon counts C^{14}, the ionization probability for the β's of average energy is 99% in 1.3 mm and 95% in only 0.84 mm.

Appendix V

SELF-ABSORPTION DATA FOR BARIUM CARBONATE AND WAX MOUNTED ON ALUMINUM

TABLE XXXVI

THIN-WINDOW COUNTER EXPERIMENTS [1,2]

Sample Thickness mg/cm²	G — Fraction of Maximum Observable Activity		J — Fraction of Maximum Observable Specific Activity	
	BaCO₃	Wax	BaCO₃	Wax
0	0.000	0.000	1.000	1.000
1	.245	.301	0.856	0.823
2	.431	.480	.761	.656
3	.560	.602	.660	.548
4	.663	.695	.586	.475
5	.745	.762	.527	.416
6	.807	.820	.475	.373
7	.854	.860	.431	.336
8	.887	.898	.392	.307
9	.914	.933	.359	.283
10	.934	.944	.330	.258
11	.947	.955	.304	.237
12	.957	.966	.282	.220
13	.965	.973	.262	.205
14	.973	.981	.246	.192
15	.978	.985	.230	.179
16	.983	.988	.217	.169
17	.987	.992	.205	.160
18	.990	.995	.194	.151
19	.993	.996	.185	.143
20	.995	.997	.176	.136

[1] P. E. Yankwich, T. H. Norris, and J. L. Huston, *Anal. Chem.*, **19**, 439 (1947).
[2] P. E. Yankwich and J. W. Weigl, *Science*, **107**, 651 (1948).

TABLE XXXVII

NUCLEOMETER EXPERIMENTS [3]

J

Fraction of Maximum
Observable Specific Activity

Sample Thickness mg/cm^2	BaCO$_3$	Wax
0	1.000	1.000
1	0.719	0.707
2	.576	.519
3	.486	.436
4	.414	.368
5	.360	.323
6	.315	.285
7	.280	.254
8	.252	.226
9	.230	.203
10	.212	.188
11	.194	.173
12	.180	.159

[3] P. E. Yankwich and J. Weigl, unpublished experiments.

NUMERICAL EXAMPLES ILLUSTRATING RADIOACTIVITY ASSAY OPERATIONS

There are a number of details of the actual operations of counting a sample of barium carbonate and calculating the activity of the organic specimen from which the carbonate is derived to which reference has been made briefly in various places in the text, but which perhaps deserve further discussion. In this appendix are collected some remarks intended to be of practical usefulness in carrying out the operations involved in radioactivity assay.

G-M Counting

In Fig. 98 is shown a typical data sheet which may be used for the recording of counting information for a mounted sample of barium carbonate. The various items will be discussed in the order of appearance on the data sheet.

Plate Number. It is ordinarily impractical to count each barium carbonate sample as soon as it is prepared, and any other plan involves storage of mounted samples; some indexing or identification system must be devised so that samples will not be mixed up. Sample holders with numbered positions are of some use, but it is better to mark the mounting disk with the number or other designation of the organic sample or to number disks consecutively, recording the disk number on a sample information sheet. The advantages associated with any of several methods are so largely determined by the operational scheme of the individual laboratory and problem that they need not be discussed here.

Date Counted. Many laboratories are located near sources of artificial background effect (high-voltage generators, cyclotrons, etc.), and a counting date helps in the assignment of non-statistical counter behavior to one of these sources rather than to the counter itself. Of course, the date can be useful in the latter regard as well, since not only do counters vary slightly in their response from day to day but also such variation may be monotonic and therefore probably due to incipient counter failure. A knowledge of the date on which the radioactivity determination was made is helpful in correcting for any of these effects.

The day-to-day response of a counting array may be checked conveniently with a standard plate made by the shellac binding technique described on page 120. The activity of the plate should be about 5,000–7,000 c/min; a sample of this strength can be counted to 0.5%

3. COUNTING DATA RECORD

Plate # _KZ–5_   Date counted: _1/3/48_

  Circuit # _126_   Conversion factor to 132s: _1.10_   M

                        Coincidence correction: _1.4_ K%/1,000 c/min

Length of BACKGROUND cycle: _4_ MIN.   Length of SAMPLE cycle: _4_ MIN.

(If automatic count, combined total times: _—_ MIN.)   SCALE: _64_

Register readings		Calculated totals	
Background	Sample	Background	Sample
1 + 40	46 + 1	104	2,945
2 + 18	47 + 4	146	3,012
2 + 0	46 + 37	128	2,981
2 + 5	46 + 63	133	3,007

mg on the plate: _78.1_ F   511   11,945

F/11.5 = _6.78_ mg/cm^2 R_b _31.9_ c/min R_s _746.6_ c/min

Thickness correction, self-absorption, divide by:

        J _0.440_

Coincidence correction, multiply by: $\left[\dfrac{K \times R_s}{10^5} + 1 \right]$ = L _1.01_

$R_s \times L = R_s$ (corrected): _754_ . R_s (corrected) $- R_b$ = Net activity N

N: _722_ c/min. Plate activity = N/J = _1,641_ c/min.

N/J $\times$ M = _1,804_ c/min on 132s H.

Standard error estimated from Table: _<1_ %.

FIG. 98

statistical accuracy in a few minutes and is sufficiently active so that coincidence losses exert a sizable effect on the activity observed. Thus, changes in electrical characteristics of the circuit can be detected which might pass unnoticed if a sample only a fifth or tenth as strong were used.

The standard sample should be the first source counted, and only after the circuit has had time to warm up. (The warm-up time varies from instrument to instrument and must be known. In many cases it is most practical to leave the circuits on all the time except over week-

RADIOACTIVITY ANALYSIS RECORD

Description: _12 Hour Feces Sample—Mouse A3_

1. Combustion and sampling data. Date burned: _1/2/48_ , by: _BC_

Total sample (wt or vol): _277 mg_ A

C: _19.4_ sample factor.

Aliquot taken (wt or vol): _14.3_ B

Dilution: Total mg. $BaCO_3$ from combustion: _96.1_ D

blank _4.0_

_____ ml $Na_2CO_3 \times 20$ equals: _____ mg $BaCO_3$ OR—

_____ mg benzoic acid $\times 11.31$ equals: _____ mg $BaCO_3$.

mg $BaCO_3$ from aliquot material alone: _92_ E

$\dfrac{E \times 6.085}{B} = $ _39_ % carbon in original material

----

2. Plating Data. Date plated: _1/3/48_ , by: _DE_

$BaCO_3$ plate	Direct plate
gross: _679.2_ tare: _601.1_	_____ G, vol plated.
net: _78.1_ F mg on the plate	(note that G may be equal to B)

4. Sample Activity Data.

c/min on plate: _1804_ H

c/min on plate: _____ H

$H/F =$ _23.2_ c/min/mg $BaCO_3$

$H/G =$ _____ c/min/cc of sample

$H/F \times D =$ _2230_ c/min in the aliquot

$(H/F \times D)/B =$ _156_ c/min/mg of the aliquot

$(H/F \times D) \times C =$ _43,200_ c/min in the whole sample

$H \times C =$ _____ c/min in the whole sample

(Note: c/min on 132s $\times 17.6$ = disintegrations/min absolute)

FIG. 99

SAMPLE # _500_

PLATE # _KZ—5_

ends.) A plot against the date should be made of the count observed. In a typical computation the authors took the mean of the standard counts obtained over 63 days; of the results observed in the next 90 days, 58 were within ±0.5% of the mean value, 28 were between ±0.5 and ±1.0%, and 4 deviated by more than 1.0%—only one of them by more than 2.0. This behavior of counter response seems to be a little better than average. Repeat determination of the standard source activity should be made when the deviation observed is so large that it may be important to the interpretation of results or whenever it is more than 5% of the observed mean. If the deviation computed the second time is about the same as that first observed a correction must be made for change in counter sensitivity. The factor $\dfrac{\text{observed count}}{\text{mean count}}$ is usually applied to the results of all counts made until the standard sample is recounted. If large deviations are observed over several days the instrument should be checked for position of the detector, grounding of the shield, coincidence correction, contamination, etc.

Conversion Factor (M) and Circuit Number. In the authors' laboratories nine counters are in daily operation, and it is nearly always impossible to count all samples derived from a single research on one counter; for this reason it is necessary that the relative sensitivities of the various instruments be determined. Four or five samples of varying thickness (so that thickness effects upon geometry, if any, may be noted) are counted on each circuit, one of which is chosen as standard. A mean ratio, usually accurate to 1 or 2%, is computed for each circuit-standard pair. This factor is determined by the counter tube and its arrangement over the sample and by certain scattering effects. If the absolute efficiency of any counter is determined, that of all the others can be quickly computed. (It is not necessary that the standard counter be preserved. The counter 132s to which reference is made in the data sheet shown was destroyed by accident several years ago, but activities are still referred to it as a matter of convenience.)

Coincidence Correction (K). In Appendix III, methods are outlined whereby coincidence correction factors at various activity levels can be determined. It is often convenient to employ the correction as a single number which is modified in a certain way, rather than to use a complete correction equation (page 296) or a value taken from a graph. Such a procedure can be followed only when the value of ν in the correction equation is such that it makes only a small contribution to the value of $(N/R) - 1$ in the activity range commonly used. This is actually the case up to 5,000 c/min with most instruments; with some this range may go as high as 15,000 c/min. The value of the correction is determined by the circuit and counter tube, and a change in either necessitates at least a brief check of the values of τ and ν.

Length of Counting Cycles. Only two factors are important in the determination of the length of counting cycles. One of these is personal convenience; the other is the nature of the background and, more particularly, its rate of fluctuation. If the background is due largely to detector contamination and cosmic rays, it is remarkably constant and needs to be determined accurately at only relatively long intervals. This situation is encountered only when ion chambers are used or when counters are operated in a laboratory which is well shielded. If the background is changing rapidly and in a random manner the counting intervals should be either short or long compared to the apparent period of fluctuations but not of approximately the same length. If the random fluctuations seem to be impressed upon a rise and fall of much longer period the counting times must be short with respect to this longer period. The counting intervals should never be so short that errors in stopping or starting the counter are appreciable; they should seldom be prolonged past 30 minutes when G-M counters are used.

Automatic Count. See page 50.

Scale. Self-explanatory.

Register Readings. The observed counts are recorded as the sum of the register and interpolate readings; the actual count is obtained by multiplying the first figure by the scale and adding to the second.

The counting error should be computed from the sum of all counts rather than the differences of pairs of counts. For example, the actual net activity computed from the data given is 714.7 c/min. On the basis of the number of events detected the predicted standard error is ±6.4 c/min; the standard deviation of all background counts is ±2.2 c/min, that of all sample counts is ±3.9 c/min, and the standard deviation of the total net counting rate is thus ±4.4 c/min, which is a good approximation to that predicted on the basis of a random disintegration process. The standard deviation of the mean net activity calculated from each background-sample pair is only ±1.8 c/min and clearly gives an erroneous picture of the counting error in this case. In nearly all calculations more reliable information is obtained when the error is evaluated from all data taken, considered as a whole, rather than as a sum of several activity determinations.

Thickness Correction (J). The correction for self-absorption depends upon the nature and thickness of the sample and mounting materials and, to a smaller degree, upon the geometry of the detection array (see pages 105, 311). The correction factor is applied to the net activity after allowance is made for coincidence losses.

Coincidence Correction Factor (L). This factor is applied to the observed sample activity before subtraction of the background; it is equal to the true activity N divided by the observed activity R and is derived from coincidence-loss experiments on the counter used. The number K is usually expressed as a percentage of the observed activity per unit count rate expressed in thousands of counts per minute. Here the coincidence loss is 1.4% per 1,000 c/min; the correction involved is $1.4 \times 747 \div 1,000 = 1.01\%$. If it is convenient to perform the correction by multiplication, as on a calculating machine, the correction factor is $1 + (1.05 \div 100) = 1.01$.

All other items are self-explanatory.

In Fig. 99 is illustrated a typical data sheet which may be used to record sampling information and assay values. The significance of the entries can be illustrated by an example: A compound labeled with C^{14} is administered to a mouse and fecal excretion is investigated by collecting samples of feces at intervals for radioactivity assay. One such sample weighs 277 mg when dried. The dry material is ground and thoroughly mixed; a 14.3-mg aliquot is then converted to barium carbonate. The sampling factor (C) is $277 \div 14.3$. The conversion to barium carbonate is effected by the second combustion technique described on page 80; the blank is known to be about 4 mg. The total weight of barium carbonate (D) is 96.1 mg; of this, about 92 mg is derived from the sample. From this fact, it can be calculated that the sample contains about 39% carbon. This value has not been determined with the best possible accuracy but is calculated for the purpose of checking the combustion by comparison with values obtained for other samples of feces. The barium carbonate is mounted on a disk for assay; (F), the weight of the mounted sample is 78.1 mg.

The sample is counted, and the data shown in Fig. 98 are obtained. The total activity of the mounted sample is 1,804 c/min.

Division of the total activity (H) of the mounted sample by the weight on the plate gives the specific activity of the barium carbonate: $1,804 \div 78.1 = 23.2$ c/min; this quantity is multiplied by the total weight of barium carbonate obtained in the combustion (D) to calculate the total activity of the aliquot.[1]

$$23.2 \times 96.1 = 2,230 \text{ c/min}$$

The specific activity of the feces sample is calculated by dividing the

[1] The total activity of the aliquot can, of course, be calculated directly from the total activity on the plate (H) by multiplying this quantity by D/F. However, if duplicate plates are to be made from a single specimen of barium carbonate, it is convenient to calculate the specific activity, since this is the quantity which is directly comparable between the duplicates.

total activity by the sample weight; the total activity is calculated by multiplying the total activity of the aliquot by 19.4.

$$\frac{2,230}{14.3} = 156 \text{ c/min/mg}; \quad 2,230 \times 19.4 = 43,200 \text{ c/min}$$

For a second illustration of the computation of the specific activity of an organic specimen, acetyl chloride will serve as an example. This substance reacts rapidly with atmospheric moisture, and in work with small quantities the operations of synthesis and weighing may permit appreciable hydrolysis of a sample before combustion. In a typical case, it may be supposed that a sample containing 10.0 mg of acetyl chloride with a specific activity of 374 c/min/mg is sealed into a capillary ampoule for combustion; the acetyl chloride has absorbed 5% by weight of water and therefore weighs 10.5 mg if it is assumed for simplicity that none of the hydrogen chloride formed has escaped. The sample is burned by the first combustion technique described on page 79, yielding 50.3 mg of barium carbonate, whose specific activity is found to be 74.4 c/min/mg. The blank is known to be negligible, and the specific activity of the acetyl chloride can therefore be calculated from the formula weights of acetyl chloride and barium carbonate:

$$\frac{2 \times \text{M.W. of BaCO}_3}{\text{M.W. of AcCl}} \times 74.4 = 374 \text{ c/min/mg AcCl}$$

It will be noted that the calculation based on the total activity of the barium carbonate and the weight of the sample gives a low value:

$$\frac{50.3 \times 74.4}{10.5} = 356 \text{ c/min/mg AcCl}$$

Ionization-Chamber Measurement

It is not practical to attempt a detailed exposition of the operation of ionization chambers because of the variety of techniques in use and because the ionization chamber is an instrument whose routine use for assay of C^{14} has not yet been standardized even to the extent that G-M counting has. Briefly, a chamber may be operated by one of two general types of techniques: the drift method, in which the observed quantity is the number of scale divisions through which a charged fiber drifts per unit of time; and the null method, in which is observed the rate at which a compensating potential must be applied to the fiber to keep it stationary. In either method, however, the observed datum can be expressed as a drift rate.

We shall consider the computations involved in translating the drift rate into terms of specific activity expressed as counts per minute per milligram of organic sample. The necessity of being able to make this conversion arises when a group of related samples, including some of very low activity, is to be assayed. For various reasons it may be desired to use an end-window G-M counter as far as possible, but the less active samples may be so weak that the determination of their activity requires utilization of the greater sensitivity of the ionization chamber. The use of the two different types of instruments makes necessary a method of expressing all activities on a common basis. The situation often arises in biological work.

Two techniques, discussed separately below, may be used to fill a chamber. In one, the entire sample of active carbon is introduced; in the other, only part. In either case, there will in general not be enough active carbon dioxide to fill the chamber, since it is necessary to have a chamber volume of 100 cc or more to secure maximum ionization efficiency and in many types of work the samples encountered are not large enough to furnish this volume of carbon dioxide. For this reason, the sample is diluted with an inactive carrier gas, since the chamber is operated at constant total pressure. The carrier may be carbon dioxide, but in the total introduction method it need not be.

Total Introduction Technique. As an example for discussion, it may be supposed that it is desired to assay a single dried lymph node from a mouse to which has been administered a compound labeled with C^{14}. The node weighs 1.71 mg. It is converted to carbon dioxide by the Van Slyke-Folch method, with the oxidation flask connected directly to the chamber (page 145). About 10 mg of benzoic acid is added to the oxidation flask as carrier, and the mixture is oxidized in the usual way. The pressure in the system at the end of the oxidation will be perhaps 0.1 atmosphere. All the active carbon dioxide is now swept into the chamber by admitting tank carbon dioxide through the oxidation flask until the pressure reaches 1 atmosphere or other standard pressure; the valve at the entrance to the chamber is then closed.

The chamber is attached to the electrometer, and the drift rate is measured; a value of 0.0562 mv/sec after subtraction of background is observed. In order to convert the drift rate to activity in terms of counts per minute it is necessary to have calibrated the chamber by determining the drift rate of a sample of carbon dioxide of known activity. The calibration is performed by introducing into the chamber carbon dioxide generated from a known weight of barium carbonate whose activity has been determined with a G-M counter. It may be supposed that the chamber used to assay the lymph node has a drift rate of 3.61 mv/sec, after subtraction of background, when filled with carbon dioxide generated from 10.2 mg of barium carbonate whose specific activity is 50.5 c/min/mg. That is, a drift rate of 3.61 mv/sec corresponds to a total activity of 515 c/min. The total activity of the lymph node is then $515 \times 0.0562/3.61 = 8.02$ c/min, and the specific activity is $8.02/1.71 = 4.68$ c/min/mg.

Partial Introduction Technique. The lymph node whose assay has been described in the foregoing section is burned (with carrier), and the carbon dioxide is converted to barium carbonate, whose weight is 92.4 mg. As much as possible of the barium carbonate is removed from the sintered-glass filter on which it is collected and is transferred to a weighed generator flask (page 144). The weight of active carbonate in the flask is found by difference to be 84.3 mg. To the flask is now added enough inactive barium carbonate to fill the chamber. The total weight of the barium carbonate (active plus inactive) is 1,004 mg. The chamber and generator are attached to the vacuum line and evacuated, and the carbon dioxide is generated from the carbonate and allowed to flow into the chamber. When the pressure reaches 1 atmosphere (or other standard pressure) the valve at the entrance to the chamber is closed.

Since there is a certain volume of the system beyond the chamber which is also filled with active gas, only a part of the sample has been introduced. Although this volume can be made quite small with respect to that of the chamber, it is not feasible to make it small enough to make the excluded fraction of the sample negligible.

A drift rate, after subtraction of background, of 0.0423 mv/sec is observed. In order to convert the drift rate to counts per minute, it is necessary to have calibrated the chamber with carbon dioxide of known specific activity. The calibration is performed by measuring the drift rate of the chamber when filled with carbon dioxide generated from barium carbonate whose specific activity has been determined with a G-M counter. When the filling technique under discussion is used, the calibration is based on the specific, rather than the total, activity of the standard since the calculation based on specific activity is not affected by the fact that not all the sample has been introduced so long as enough of the standard is used to fill the chamber to standard pressure.

It may be supposed that the chamber used has a drift rate, after subtraction of background, of 20.34 mv/sec when filled with carbon dioxide generated from barium carbonate whose specific activity is 3.51 c/min/mg. Then the specific activity of the mixed active and inactive barium carbonate is $3.51 \times 0.0423 \div 20.34 = 0.00732$ c/min/mg.

The specific activity of the barium carbonate obtained in the combustion is $0.00732 \times 1,004/84.3 = 0.0869$ c/min/mg.

The total activity of the active barium carbonate (and of the lymph node) is $92.4 \times 0.0869 = 8.02$ c/min, and the specific activity of the node itself is $8.02/1.71 = 4.68$ c/min/mg.

Appendix VII

FLOW IN VACUUM SYSTEMS

The ability of a system to transport gases is usually expressed in terms of conductance, which is the quantity transfer divided by the pressure differential for the system. Compared to the conductance of the same system at higher pressure the conductance of a system at low pressures is often very small. This flow rate is so slow that it is often the limiting factor in the evacuation of a system or in a vacuum-distillation transfer of a compound. Flow rates thus become very important considerations in the design of vacuum systems for specific purposes. It is desirable to be able to make estimates of the size needed for the parts of such systems and to calculate the rate of flow in these systems. Much of this design work, especially for small systems, has been and still is done by trial and error, but a great deal of qualitative and quantitative information is available as a help.

Gas flow is of three types: turbulent, viscous (or laminar), and molecular. Turbulent flow occurs only at high velocities, which are rarely found in vacuum systems, and so it will not be described here.

In order to distinguish between viscous and molecular flow it is desirable to introduce the concept of *mean free path*, which is the average distance a molecule travels before it collides with another. The mean free path, λ, of a gas may be calculated by the following closely approximate formula (Maxwell):

$$\lambda = \frac{kT}{\sqrt{2}\,\pi P \sigma^2} \qquad \begin{aligned} k &= \text{Boltzmann's constant.} \\ T &= \text{absolute temperature.} \\ P &= \text{pressure.} \\ \sigma &= \text{effect diameter of the molecules.} \end{aligned} \qquad (1)$$

In Table XXXVIII the mean free path for a number of gases at room temperature is listed at 1 atmosphere and at 1 micron pressure (1 micron $= 10^{-3}$ mm Hg); the mean free path at other pressures and temperatures may be conveniently estimated by simple relations using the above equation.

In viscous flow, the gas near the walls of the tube is almost stationary except for diffusion. Farther from the wall the gas flows smoothly, so that, if lines connecting regions of equal velocity are drawn on a longitudinal section view of the tube, there would be formed long gently curved lines. The maximum velocity of flow is found in the center of the tube. Such flow occurs only when the mean free path of the gas is small compared to the diameter of the tube in which the gas is flowing. If the pressure in the tube is reduced, for example when the system is evacuated or a transfer is being completed, the mean free path of the gas increases until eventually almost all the collisions of a molecule will be with the tube and not with the other molecules. Under these conditions the molecules will migrate independently of each other, and the

TABLE XXXVIII

Mean Free Path, λ, of a Number of Gases at 25° C

Gas	Molecular Weight	λ, mm, at 1 micron	λ, mm, at 100 microns
H_2	2.0	95	0.95
CH_4	16.0	41	0.41
NH_3	17.0	36	0.36
H_2O	18.0	34	0.34
N_2	28.0	50	0.50
Air	(28.7)	51	0.51
O_2	32.0	54	0.54
HCl	36.5	36	0.36
CO_2	44.0	34	0.34

phenomenon, which is essentially a diffusion process, is called molecular flow. The rate of flow of gases for a given pressure differential under such conditions is much slower than for viscous flow. The flow of gases in a tube for a given pressure differential decreases with decreasing pressure until the region of molecular flow is reached. There the flow depends only on the pressure differential and the characteristics of the system and gas.

Viscous flow of gases occurs when the mean free path of the molecules in the tube is small (less than $1/100$) compared to the diameter of the tube.[1] The flow is almost completely molecular when the mean free path of the gas is of the same order of magnitude ($1/3$ or greater) as the diameter of the tube. For air at 20° C the mean free path of the molecules is about $5/P$ cm, where P is the pressure in the system in microns. This is a very convenient approximation, for combination of this factor with the limiting mean free paths given above enables one to determine easily the type of flow in a system for air. Between these two arbitrary limiting figures for flow types, there is a region in which both molecular

[1] R. Loevinger, private communication.

and viscous flow occur, but the total flow is not the sum of the two flow types.

The following equations are presented to help estimate the rate of flow in vacuum systems of gases at reduced pressures; by use of these equations, comparative estimates can be made for the size of lines and stopcocks needed to obtain a given minimum pressure in a reasonable length of time. These equations are accurate only for round tubes whose entrance resistance is small compared to the resistance of flow in the tube; this is true when the length of the tube is equal to or greater than about 25 diameters. However, useful estimations may be made even when the length compared to the diameter is not so great or the tube is not circular (the principal error is that the flow rates so calculated will be high).

In this section equations for conductance are presented in units of liters per second per micron pressure differential.

For the conductance of a long circular pipe Knudsen has derived the following formula:

$$C = \left[\frac{\pi D^4}{128n}\frac{\bar{P}}{L}\right] + \left[\frac{1}{6}\sqrt{\frac{2kT}{m}}\frac{D^3}{L}\right]\left[\frac{1 + \sqrt{\frac{m}{kT}}\frac{D\bar{P}}{n}}{1 + 1.24\sqrt{\frac{m}{kT}}\frac{D\bar{P}}{n}}\right] \quad \text{cgs unit} \quad (2)$$

where D = diameter of pipe, L = length of pipe, n = viscosity of gas, k = Boltzmann's constant, T = absolute temperature, m = mass of molecule, and $\bar{P}$ = average pressure. When the data for air at 20° C are introduced, this equation becomes [1]

$$C = \left[0.182\frac{D^4\bar{P}}{L}\right] + \left[12.1\frac{D^3}{L}\right]\left[\frac{1 + 0.256D\bar{P}}{1 + 0.316D\bar{P}}\right] \text{ l/sec} \quad \begin{array}{l} L \text{ and } D \text{ in cm} \\ P \text{ in microns} \end{array}$$

$$(3)$$

or

$$C = 12.1\frac{D^3}{L}(J) \text{ l/sec} \quad (4)$$

where

$$(J) = \frac{1 + 0.271D\bar{P} + 0.00479 (D\bar{P})^2}{1 + 0.316D\bar{P}} \quad (5)$$

Calculated values of J for given values of $D\bar{P}$ are listed in Table XXXIX; by means of these data the conductance of a simple system may be easily calculated. If the system is made of several parts in series the total conductance is the reciprocal of the sum of the reciprocals

TABLE XXXIX [1]

VALUES OF $D\bar{P}$ AND J FOR AIR AT 20° C (EQUATIONS 4 AND 5)

$D\bar{P}$ (cm-microns) $\lessgtr$ 10	20	40	60	80	100	200	400	600	800	1,000	2,000	4,000	10,000
J (equation 5) 1.0	1.1	1.4	1.7	2.0	2.3	3.8	6.9	9.9	13	16	31	62	153
Molecular-flow region		Transition region							Viscous-flow region				
←								→					

of the individual parts; if the parts are in parallel the conductance is the sum of the conductances of the parts:

$$C = \frac{1}{\dfrac{1}{C_1} + \dfrac{1}{C_2} + \dfrac{1}{C_3} + \cdots} \qquad \text{Series system} \qquad (6)$$

$$C = C_1 + C_2 + C_3 + \cdots \qquad \text{Parallel system} \qquad (7)$$

At low pressures where only molecular conductance is effective the first bracket of equation 2 is negligible and the last bracket becomes unity, or, for air at 20° C:

$$C = 12.1 \frac{D^3}{L} \, \text{l/sec} \qquad \text{Molecular conductance} \qquad (8)$$

If the pressure in a system is high and only viscous conductance is important, the first term only of equation 2 is significant and conductance for air at 20° C is:

$$C = 0.182 \frac{D^4 \bar{P}}{L} \, \text{l/sec} \qquad \text{Viscous conductance} \qquad (9)$$

Appendix VIII

VACUUM GAUGES AND MANOMETERS

The pressure in a closed system can be determined by any of several instruments, but no one gauge is available that can cover the entire range of pressures and still withstand all corrosive vapors encountered in the vacuum work described in this book. In Fig. 50 the useful pressure ranges for most common gauges are shown, and in the following sections some of those most often used in synthetic work are described briefly. (The reader is referred to the numerous books on the subject of vacuum techniques for more detailed descriptions.)

Absolute Differential Manometer. Range: 1 atm to 0.1 mm Hg.

This gauge may be filled with mercury, oil, sulfuric acid, silicon hydrocarbons, fluorinated hydrocarbons, dibutylphthalate, etc.; the choice depends on the desired pressure range, corrosion problems, and accuracy of the manometer. A convenient manometer design for vacuum lines is shown in Fig. 100. Tubing of adequate diameter should be used to reduce surface tension effects, and a small constriction at the bottom of the U is desirable to prevent too rapid motion of the liquid column.

To manifold

FIG. 100. Absolute differential manometer.

Barometer Type Manometer (Mercury Filled). Range: Atmospheric pressure to 1 mm Hg.

This manometer is particularly useful when it is necessary to fill a system with an inert gas and maintain a slight positive pressure of this gas while reagents are introduced (see page 179 and Fig. 72). To make accurate pressure readings with this manometer, it is necessary to know the atmospheric pressure.

Brass Vacuum Gauge (Bourdon Type). Range: 0 to 30 inches vacuum.

This gauge is a mechanical unit in which an indicator is actuated by movement of a curved flattened spring tube which is connected to the vacuum system. The gauge can be sealed with hard wax to a glass joint; it makes a very convenient unit which can often be used in place of a mercury manometer. The gauge is small in volume, is easily detached from the vacuum line, is not rapidly corroded, and responds quickly to pressure change. It is particularly useful in closed systems where liquids are refluxed (see page 193) and where it is desired to avoid pressures of more than 1 atmosphere.

McLeod Gauge (Mercury Filled). Range: 10 mm to 5×10^{-6} mm Hg.

The McLeod gauge is valuable as a low-pressure absolute instrument (the pressure calibration can be determined from the geometry and other measurable characteristics of the gauge). With the McLeod gauge, low gas pressures are measured by compressing a large known volume of gas into a capillary tube of known volume per unit of length. At the smaller volume, the pressure is measured by a differential manometer arrangement; by application of ideal gas laws, the original pressure of the gas may be calculated. The gauge is not accurate when used with easily condensible gases which do not obey the ideal gas laws. To prevent diffusion of mercury vapor, the gauge should be protected from the system with a cold trap. The McLeod gauge is not of the continuous reading type and in addition occupies a considerable amount of space on the vacuum-line bench; many models of this gauge are fragile. For synthetic organic work, the more recently developed electric gauges are generally more useful.

Pirani Gauge. Range: 100 microns to 10^{-6} mm Hg.

The operation of the Pirani gauge is based on the principle that at low pressure the heat conductivity of a gas is a function of the pressure. The heat conductivity of the gas is indirectly measured by determining, with a Wheatstone bridge, the resistance of a hot wire. This gauge is useful in organic systems, but the vacuum thermocouple unit (see below) is somewhat simpler and generally can be used instead of a Pirani gauge.

Vacuum Thermocouple Gauge. Range: 500 microns to 1 micron.

The principle of operation of this gauge is the same as that of the Pirani gauge, but the temperature of the hot wire is measured by means of a thermocouple attached to the wire. In Fig. 101 is shown an easily constructed electrical circuit for use with this gauge. The gauge is available commercially with either a glass or a metal envelope. For routine organic work it is very satisfactory. It is rugged, inexpensive, and, except for a small time lag, continuous-reading. The gauge should be calibrated for different gases, although calibration against air is

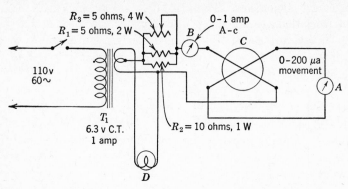

FIG. 101. Schematic electrical circuit for use with a vacuum thermocouple gauge: *A*, milliammeter; *B*, a-c ammeter; *C*, vacuum thermocouple gauge; *D*, pilot light.

usually accurate enough for organic work where relative pressures are important, especially in leak hunting, etc.

Phillips Ionization Gauge. Range: 20 microns to 2×10^{-5} mm Hg.

This gauge measures the pressure in a system by measuring the ionization current of a high-voltage discharge. A magnetic field set across the electrodes forces the electrons to move in spirals so the effective path of the electrons is several hundred times the direct path; thus the probability of ionization and therefore the sensitivity is improved. The instrument is continuous-reading and has no time lag. In its pressure range, the gauge is reliable and sensitive and is an excellent instrument for the high-vacuum side of a diffusion pump which is to be used in a system with organic compounds.

Ionization Gauge. Range: 100 microns to 10^{-7} mm Hg.

This continuous-reading gauge is by far the most sensitive of the vacuum measuring units available today. Two electrical circuits commonly used for this gauge are shown in Fig. 102. A heated cathode emits electrons which pass to either the negative grid or anode, depending on the circuit. In passing to the anode or beyond the grid these electrons ionize a given number of gas molecules; the positive ions thus formed are collected on the circuit connected to the microammeter, which is maintained at a positive potential with respect to the cathode. The positive-ion current flow is proportional to the number of gas molecules present and to the ionizing current. The circuit using the external collector is more common as there is direct proportionality between pressure and ionization current, but the internal collector arrangement is more sensitive.

The ionization gauge must be calibrated against the gas used. It has a low maximum pressure reading; the filament is easily burned out if

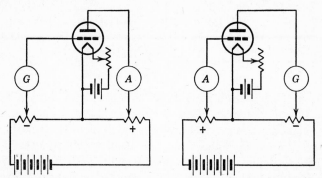

FIG. 102. Schematic electrical circuits for use with ionization gauge.

air is let into the system. The tube is useful in high-vacuum systems for leak hunting. A thoriated-tungsten filament is more sensitive to gas contamination than a pure-tungsten filament.

Alphatron Gauge.[1]   Range: 10 mm to 1 micron.

This gauge operates on a principle similar to that of the ionization gauge; the pressure is measured as a function of the ionization current produced by α particles from a sealed radium source. The gauge has many advantages, which include a wide range of sensitive operation, continuous readings, and stability to air, but it necessitates an expensive direct-current amplifier.

[1] J. R. Downing and G. Mellen, *Rev. Sci. Instruments*, **17**, 218 (1946).

Appendix IX

AN INDUCTION STIRRER

FOR USE WITH VACUUM OR CLOSED SYSTEMS

Numerous devices for agitation of solutions have been developed for use with closed systems. These include liquid seal (oil or mercury) stirrers, magnetic stirrers which utilize a small piece of a rotating metal driven by external permanent magnet, shakers which make use of a flexible connecting line, etc. For small vacuum systems these are often unsatisfactory since they are unable to withstand a large pressure differential, are too large and bulky, or lack sufficient stirring power. As a solution for these difficulties a simple induction stirrer of considerable power has been developed which may be used with vacuum systems. An improved design [1] based upon an earlier model [2] is described here.

This induction stirrer consists of a three-phase selsyn generator stator and a glass-inclosed armature and bearing system. The unit is particularly suited for use with small-scale reaction vessels; sufficient power to stir viscous solutions is developed. The maximum speed of the stirrer is about 3,000 rpm and can be controlled with a variable transformer.

In Figs. 103 and 104 two models of the stator and bearing system are shown. Figure 103 is a corrosion-resistant model in which Teflon [3] is used for the bearing material; the unit shown in Fig. 104 employs a ball bearing. The stirrer is so designed that it has good vacuum characteristics; the rotor is solid, and outgassing from windings is thus avoided; holes are provided in all solid bearings to permit rapid evacuation of otherwise inclosed spaces; gas volumes are kept small.

Armature. The core of the armature (see Fig. 105) is turned from soft iron. A light push fit is provided for the ball bearing; the copper shell, which is made from 0.035-inch wall, $1\frac{1}{4}$-inch O.D. copper tubing, and the iron core are soft-soldered together and made vacuum-tight at the edges. After completion, the entire armature except for the lower

---

[1] B. M. Tolbert, J. C. Reid, and W. G. Dauben, unpublished experiments.

[2] W. G. Dauben, J. C. Reid, and P. E. Yankwich, *Anal. Chem.*, **19**, 828 (1947).

[3] Polymerized tetrafluorethylene. Made by E. I. du Pont de Nemours and Co., Wilmington, Del.

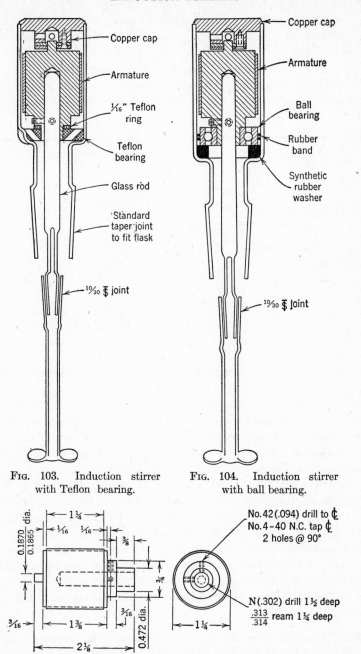

FIG. 103.   Induction stirrer with Teflon bearing.

FIG. 104.   Induction stirrer with ball bearing.

FIG. 105.   Armature for induction stirrer.   The body is soft iron, and the shell is copper; all dimensions are given in inches.

bearing surface is painted with a corrosion-resistant paint [4] and baked at 250° F for 12 hours. The same armature is used with either ball or Teflon bearings.

Cap. The cap is machined from hard copper and should fit the glass shell loosely (see Fig. 106). The cap, with screws in place, is also painted and baked, as is the armature. The Teflon bearings (made from $\frac{1}{16}$-

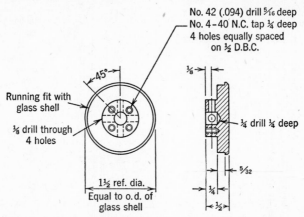

No. 42 (.094) drill $\frac{5}{16}$ deep
No. 4-40 N.C. tap $\frac{1}{4}$ deep
4 holes equally spaced on $\frac{1}{2}$ D.B.C.

45°

Running fit with glass shell

$\frac{1}{8}$ drill through 4 holes

$\frac{1}{8}$

$\frac{1}{4}$ drill $\frac{1}{4}$ deep

$\frac{5}{32}$

$1\frac{1}{2}$ ref. dia.
Equal to o.d. of glass shell

$\frac{1}{4}$

$\frac{1}{2}$

FIG. 106. Cap for induction stirrer; material, copper. All dimensions are in inches.

inch sheet) in the cap should fit loosely on the upper armature shaft, for Teflon expands when it is warmed.

Bearings (Lower). The ball bearing (open type, $1\frac{1}{4}$-inch O.D., $1\frac{5}{16}$-inch I.D. [5] is centered in the glass shell by two or three small rubber bands and supported on an oil-resistant synthetic rubber washer; it is lubricated with a non-volatile, non-reactive oil (some types of diffusion pump oil are very good for this purpose.[6]

The plastic bearing is machined from $\frac{1}{4}$-inch Teflon sheet to give a slide fit inside the glass shell and a loose bearing fit on the armature. A ring of $\frac{1}{16}$-inch Teflon provides a horizontal Teflon-to-Teflon bearing that has less friction resistance than a plastic to iron bearing; even so, wear is appreciable, and such bearings have a limited life. Rotation of the bearing is prevented by a V cut in the Teflon and an indentation on the lower end of the glass shell. Four 3-mm holes ($\frac{1}{8}$-inch) bored slantwise through the body of the plastic permit evacuation of the upper chamber of the stirrer.

[4] Plastic Paint 4A, Interchemical Corp., 1073 Howard St., San Francisco, Calif.

[5] Ball bearing No. 6201, S.K.F. Industries, Inc., 440 East 34 Street, New York, N. Y.

[6] For example, D.C. 703 Silicone Fluid, Dow Corning Corp., Midland, Mich.

Stator. The stator is the field coil of a selsyn generator [7] (1½-inch I.D.). When the unit is operated above 30 volts a water jacket or air blast should be provided to prevent overheating of the windings. If this stator is supported on a cork ring which rests on the rest of the equipment, no alignment problem is encountered when the stirrer is assembled.

The power supply for the stator is conveniently made from a variable transformer and a 50- to 100-μf condenser [8] (note: electrolytic condensers will not work on alternating current). In Fig. 107 a schematic

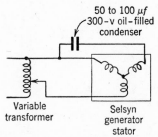

50 to 100 μf
300-v oil-filled
condenser

Variable transformer

Selsyn generator stator

FIG. 107. Electrical circuit for use with induction stirrer.

diagram of the electrical circuit is shown; this arrangement is a typical capacitor-induction-type motor circuit and permits operation of the motor on a 110-volt, 60-cycle single-phase line.

Stirrers. Any type of stirrer desired may be used with this motor; the arrangement shown is convenient because various models and lengths of stirrers may be used without need to open the armature housing. The ground joint is waxed in with a low-melting solid (such as deKhotinsky cement or sealing wax).

Cap to Glass Body Seal. The cap is sealed to the glass shell with a low-melting sealing compound (see above). In this process both the cap and glass are warmed; the edges are covered with a thick layer of melted wax and the parts are brought together. Enough wax should be used so that a definite fillet is formed on the inside surface of the stirrer; excess wax on the outside may be cut off.

[7] Selsyn Generator, Model 2J55V1, 110-volt, 60-cycle, General Electric Co., Schenectady, N. Y.

[8] Pyranol capacitor, Catalogue No. 67X18X, Model 9CE1A318, 330-volt, 60-cycle, 50-μf.

BIBLIOGRAPHY

Reviews

H. A. Barker and M. Doudoroff, "Bacterial Metabolism," *Ann. Rev. Biochem.*, **15**, 475 (1946).

R. O. Belkengren, "The Use of the Heavy Carbon Isotope as a 'Tracer' in Plant Metabolism," Thesis, University of Minnesota, 1941.

Konrad Bloch, "The Metabolism of Acetic Acid in Animal Tissues," *Physiol. Revs.*, **27**, 574 (1947).

J. M. Buchanan, "Glycogen Formation," Thesis, Harvard University, 1943; with A. B. Hastings, "The Use of Isotopically Marked Carbon in the Study of Intermediary Metabolism," *Physiol. Revs.*, **26**, 120 (1946).

Melvin Calvin, "Radiocarbon and Its Application in Chemistry and Biology," paper presented at Seventh Solvay International Institute of Chemistry, Brussels, Belgium, September, 1947; "Investigation of Reaction Mechanisms and Photosynthesis with Radiocarbon," *Nucleonics*, **2**, No. 3, 40 (1948).

S. F. Carson, "The Role of Carbon Dioxide in Cellular Metabolism," Thesis, Stanford University, 1941.

E. A. Evans, "Metabolic Cycles and Decarboxylation," *Symp. on Resp. Enzymes*, 197, Madison, Wisconsin (1941); "Pyruvate Oxidation and the Citric Acid Cycle," *Bull. Johns Hopkins Hosp.*, **69**, 225 (1941); "Carbohydrate Metabolism," *Ann. Rev. Biochem.*, **13**, 187 (1944); "The Fixation of CO_2 by Animal Tissues," *Harvey Lectures Ser.*, **39**, 273–287 (1943–1944).

J. Franck and H. Gaffron, "Photosynthesis, Facts and Interpretations," *Advances in Enzymol.*, **1**, 199 (1941).

J. G. Hamilton, "The Use of Radioactive Tracers in Biology and Medicine," *Radiology*, **39**, 541 (1942).

Martin D. Kamen, "Survey of Contemporary Knowledge of Biogeochemistry," *Bull. Am. Museum Nat. Hist.*, **87**, 105 (1946); "Use of Isotopes in Biochemical Research: Fundamental Aspects," *Ann. Rev. Biochem.*, **16**, 631 (1947).

H. A. Krebs, "Carbon Dioxide Assimilation in Heterotrophic Organisms," *Ann. Rev. Biochem.*, **12**, 529 (1943).

Warren W. Miller and T. D. Price, "Research with Carbon 14," *Nucleonics*, **1**, No. 3, 4 (1947); **1**, No. 4, 11 (1947).

D. Rittenberg and D. Shemin, "Isotope Technique in the Study of Intermediary Metabolism," *Currents in Biochem. Research*, p. 261, 1946.

Jacob Sacks, "Radioactive Isotopes as Indicators in Biology," *Chem. Revs.*, **42**, 411 (1948).

Elmer Stotz, "Pyruvate Metabolism," *Advances in Enzymol.*, **5**, 153 (1945).

C. B. Van Niel, "The Bacterial Photosyntheses and Their Importance for the General Problem of Photosynthesis," *Advances in Enzymol.*, **1**, 263 (1941); with S. Ruben, S. F. Carson, M. D. Kamen, and J. W. Foster, "Radioactive Carbon as an Indicator of Carbon Dioxide Utilization: VIII. The Role of Carbon Dioxide in Cellular Metabolism," *Proc. Natl. Acad. Sci. U. S.*, **28**, 8 (1942).

D. Wright Wilson, "The Use of C^{13} and C^{14} in Medical Research," *J. Franklin Inst.* **244**, 209 (1947).

H. G. Wood, "The Fixation of Carbon Dioxide and the Interrelationships of the Tri carboxylic Acid Cycle," *Physiol. Revs.*, **26**, 198 (1946).

Amino Acids and Proteins

K. I. Altman, G. W. Casarett, R. E. Masters, T. R. Noonan, and K. Salomon, "Hemin Synthesis with Glycine Containing C^{14} in the Alpha Carbon Atom," *Federation Proc.*, **7**, 2 (1948).

Konrad Bloch and Ernest Borek, "Biological Acetylation of Natural Amino Acids," *J. Biol. Chem.*, **164**, 483 (1946).

Henry Borsook, Clara L. Deasy, Jacob W. Dubnoff, C. T. O. Fong, William D. Fraser, A. J. Haagen-Smith, Geoffrey Keighley, and Peter H. Lowy, "Protein and Peptide Turnover with Respect to Lysine in Guinea Pig Liver Homogenate," *Federation Proc.*, **7**, 147 (1948).

Henry Borsook, Clara L. Deasy, A. J. Haagen-Smith, Geoffrey Keighley, and Peter H. Lowy, "α-Aminoadipic Acid: A Product of Lysine Metabolism," *J. Biol. Chem.*, **173**, 423 (1948); "Isolation of a Peptide in Guinea Pig Liver Homogenate and Its Turnover of Leucine," *J. Biol. Chem.*, **174**, 1041 (1948).

G. Ehrensvard, E. Sperber, E. Saluste, L. Reio, and R. Stjernholm, "Metabolic Connection between Proline and Glycine in the Amino Acid Utilization of *Torpulis utilis*," *J. Biol. Chem.*, **169**, 759 (1947).

I. D. Frantz, R. B. Loftfield, and W. W. Miller, "Incorporation of C^{14} from Carboxyl-Labeled DL-Alanine into the Proteins of Liver Slices," *Science*, **106**, 544 (1947).

I. D. Frantz, P. C. Zamecnik, J. W. Reese, and Mary L. Stephenson, "The Effect of Dinitrophenol on the Incorporation of Alanine Labeled with Radioactive Carbon into the Proteins of Slices of Normal and Malignant Rat Liver," *J. Biol. Chem.*, **174**, 773 (1948).

Felix Friedberg, Martin P. Schulman, and David M. Greenberg, "The Effect of Growth on the Incorporation of Glycine Labeled with Radioactive Carbon in the Protein of Liver Homogenates," *J. Biol. Chem.*, **173**, 437 (1948).

Felix Friedberg, Theodore Winnick, and David M. Greenberg, "Peptide Synthesis *in Vivo*," *J. Biol. Chem.*, **169**, 763 (1947); "Incorporation of Labeled Glycine into the Protein of Tissue Homogenates," *J. Biol. Chem.*, **171**, 441 (1947).

David M. Greenberg and Theodore Winnick, "Studies in Protein Metabolism with Compounds Labeled with Radioactive Carbon: II. The Metabolism of Glycine in the Rat," *J. Biol. Chem.*, **173**, 199 (1948).

Moisés Grinstein, Martin D. Kamen, and Carl V. Moore, "Observation on the Utilization of Glycine in the Biosynthesis of Hemoglobin," *J. Biol. Chem.*, **174**, 767 (1948).

S. Gurin and Adelaide M. Delluva, "The Biological Synthesis of Radioactive Adrenalin from Phenylalanine," *J. Biol. Chem.*, **170**, 545 (1947).

S. Gurin and D. Wright Wilson, "The Intermediary Metabolism of Alanine Containing C^{13}," *Federation Proc.*, **1**, 114 (1942).

C. Heidelberger, M. E. Gullberg, A. F. Morgan, and S. Lepkovsky, "Concerning the Mechanism of the Mammalian Conversion of Tryptophan to Kynurenine, Kynurenic Acid, and Nicotinic Acid," *J. Biol. Chem.*, **175**, 471 (1948).

J. M. Hundley and H. W. Bond, "A Study of the Conversion of Isotopic Nicotinic Acid to N-Methylnicotinamide," *J. Biol. Chem.*, **173**, 513 (1948).

E. C. Kooyman and D. H. Campbell, "On the Dynamic State of Antibodies," *J. Am. Chem. Soc.*, **70**, 1293 (1948).

Victor Lorber and N. S. Olsen, "Metabolism of Glycine by the Completely Isolated Mammalian Heart Investigated with Carboxyl-Labeled Glycine," *Proc. Soc. Exptl. Biol. Med.*, **61**, 227 (1946).

C. G. Mackenzie, J. R. Rachele, N. Cross, J. P. Chandler, and V. du Vigneaud, "Study of the Oxidation of the Labile Methyl Group of Dietary Methionine Labeled with C^{14}," *Federation Proc.*, **7**, 170 (1948).

N. Olsen, A. Hemingway, and A. O. Nier, "The Metabolism of Glycine: I. Studies with the Stable Isotope of Carbon," *J. Biol. Chem.*, **148**, 611 (1943).

J. C. Reid and H. B. Jones, "Radioactivity Distribution in the Tissues of Mice Bearing Melanosarcoma after Administration of DL-Tyrosine Labeled with Radioactive Carbon," *J. Biol. Chem.*, **174**, 427 (1948).

Vincent du Vigneaud, G. W. Kilmer, J. R. Rachele, and Mildred Cohn, "On the Mechanism of the Conversion *in Vivo* of Methionine to Cystine," *J. Biol. Chem.*, **155**, 645 (1944).

S. Weinhouse and R. H. Millington, "Ketone Body Formation from Tyrosine," *J. Biol. Chem.*, **175**, 995 (1948).

Theodore Winnick, Felix Friedberg, and David M. Greenberg, "Incorporation of C^{14}-Labeled Glycine into Intestinal Tissue and Its Inhibition by Azide," *Arch. Biochem.*, **15**, 160 (1947); "Studies in Protein Metabolism with Compounds Labeled with Radioactive Carbon: I. Metabolism of DL-Tyrosine in the Normal and Tumor-Bearing Rat," *J. Biol. Chem.*, **173**, 189 (1948); "Incorporation of C^{14}-Labeled Glycine into the Protein of Tissue Homogenates," *Federation Proc.*, **7**, 200 (1948); "The Utilization of Labeled Glycine in the Process of Amino Acid Incorporation by the Protein of Liver Homogenate," *J. Biol. Chem.*, **175**, 117 (1948).

Theodore Winnick, I. Moring-Claesson, and D. M. Greenberg, "Distribution of Radioactive Carbon among Certain Amino Acids of Liver Homogenate Protein Following Uptake Experiments with Labeled Glycine," *J. Biol. Chem.*, **175**, 127 (1948).

P. C. Zamecnik, I. D. Frantz, R. B. Loftfield, and M. L. Stephenson, "Incorporation *in Vitro* of Radioactive Carbon from Carboxyl-Labeled DL-Alanine and Glycine into Proteins of Normal and Malignant Rat Livers," *J. Biol. Chem.*, **175**, 291 (1948).

Carbohydrates and Fats

C. B. Anfinsen, Anne Beloff, A. B. Hastings, and A. K. Solomon, "The *in Vitro* Turnover of Dicarboxylic Amino Acids in Liver Slice Proteins," *J. Biol. Chem.*, **168**, 771 (1947).

H. S. Anker, "On the Fate of Labeled Pyruvic Acid in the Intact Animal," *Federation Proc.*, **7**, 142 (1948).

E. G. Ball, H. F. Tucker, A. K. Solomon, and B. Vennesland, "The Source of Pancreatic Juice Bicarbonate," *J. Biol. Chem.*, **140**, 119 (1941).

Konrad Bloch and W. Kramer, "Synthesis of Fatty Acids in Rat Liver Slices," *Federation Proc.*, **7**, 143 (1948); "The Effect of Pyruvate and Insulin on Fatty Acid Synthesis *in Vivo*," *J. Biol. Chem.*, **173**, 813 (1948).

J. M. Buchanan, A. Baird Hastings, and F. B. Nesbett, "Glycogen Formation from Pyruvate *in Vitro* in the Presence of Radioactive Carbon Dioxide," *J. Biol. Chem.*, **145**, 715 (1942); "The Role of Carboxyl-Labeled Acetic, Propionic and Butyric Acids in Liver Glycogen Formation," *J. Biol. Chem.*, **150**, 413 (1943).

J. M. Buchanan, W. Sakami, and S. Gurin, "A Study of the Mechanism of Fatty Acid Oxidation with Isotopic Acetoacetate," *J. Biol. Chem.*, **169**, 411 (1947).

J. M. Buchanan, W. Sakami, S. Gurin, and D. W. Wilson, "A Study of the Intermediates of Acetoacetate Oxidation with Isotopic Carbon," *J. Biol. Chem.*, **157**, 747 (1945); "A Study of the Intermediates of Acetate and Acetoacetate Oxidation with Isotopic Carbon," *J. Biol. Chem.*, **159**, 695 (1945); "Intermediates in the Biological Oxidation of Isotopic Acetoacetate," *J. Biol. Chem.*, **169**, 403 (1947).

S. F. Carson, S. Ruben, M. D. Kamen, and J. W. Foster, "Radioactive Carbon as an Indicator of Carbon Dioxide Utilization: VI. On the Possibility of Carbon Dioxide Reduction via the Carboxylase System," *Proc. Natl. Acad. Sci. U. S.*, **27**, 475 (1941).

I. L. Chaikoff, S. R. Lerner, C. Entenman, and W. G. Dauben, "On the Conversion of Palmitic Acid Labeled with Radioactive Carbon to Glucose by the Alloxan-Diabetic Rat," *J. Biol. Chem.*, **174**, 1045 (1948).

J. B. Conant, R. D. Cramer, A. B. Hastings, F. W. Klemperer, A. K. Solomon, and B. Vennesland, "Metabolism of Lactic Acid Containing Radioactive Carboxyl Carbon," *J. Biol. Chem.*, **137**, 557 (1941).

D. I. Crandall, S. Gurin, and D. W. Wilson, "Studies on the Formation of Isotopic Acetoacetate in Homogenized Liver," *Federation Proc.*, **6**, 246 (1947).

A. M. Delluva and D. W. Wilson, "A Study with Isotopic Carbon of the Assimilation of Carbon Dioxide in the Rat," *J. Biol. Chem.*, **166**, 739 (1946).

E. A. Evans, "The Utilization of Carbon Dioxide in the Synthesis of α-Ketoglutaric Acid," *J. Biol. Chem.*, **136**, 301 (1940); "The Role of Carbon Dioxide in the Synthesis of Urea in Rat Liver Slices," *J. Biol. Chem.*, **136**, 805 (1940).

E. A. Evans and L. Slotin, "Carbon Dioxide Utilization by Pigeon Liver," *J. Biol. Chem.*, **141**, 439 (1941); with B. Vennesland, "Carbon Dioxide Assimilation in Cell-Free Liver Extracts," *J. Biol. Chem.*, **143**, 565 (1942); "The Mechanism of Carbon Dioxide Fixation in Cell-Free Extracts of Pigeon Liver," *J. Biol. Chem.*, **147**, 771 (1943).

N. F. Floyd, G. Medes, and S. Weinhouse, "Fatty Acid Metabolism: VI. Conversion of Acetoacetate to Citrate in Animal Tissues Studied with Isotopic Carbon," *J. Biol. Chem.*, **171**, 633 (1947).

S. Grisolia and B. Vennesland, "Carbon Dioxide Fixation in Isocitric Acid," *J. Biol. Chem.*, **170**, 461 (1947).

S. Gurin, A. M. Delluva, and D. W. Wilson, "The Metabolism of Isotopic Lactic Acid and Alanine in the Phlorhizinized Animal," *J. Biol. Chem.*, **171**, 101 (1947).

A. B. Hastings and J. M. Buchanan, "The Role of Intracellular Cations on Liver Glycogen Formation *in Vitro*," *Proc. Natl. Acad. Sci. U. S.*, **28**, 478 (1942).

A. B. Hastings and G. B. Kistiakowsky, "Biological Studies with Radioactive Carbon," *J. Applied Phys.*, **12**, 322 (1941); with R. D. Cramer, F. W. Klemperer, A. K. Solomon, and B. Vennesland, "Liver Glycogen from Lactic Acid Containing Radioactive Carboxyl Carbon," *Science*, **91**, 421 (1940).

N. Lifson, V. Lorber, and H. G. Wood, "Position of Carboxyl Carbon of Fed Acetic Acid in Glucose from Rat Liver Glycogen," *Federation Proc.*, **4**, 47 (1945); with W. Sakami, "Pathways of Conversion of Butyrate Carbon to Rat Liver Glycogen," *Federation Proc.*, **4**, 47 (1945).

V. Lorber, A. Hemingway, and A. O. Nier," Assimilation of Carbon Dioxide by the Isolated Mammalian Heart," *J. Biol. Chem.*, **151**, 647 (1943).

V. Lorber, N. Lifson, and H. G. Wood, "Incorporation of Acetate Carbon into Rat Liver Glycogen by Pathways Other than Carbon Dioxide Fixation," *J. Biol. Chem.*, **161**, 411 (1945).

V. Lorber, N. Lifson, H. G. Wood, and J. Barcroft, "The Metabolism of Acetate by the Completely Isolated Mammalian Heart Investigated with Carboxyl-Labeled Acetate," *Am. J. Physiol.*, **147**, 557 (1946).

G. Medes, S. Weinhouse, and N. F. Floyd, "Acetate Utilization by Animal Tissues Using Isotopic Carbon as a Tracer," *Federation Proc.*, **4**, 98 (1945); "Fatty Acid Metabolism: II. The Breakdown of Carboxyl-Labeled Butyric Acid by Liver Tissue," *J. Biol. Chem.*, **157**, 35 (1945); "Ketone Body Formation from Acetate in Kidney with Isotopic Carbon as a Tracer," *J. Biol. Chem.*, **157**, 751 (1945); "Fatty Acid Metabolism: IV. Ketone Bodies as Intermediates of Acetate Oxidation in Animal Tissues," *J. Biol. Chem.*, **162**, 1 (1946).

R. E. Olson, O. N. Miller, Y. J. Topper, and F. J. Store, "The Effect of Vitamin Deficiencies upon the Metabolism of Cardiac Muscle *in Vitro:* II. The Effect of Biotin Deficiency in Ducks with Observations on the Metabolism of Radioactive Carbon-Labeled Succinate," *J. Biol. Chem.*, **175**, 503 (1948).

D. Rittenberg and Konrad Bloch, "Some Biological Reactions of Acetic Acid," *J. Biol. Chem.*, **157**, 749 (1945); "The Utilization of Acetic Acid for the Synthesis of Fatty Acids," *J. Biol. Chem.*, **160**, 417 (1945).

M. Schlamowitz and D. M. Greenberg, "On the Mechanism of Enzymatic Conversion of Glucose-1-Phosphate to Glucose-6-Phosphate," *J. Biol. Chem.*, **171**, 293 (1947).

A. K. Solomon, B. Vennesland, F. W. Klemperer, J. M. Buchanan, and A. B. Hastings, "The Participation of Carbon Dioxide in the Carbohydrate Cycle," *J. Biol. Chem.*, **140**, 171 (1941).

H. E. Swendseid, R. H. Barnes, A. Hemingway, and A. O. Nier, "The Formation of Acetone Bodies from Acetic Acid," *J. Biol. Chem.*, **142**, 47 (1942).

M. F. Utter and H. G. Wood, "Fixation of Carbon Dioxide in Oxalacetate by Pigeon Liver," *J. Biol. Chem.*, **160**, 375 (1945).

B. Vennesland, E. A. Evans, and K. I. Altman, "The Effects of Triphosphopyridine Nucleotide and of Adenosine Triphosphate on Pigeon Liver Oxalacetic Carboxylase," *J. Biol. Chem.*, **171**, 675 (1947).

B. Vennesland, A. K. Solomon, J. M. Buchanan, R. D. Cramer, and A. B. Hastings, "Metabolism of Lactic Acid Containing Radioactive Carbon in the α or β Position," *J. Biol. Chem.*, **140**, 371 (1942).

B. Vennesland, A. K. Solomon, J. M. Buchanan, and A. B. Hastings, "Glycogen Formation from Glucose in the Presence of Radioactive Carbon Dioxide," *J. Biol. Chem.*, **140**, 379 (1942).

S. Weinhouse, G. Medes, and N. F. Floyd, "Ketone Body Formation from Fatty Acids Using Heavy Carbon as a Tracer," *Am. J. Med. Sci.*, **207**, 812 (1944); "The Mechanism of Fatty Acid Oxidation," *J. Biol. Chem.*, **153**, 689 (1944); "Fatty Acid Metabolism. The Mechanism of Ketone Body Synthesis from Fatty Acids with Isotopic Carbon as Tracer," *J. Biol. Chem.*, **155**, 143 (1944); "Fatty Acid Metabolism: III. Reactions of Carboxyl-Labeled Acetic Acid in Liver and Kidney," *J. Biol. Chem.*, **158**, 411 (1945); "Fatty Acid Metabolism: V. The Conversion of Fatty Acid Intermediates to Citrate Studied with the Aid of Isotopic Carbon," *J. Biol. Chem.*, **166**, 691 (1946).

S. Weinhouse, G. Medes, N. F. Floyd, and L. Noda, "Intermediates of Acetate Oxidation in Kidney," *J. Biol. Chem.*, **161**, 745 (1945).

H. G. Wood, N. Lifson, and V. Lorber, "The Position of Fixed Carbon in Glucose from Rat Liver Glycogen," *J. Biol. Chem.*, **159**, 475 (1945).

H. G. Wood, B. Vennesland, and E. A. Evans, "The Mechanism of Carbon Dioxide

Fixation by Cell-Free Extracts of Pigeon Liver: Distribution of Labeled Carbon Dioxide in the Products," *J. Biol. Chem.*, **159**, 153 (1945).

H. G. Wood, C. H. Werkman, A. Hemingway, and A. O. Nier, "Mechanism of Carbon Dioxide in the Krebs Cycle," *J. Biol. Chem.*, **139**, 483 (1941); "Fixation of Carbon Dioxide by Pigeon Liver in the Dissimilation of Pyruvic Acid," *J. Biol. Chem.*, **142**, 31 (1942).

Microbiology

H. A. Barker and S. R. Elsden, "Carbon Dioxide Utilization in the Formation of Glycine and Acetic Acid," *J. Biol. Chem.*, **167**, 619 (1947).

H. A. Barker and M. D. Kamen, "Carbon Dioxide Utilization in the Synthesis of Acetic A id by *Clostridium Thermoaceticum*," *Proc. Natl. Acad. Sci. U. S.*, **31**, 219 (1945).

H. A. Barker, M. D. Kamen, and B. T. Bornstein, "The Synthesis of Butyric and Caproic Acids from Ethanol and Acetic Acid by *Clostridium Kluyveri*," *Proc. Natl. Acad. Sci. U. S.*, **31**, 373 (1946).

H. A. Barker, M. D. Kamen, and V. Haas, "Carbon Dioxide Utilization in the Synthesis of Acetic and Butyric Acids by *Butyribacterium Rettgeri*," *Proc. Natl. Acad. Sci. U. S.*, **31**, 355 (1945).

H. A. Barker, S. Ruben, and J. V. Beck, "Radioactive Carbon as an Indicator of Carbon Dioxide Reduction: IV. The Synthesis of Acetic Acid from Carbon Dioxide by *Clostridium Acidi-Urici*," *Proc. Natl. Acad. Sci. U. S.*, **26**, 477 (1940).

H. A. Barker, S. Ruben, and M. D. Kamen, "The Reduction of Radioactive Carbon Dioxide by Methane-Producing Bacteria," *Proc. Natl. Acad. Sci. U. S.*, **26**, 426 (1940).

H. A. Barker, B. E. Volcani, and B. D. Cardon, "Tracer Experiments on the Mechanism of Glycine Fermentation by *Diplococcus Glycinophilus*," *J. Biol. Chem.*, **173**, 803 (1948).

R. W. Brown, H. G. Wood, and C. H. Werkman, "Fixation of Carbon Dioxide in Lactic Acid by *Clostridium butylicum*," *Arch. Biochem.*, **5**, 423 (1944).

S. F. Carson, J. W. Foster, S. Ruben, and H. A. Barker, "Radioactive Carbon as an Indicator of Carbon Dioxide Utilization: V. Studies on Propionic Acid Bacteria," *Proc. Natl. Acad. Sci. U. S.*, **27**, 229 (1941).

S. F. Carson, J. W. Foster, S. Ruben, and M. D. Kamen, "Radioactive Carbon as a Tracer in the Synthesis of Propionic Acid from Carbon Dioxide by the Propionic Acid Bacteria," *Science*, **92**, 433 (1940); "Radioactive Carbon as an Indicator of Carbon Dioxide Utilization: VII. The Assimilation of Carbon Dioxide by Molds," *Proc. Natl. Acad. Sci. U. S.*, **27**, 590 (1941).

S. F. Carson and S. Reuben, "Carbon Dioxide Assimilation by Propionic Acid Bacteria Studied by the Use of Radioactive Carbon," *Proc. Natl. Acad. Sci. U. S.*, **26**, 422 (1940).

N. Gross and C. H. Werkman, "Isotopic Composition of Acetylmethylcarbinol Formed by Yeast Juice," *Arch. Biochem.*, **15**, 125 (1947); with H. G. Wood, "Fixation of Heavy Carbon Acetaldehyde by Active Juices," *J. Bact.*, **44**, 257 (1942).

G. Kalnitsky and C. H. Werkman, "Enzymatic Decarboxylation of Oxalacetate and Carboxylation of Pyruvate," *Arch. Biochem.*, **4**, 25 (1944); "Fixation of Carbon Dioxide by Cell-Free Extract of *E. coli*," *J. Bact.*, **44**, 256 (1942); with H. G. Wood, "Carbon Dioxide Fixation and Succinic Acid Formation by a Cell-Free Enzyme Preparation of *E. coli*," *Arch. Biochem.*, **2**, 269 (1943).

L. O. Krampitz, H. G. Wood, and C. H. Werkman, "Enzymatic Fixation of Carbon Dioxide in Oxalacetate," *J. Biol. Chem.*, **147**, 243 (1943).

G. Krotkov and H. A. Barker, "Utilization of Acetate by Tobacco Leaves as Determined with Carbon 14," *Am. J. Botany*, **35**, 12 (1948).

F. Lipmann and L. C. Tuttle, "Keto Acid Formation through the Reversal of the Phosphoroclastic Reaction," *J. Biol. Chem.*, **154**, 725 (1944); "On the Condensation of Acetyl Phosphate with Formate or Carbon Dioxide in Bacterial Extracts," *J. Biol. Chem.*, **158**, 505 (1945).

Y. Nishina, S. Endo, and H. Nakayama, "Experiments on the Bacterial Synthesis of Some Dicarboxylic Acid by Means of Radioactive Carbonic Acid," *Sci. Papers Inst. Phys. Chem. Research, Tokyo*, **38**, 341 (1941).

S. Ruben and M. D. Kamen, "Radioactive Carbon in the Study of Respiration in Heterotrophic Systems," *Proc. Natl. Acad. Sci. U. S.*, **26**, 418 (1940); "Nonphotochemical Reduction of Carbon Dioxide by Biological Systems," *J. Applied Phys.*, **12**, 321 (1941).

H. D. Slade and C. H. Werkman, "Assimilation of Acetic and Succinic Acids Containing Heavy Carbon by *Aerobacter Indologenes*," *Proc. Soc. Exptl. Biol. Med.*, **51**, 65 (1942); "Assimilation of Acetic and Succinic Acids Containing Heavy Carbon by *Aerobacter Indologenes*," *Arch. Biochem.*, **2**, 97 (1943).

H. D. Slade, H. G. Wood, A. O. Nier, A. Hemingway, and C. H. Werkman, "Assimilation of Heavy Carbon Dioxide by Heterotrophic Bacteria," *J. Biol. Chem.*, **143**, 133 (1942).

H. Strecker, L. O. Krampitz, and H. G. Wood, "The Role of Acetylphosphate in the Phosphoroclastic and Dismutation Reactions of Pyruvate," *Federation Proc.*, **7**, 194 (1948).

M. F. Utter and C. H. Werkman, "Formation and Reactions of Acetyl Phosphate in *E. coli*," *Arch. Biochem.*, **5**, 413 (1944).

M. F. Utter, C. H. Werkman, and F. Lipmann, "Reversibility of the Phosphoroclastic Split of Pyruvate," *J. Biol. Chem.*, **154**, 723 (1944); "Reversibility of the Phosphoroclastic Split of Pyruvate," *J. Biol. Chem.*, **158**, 521 (1945).

C. B. Van Niel, J. O. Thomas, S. Ruben, and M. D. Kamen, "Radioactive Carbon as an Indicator of Carbon Dioxide Utilization: IX. The Assimilation of Carbon Dioxide by Protozoa," *Proc. Natl. Acad. Sci. U. S.*, **28**, 157 (1942).

D. Watt and L. O. Krampitz, "α-Acetolactic Acid, an Intermediate in Acetylmethylcarbinol Formation," *Federation Proc.*, **6**, 301 (1947).

S. Weinhouse and R. H. Millington, "Acetate Metabolism in Yeast Studied with Isotopic Carbon," *J. Am. Chem. Soc.*, **69**, 3089 (1947).

C. H. Werkman and H. G. Wood, "Heterotrophic Assimilation of Carbon Dioxide," *Advances in Enzymol.*, **2**, 135 (1942).

A. G. C. White and C. H. Werkman, "Assimilation of Acetate by Yeast," *Arch. Biochem.*, **13**, 27 (1947).

J. Wilson, L. O. Krampitz, and C. H. Werkman, "Reversibility of a Phosphoroclastic Reaction," *Biochem. J.*, **42**, 598 (1948).

H. G. Wood, R. W. Brown, and C. H. Werkman, "Mechanism of the Butyl Alcohol Fermentation with Heavy Carbon Acetic and Butyric Acids and Acetone," *Arch. Biochem.*, **6**, 243 (1945).

H. G. Wood, C. H. Werkman, A. Hemingway, and A. O. Nier, "Heavy Carbon as a Tracer in Bacterial Fixation of Carbon Dioxide," *J. Bact.*, **41**, 20 (1941); "Heavy Carbon as a Tracer in Bacterial Fixation of Carbon Dioxide," *J. Biol. Chem.*, **135**,

789 (1940); "The Position of Carbon Dioxide Carbon in Succinic Acid Synthesized by Heterotrophic Bacteria," *J. Biol. Chem.*, **139**, 377 (1941); "Position of the Carbon Dioxide Carbon in Propionic Acid Synthesized by *Propionibacterium*," *Proc. Soc. Exptl. Biol. Med.*, **46**, 313 (1941).

Organic Reaction Mechanisms

M. B. Allen and S. Ruben, "Tracer Studies with Radioactive Carbon and Hydrogen. The Synthesis and Oxidation of Fumaric Acid," *J. Am. Chem. Soc.*, **64**, 948 (1942).

M. Calvin and R. M. Lemmon, "The Decarbonylation of Ethyl Pyruvate," *J. Am. Chem. Soc.*, **69**, 1232 (1947).

W. G. Dauben, J. C. Reid, P. E. Yankwich, and M. Calvin, "The Willgerodt Reaction," *J. Am. Chem. Soc.*, **68**, 2117 (1946).

W. E. Doering, T. I. Taylor, and E. F. Schoenewaldt, "Mechanism of the Conversion of Phenylglyoxal to Mandelic Acid," *J. Am. Chem. Soc.*, **70**, 455 (1948).

B. A. Fries and M. Calvin, "Preparation of 1-C^{14}-Propene-1 and the Mechanism of the Permanganate Oxidation of Propene," *J. Am. Chem. Soc.*, **70**, 2235 (1948).

P. Nahinsky, C. N. Rice, S. Ruben, and M. D. Kamen, "Tracer Studies with Radioactive Carbon. The Synthesis and Oxidation of Several Three-Carbon Acids," *J. Am. Chem. Soc.*, **64**, 2299 (1942).

P. Nahinsky and S. Ruben, "Tracer Studies with Radioactive Carbon: The Oxidation of Propionic Acid," *J. Am. Chem. Soc.*, **63**, 2275 (1941).

O. K. Neville, "C^{14} Tracer Studies in Rearrangements of Unsymmetrical α-Diketones: Phenylglyoxal to Mandelic Acid," Abstracts New York Meeting, Am. Chem. Soc., September 1947, p. 63L; see, also, *J. Am. Chem. Soc.*, **70**, 3499 (1948).

J. W. Otvos, D. P. Stevenson, C. D. Wagner, and O. Beeck, "Isomerization of n-Butane-1-C^{13}," *J. Chem. Phys.*, **16**, 745 (1948).

S. Ruben, M. B. Allen, and P. Nahinsky, "Tracer Studies with Radioactive Carbon. The Exchange between Acetic Anhydride and Sodium Acetate," *J. Am. Chem. Soc.*, **64**, 3050 (1942).

E. M. Shantz and D. Rittenberg, "Retention of the Carbon Skeleton in the Kindler-Willgerodt Reaction," *J. Am. Chem. Soc.*, **68**, 2109 (1946).

D. P. Stevenson, C. D. Wagner, O. Beeck, and J. W. Otvos, "Isotope Effect in the Thermal Cracking of Propane-1-C^{13}," *J. Chem. Phys.*, **16**, 993 (1948).

H. G. Wood, R. W. Brown, C. H. Werkman, and C. G. Stuckwisch, "The Degradation of Heavy-Carbon Butyric Acid from the Butyl Alcohol Fermentation," *J. Am. Chem. Soc.*, **66**, 1812 (1944).

H. G. Wood, C. H. Werkman, A. Hemingway, and A. O. Nier, "Note on the Degradation of Propionic Acid Synthesized by *Propionibacterium*," *Iowa State Coll. J. Sci.*, **15**, 213 (1941).

H. G. Wood, C. H. Werkman, A. Hemingway, A. O. Nier, and C. G. Stuckwisch, "Reliability of Reactions Used to Locate Assimilated Carbon in Propionic Acid," *J. Am. Chem. Soc.*, **63**, 2140 (1941).

Pharmacology

W. Bloom, H. J. Curtis, and F. C. McLean, "The Deposition of Carbon 14 in Bone," *Science*, **105**, 45 (1947).

C. Heidelberger and H. B. Jones, "The Metabolism in the Mouse of 1,2,5,6-Dibenzanthracene Labeled in the 9-Position with C^{14}," *Cancer Research*, **7**, 720 (1947);

"The Distribution of Radioactivity in the Mouse Following Administration of Dibenzanthracene Labeled in the 9 and 10-Positions with Carbon 14," *Cancer*, **1**, No. 2, 252 (1948).

Charles Heidelberger, Martha R. Kirk, and Marion S. Perkins, "The Metabolic Degradation in the Mouse of Dibenzanthracene Labeled in the 9 and 10-Positions with Carbon 14," *Cancer*, **1**, No. 2, 261 (1948).

J. H. Lawrence and C. A. Tobias, "Is CO Oxidized to CO_2 in the Human Body?" *Air Surgeon's Bull.*, **2**, 452 (1945).

C. A. Tobias, J. H. Lawrence, F. J. W. Roughton, W. S. Root, and M. I. Gregersen, "The Elimination of Carbon Monoxide from the Human Body with Reference to the Possible Conversion of CO to CO_2," *Am. J. Physiol.*, **145**, 253 (1945).

Photosynthesis

S. Aronoff, A. Benson, W. Z. Hassid, and M. Calvin, "Distribution of C^{14} in Photosynthesizing Barley Seedlings," *Science*, **105**, 664 (1947).

A. Benson and M. Calvin, "The Dark Reduction of Photosynthesis," *Science*, **105**, 648 (1947).

A. H. Brown, E. W. Fager, and H. Gaffron, "Use of C^{14} in the Study of Photosynthesis," *Federation Proc.*, **6**, 242 (1947).

A. H. Brown and J. Franck, "On the Participation of Carbon Dioxide in the Photosynthetic Activity of Illuminated Chloroplast Suspensions," *Arch. Biochem.*, **16**, 55 (1948).

M. Calvin and A. Benson, "The Path of Carbon in Photosynthesis," *Science*, **107**, 476 (1948).

A. Frenkel, "Photosynthesis with Radioactive Carbon. Distribution of the Intermediate Products in the Plant Cell," *Plant Physiol.*, **16**, 654 (1941).

M. D. Kamen and S. Ruben, "Synthesis *in Vivo* of Organic Molecules Containing Radioactive Carbon," *J. Applied Phys.*, **12**, 310 (1941); "Studies in Photosynthesis with Radiocarbon," *J. Applied Phys.*, **12**, 326 (1941).

L. G. Livingstone and G. Medes, "The Biosynthesis of C^{13} Compounds: I. The Biosynthesis of C^{13}-Labeled Starch," *J. Gen. Physiol.*, **31**, 75 (1947).

R. Overstreet, S. Ruben, and T. C. Broyer, "The Absorption of Bicarbonate Ion by Barley Plants as Indicated by Studies with Radioactive Carbon," *Proc. Natl. Acad. Sci. U. S.*, **26**, 688 (1940).

G. S. Rabideau and G. O. Burr, "The Use of the C^{13} Isotope as a Tracer for Transport Studies in Plants," *Am. J. Botany*, **32**, 349 (1945).

S. Ruben, W. Z. Hassid, and M. D. Kamen, "Radioactive Carbon in the Study of Photosynthesis," *J. Am. Chem. Soc.*, **61**, 661 (1939); "Photosynthesis with Radioactive Carbon: II. Chemical Properties of the Intermediates," *J. Am. Chem. Soc.*, **62**, 3443 (1940).

S. Ruben and M. D. Kamen, "Photosynthesis with Radioactive Carbon: IV. Molecular Weight of the Intermediate Products and a Tentative Theory of Photosynthesis," *J. Am. Chem. Soc.*, **62**, 3451 (1940).

S. Ruben, M. D. Kamen, W. Z. Hassid, and D. C. Devault, "Photosynthesis with Radiocarbon," *Science*, **90**, 2346 (1939).

S. Ruben, M. D. Kamen, and L. H. Perry, "Photosynthesis with Radioactive Carbon: III. Ultracentrifugation of Intermediate Products," *J. Am. Chem. Soc.*, **62**, 3450 (1940).

J. H. C. Smith and D. B. Cowie, "Absorption and Utilization of Radioactive Carbon Dioxide by Sunflower Leaves," *Plant Physiol.*, **16**, 257 (1941).

W. Stepka, A. A. Benson, and M. Calvin, "The Path of Carbon in Photosynthesis: II. Amino Acids," *Science*, **108**, 304 (1948).

H. G. Wood and G. O. Burr, "Photosynthesis with $C^{13}O_2$ and the Distribution of Heavy Carbon in the Sugars," *Federation Proc.*, **6**, 303 (1947).

Miscellaneous Compounds

W. D. Armstrong, J. Schubert, and A. Lindenbaum, "Distribution of Radioactive Carbon Dioxide Eliminated as Carbonate in the Body and Excreta of the Mature Rat," *Proc. Soc. Exptl. Biol. Med.*, **68**, 233 (1948).

J. M. Buchanan and J. C. Sonne, "The Utilization of Formate in Uric Acid Synthesis," *J. Biol. Chem.*, **166**, 781 (1946).

J. M. Buchanan, J. C. Sonne, and A. M. Delluva, "Biological Precursors of Uric Acid: II. The Role of Lactate, Glycine and Carbon Dioxide as Precursors of the Carbon Chain and Nitrogen Atom 7 of Uric Acid," *J. Biol. Chem.*, **173**, 81 (1948).

R. G. Gould, I. M. Rosenberg, M. Sirrex, and A. B. Hastings, "Rate of $C^{14}O_2$ Excretion Following Intraperitoneal Administration of Isotopic Bicarbonate and Acetate," *Federation Proc.*, **7**, 156 (1948).

C. G. Mackenzie and V. du Vigneaud, "The Source of Urea Carbon," *J. Biol. Chem.*, **172**, 353 (1948).

D. Rittenberg and Heinrich Waelsch, "The Source of Carbon for Urea Formation," *J. Biol. Chem.*, **136**, 799 (1940).

J. C. Sonne, J. M. Buchanan, and A. M. Delluva, "Biological Precursors of Uric Acid Carbon," *J. Biol. Chem.*, **166**, 395 (1946); "Biological Precursors of Uric Acid: I. The Role of Lactate, Acetate and Formate in the Synthesis of the Ureide Groups of Uric Acid," *J. Biol. Chem.*, **173**, 69 (1948).

AUTHOR INDEX

SUBJECT INDEX *

* Page numbers appearing after the name of a chemical compound without descriptive notation refer to the appearance of the compound in a chemical reaction or in a table. A compound used as a starting material or an important reagent in a reaction is indexed with a notation of the reaction product.

Permanganate, in degradation of propionic acid, 249–250
in degradation of propylene, 260
in oxidation of butyl lactate, 210
Persulfate oxidation, 82, 94–96
Phenanthrene-9-C^{14} synthesis, 234–235
Phenol in acetate synthesis, 194
Phenylacetamide-1-C^{14}, synthesis, 181
Phenylacetamide-2-C^{14} synthesis, 196–197
Phenyl acetate-1-C^{14} synthesis, 237
Phenylacetic acid, isotopic, plating, 112
Phenylacetic acid-carboxyl-C^{14} synthesis, 181
phenylacetamide from, 172, 181
Phenylalanine-α, carboxyl-C^{14} synthesis, 223
Phenylglyoxal-α-C^{14}, 214
Phenylmagnesium bromide, 180
p-Phenylphenacylacetate, plating, 112
Philips ionization gauge, 141, 334
Phosgene-C^{11} and phosgene-C^{14}, 152, 158
synthesis, 155–156
urea from, 157
3-Phosphoglyceric acid, plating, 112
Phosphoric acid in generation of CO_2, 154
Phosphorus, red, 226–227
reduction with, 223–225
Phosphorus tribromide in acetyl bromide synthesis, 210
Phosphorus trichloride in acetyl chloride synthesis, 176–177
Phosphorus triiodide in methyl iodide synthesis, 169
Phosphoserine, plating, 112
Photoelectron production with annihilation radiations, 26
Photographic method of particle detection, 77–78
Photosensitivity, of G-M counter cathodes, 60
of oxide-coated cathodes, 70
Photosynthetic methods, 263
2-Phthalimidoacetonitrile-1-C^{13}, 215
Phthalimidomalonic ester. See Diethyl phthalimidomalonate.
Piperidine in plate making, 112
Pirani gauge, 333
Plant cells, plates, 113
Plant materials, 266

Plate maker, 118
Plate making, solvent and solute rules, 110–113
use of turntable, 111
Plate number, 319
Plates of pure substances, 109, 112
Plating of extracts, 113–114
Poisson relation, 284
application to radioactive decay, 17
Polystyrene in ion-chamber insulators, 53
Porous media, in sample preparation, 106–108
reproducibility, 108
self-absorption corrections, 107–108
Positron, 3, 19
of C^{11}, maximum energy, 22
Potassium. See also Bicarbonate; Permanganate; etc.
in cyanide synthesis, 160–161
in oxalic acid synthesis, 191
Powder samples, compacted, preparation, 121–122
Precipitation flask for barium carbonate, 85
Probable error, definition, 285
Probability constant, 284
values for various named errors, 285
Probability integral, 284
Propanol, in plate making, 119
propyl propionate from, 203
n-Propanol-1-C^{13} synthesis, 202
n-Propanol-1-C^{14} synthesis, 203
Propene-1-C^{14}, degradation, 259–260
synthesis, 206
Propionic acid, isotopic, degradation, 249–250
Propionic acid-1-C^{11} synthesis, 176
Propionic acid-2-C^{13} synthesis, 192
Propionic acid-3-C^{13} synthesis, 193
Proportional region, 33
Propyl-1-C^{14} bromide, 202
propene from, 206
Propylene. See Propene.
Propyl-1-C^{13} iodide, 202
Propyl propionate-1-C^{14}, 203
Propyl-1-C^{14}-trimethylammonium bromide, 207
Propyl-1-C^{14}-trimethylammonium hydroxide, 206
Protein, samples on filter paper, 117